ANIMALS *in* ACTION
THE LIVING COUNTRYSIDE

A Reader's Digest selection

ANIMALS IN ACTION

First Edition Copyright © 1990
The Reader's Digest Association Limited, Berkeley Square House,
Berkeley Square, London W1X 6AB

Copyright © 1990
Reader's Digest Association Far East Limited
Philippines Copyright 1990
Reader's Digest Association Far East Ltd

Originally published as a partwork,
The Living Countryside
Copyright © 1981, 1982, 1983, 1984
Eaglemoss Publications Ltd and Orbis Publishing Ltd

PRINTED IN SPAIN

Front cover picture: Two young foxes emerge from their earth. Foxes
are acutely aware of their surroundings, they have a strong sense of
smell and their pointed ears are sensitive scanners.

ISBN 0 276 42027 6

ANIMALS *in* ACTION
THE LIVING COUNTRYSIDE

PUBLISHED BY THE READER'S DIGEST ASSOCIATION LIMITED
LONDON   NEW YORK   MONTREAL   SYDNEY   CAPE TOWN

Originally published in partwork form
by Eaglemoss Publications Limited and Orbis Publishing Limited

Consultant

Robert Gibbons

Contributors

Jeremy Bradshaw	Peter Evans	Denis Owen
Carolyn Boulton	Chris Feare	Valerie Russell
Andrew Campbell	Jim Flegg	Keith Snow
Michael Chinery	W J Griffiths	Ian Spellerberg
John Cloudsley-Thompson	Paul Hillyard	Michael Stoddart
David Corke	Ian Linn	Michael Tweedie
Oliver Dansie	Roger Lovegrove	Juliet Walker
Euan Dunn	Nigel Matthews	Alwyne Wheeler
Keith Easton	Pat Morris	D W Yalden

Contents

ANIMALS *in* ACTION

Introduction

One of the key characteristics that sets animals apart from plants is their mobility. Although there are plants that move, and there are animals that do not move, in general animals are notable for their activity.

With mammals, of which there are about 60 different species in the British Isles, action pervades every aspect of their lives. Hunting, feeding, courtship, mating, home-making, dispersing and playing all involve a variety of actions. Birds are at least as energetic, and usually much more visible, since they are mainly active in daylight and somewhat bolder around humans than wild mammals. And it is generally true that the smaller the bird, the more active it is – try watching a blue tit for a few minutes to see how much energy it uses.

Mammals and birds are warm-blooded creatures, able to maintain body temperature and activity whatever the weather, as long as they can find sufficient food. Lower down the evolutionary scale are the cold-blooded reptiles and amphibia, and below them the insects and other invertebrates. Reptiles and amphibia can be highly active at certain stages of their lives, but they also spend long periods totally immobile, with body functions reduced to a minimum, when the outside temperature is too low or food is unavailable.

Some invertebrates, such as dragonflies and butterflies, are as active as birds – except during cold weather when their bodies slow right down – but others have a quite different pattern of activity. At first sight, a starfish or a garden snail may not seem to be active at all. It is only when you look more closely at these animals, at all the phases of their lives, that you can appreciate just how active they really are.

Left: A pole cat jumping across a stream. Many animals expend a great deal of energy as they pursue their daily activities.

Hunting and feeding

All animals have to feed to stay alive, but the food they consume and their ways of finding it and eating it vary enormously. Feeding can be divided roughly into three types: herbivorous, carnivorous, and parasitic, but there is plenty of overlap. Many carnivores – flesh-eaters – also eat vegetable material, for example, badgers eat roots, fruit and nuts as well as worms, insects and other small creatures.

Carnivorous animals include those that actively hunt and kill living animals – the predatory species – as well as those that rely mainly on carrion – the scavengers. Predatory species generally occur in small numbers and are usually at the top of the food chain. Good examples include falcons and owls, weasels and stoats, and dragonflies. They are all highly active, alert animals, with the ability to outfly, outrun or outwit their prey before overpowering it. Scavengers may prey on weak or sick individuals, but are rarely able to attack normally mobile, healthy animals, and they therefore rely on carrion. Scavengers include such diverse species as magpies and pond-skaters.

Herbivores – plant-eating animals – include a wide range of species, from grazing mammals such as deer, through seed-eating birds such as finches and crossbills, to insects such as aphids or butterflies. As a general rule, herbivores are far more numerous than carnivores, because their chosen food is more readily available and does not have to be hunted. On the other hand, their abundance means that they form a large part of the prey of carnivores.

A totally different way of life is that of the parasite. Parasites normally feed on, or in, their prey in such a way that they do not kill it. Familiar examples include fleas, ticks and tapeworms.

Left: Short-eared owls can catch several thousand field voles a year by gliding silently in on their unsuspecting prey. The short-eared owl hunts primarily by day, using wind currents to carry it great distances without a single beat of its broad wings.

CHECKLIST
This checklist is a guide to the animals featured in the following section. Each species has been chosen for its method of hunting and feeding. The animals listed in **bold** *have their own chapter.*

Bats
Bullfinch
Carp
Dace
Dragonflies
European polecat
Ferrets
Fox
Froghopper
Great black-backed gull
Harriers
John dory
Ladybirds
Long-eared owl
Mole
Moths
Otter
Pike
Portuguese man o'war
Rabbit
Short-eared owl
Starfishes
Stone loach
Squirrels
Tiger beetles
Wasps
Wolf spider

Left: A barn owl bringing food to the nest. Barn owls survive on a carnivorous diet and are very efficient at controlling farmyard pests. Their eyes are specially adapted to see in the dark, enabling them to fly in safety and hunt with astonishing efficiency, even on the darkest night.

MAMMAL TEETH: MEAT-EATERS

Meat-eating mammals have sharp teeth with prominent canines—the fangs—and cheek teeth that are designed for slicing meat and gnawing bones.

Mammals that hunt and eat other animals are known as carnivores. In Britain, they include members of the dog, weasel and cat families. Moles, hedgehogs, shrews and bats eat insects and are called insectivores. The herbivores– plant-eaters–appear in the next chapter.

Mammals have two sets of teeth: milk teeth (while the mammal is young), and the adult set. The milk teeth are used during the weaning period while the young mammal is starting to eat solid food. In almost all species of mammals, the milk teeth are like smaller versions of the adult incisors, canines and premolars. There are no milk molars, but the adult molars appear before all the milk teeth have been lost. The various types of adult teeth are specialized for the different processes of biting and chewing.

Structure The pearly white enamel, which covers the outside of the tooth, is composed of 96% mineral salts for maximum hardness. Tooth enamel is the hardest substance produced in the body of mammals. Inside the enamel layer, most of the tooth is dentine which is very like bone in structure, but harder. Unlike bone, dentine which has finished growing has no living cell bodies inside it. The living part of the tooth is a pulp-filled cavity, containing the blood vessels and nerves which keep the tooth alive. The tooth is fixed in its socket by a root held firm by a modified form of bone called cement.

The fox has four canine teeth which are the largest and most obvious of its 42 teeth. Canines are used for attack by all carnivores, and for defence against attack by larger animals. In front of the canine teeth are the smaller incisors. All true carnivores have 12 incisors, six in the top jaw and six in the bottom. The incisors are used for nibbling small pieces of meat off a bone, and for grooming. Behind the canines are the cheek teeth. The ones immediately behind the canines are the premolars and those right at the back of the mouth are the molars. Front teeth are for biting and nibbling, cheek teeth mainly for cutting and chewing.

All the true carnivores (members of the dog, weasel and cat families) have two cheek teeth, the carnassials, on each side of the

The fox (above) has 42 teeth, of which the canines are its main weapon of attack. When a fox pounces on a rabbit, the canines bite through its neck or the back of its head. Like the front teeth of all mammals, the canine (below) has only one point (cusp) and only one root.

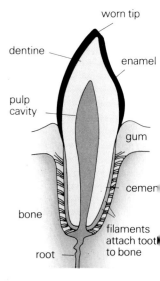

worn tip

dentine

enamel

pulp cavity

gum

cement

bone

filaments attach tooth to bone

root

mouth, which are enlarged and modified for cutting through meat or bones. In the top jaw the hindmost of the premolars is large, three-pointed and flattened on the inner surface. It works against the first of the molars in the lower jaw, this tooth being large and flattened on the outer surface. When a fox closes its jaws the flattened surfaces of the upper and lower carnassials shear across each other in a very effective cutting action. It is to bring their carnassials into action, that foxes and dogs, and other carnivores, chew at meat with the sides of the mouth.

Although the fox is a meat-eater, it is also a scavenger and general feeder (an omnivore). This is one reason why there are a large number of molars and premolars—some for biting, others for chewing or crushing insects.

A mole has 44 teeth, all of which are sharp-pointed for catching and holding worms. Moles are fierce territorial animals and use their enlarged upper canines for fighting. Moles are unusual in not having any proper milk teeth.

Hedgehogs have slightly fewer teeth than moles, but all the teeth are pointed for eating invertebrates. Their milk teeth start to be replaced when the hedgehog is nearly four weeks old.

Shrews' teeth are adapted for eating insects. The very large front teeth, top and bottom, project beyond the jaw and enable shrews to pick up small insects. The cheek teeth are many-pointed; some of them are wide and are used for crunching tough chitin-covered insects.

Bats crunch insects, too, and their cheek teeth are very similar to those of shrews. The pointed incisors and canines help hold and kill insects. Baby bats have small milk teeth which drop out shortly after birth. They may be used for clinging on to the mother's fur.

Telling mammals by their teeth Each species of adult mammal has a fixed number of teeth of each type, whether they are incisors, canines, premolars or molars. If you find the skull of a dead mammal in the countryside, the numbers and types of teeth are the best guide to identify the species. The simplest way of noting the numbers and types is to count the teeth on one side of the jaw only (there should be exactly the same number on the other side) and to write the numbers down in a standard way, called the dental formula. The top row of figures in the examples below gives the number of teeth of one side of the upper jaw, while the lower row of figures represents one side of the lower jaw.

Fox	$I\frac{3}{3}$	$C\frac{1}{1}$	$PM\frac{4}{4}$	$M\frac{2}{3}$
Hedgehog	$I\frac{3}{3}$	$C\frac{1}{1}$	$PM\frac{3}{2}$	$M\frac{3}{3}$
Mole	$I\frac{3}{3}$	$C\frac{1}{1}$	$PM\frac{4}{4}$	$M\frac{3}{3}$
Weasel	$I\frac{3}{3}$	$C\frac{1}{1}$	$PM\frac{3}{3}$	$M\frac{1}{2}$
Wild cat	$I\frac{3}{3}$	$C\frac{1}{1}$	$PM\frac{3}{2}$	$M\frac{1}{1}$

I incisors **C** canines **PM** premolars **M** molars

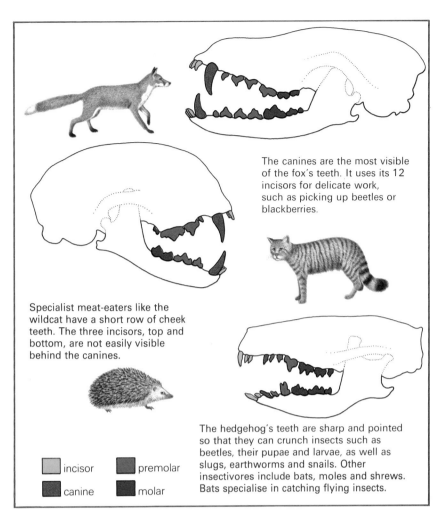

The canines are the most visible of the fox's teeth. It uses its 12 incisors for delicate work, such as picking up beetles or blackberries.

Specialist meat-eaters like the wildcat have a short row of cheek teeth. The three incisors, top and bottom, are not easily visible behind the canines.

The hedgehog's teeth are sharp and pointed so that they can crunch insects such as beetles, their pupae and larvae, as well as slugs, earthworms and snails. Other insectivores include bats, moles and shrews. Bats specialise in catching flying insects.

☐ incisor ☐ premolar
☐ canine ☐ molar

Right: With wide open mouth, the bat can catch insects in flight. The large gap between the left and right upper incisors may help the bat direct its echo-location ultrasonic squeaks— the sounds that it uses to navigate.

Below: The mole has more teeth than any other mammal in Britain. All its teeth are sharp-pointed: a bite will paralyse a worm, so that it can be stored until the mole is hungry.

MAMMAL TEETH: HERBIVORES

Seed-nibbling mice, nut-cracking squirrels and grass-grazing horses are just a few of the wide range of mammals that have teeth adapted for feeding on plant material.

Eating plants wears out teeth faster than crunching or gnawing at even the hardest bones. Plants are less nutritious than meat, so herbivores spend longer feeding, and their teeth wear more quickly. Additionally, grass, the main diet of most specialist plant-eaters, contains abrasive silica salts in its stems and leaves which act like sandpaper when the teeth bite and grind.

While a meat-eating mammal normally retains the enamel covering of its teeth in good condition the whole of its life, a herbivore grinds down the enamel, and then the dentine is exposed. The bone-like dentine and enamel wear down gradually, the former at a quicker rate so that the enamel appears as ridges. Herbivores have different sets of teeth for biting and chewing, which are separated by a gap, known as the diastema. The incisors nip off the plant, and the cheek teeth grind and chew each mouthful before it is swallowed.

Horses and ponies have a maximum of 40 teeth, many more than the other species of herbivore. The row of six incisors in the top jaw are used to crop grass by biting against a similar row in the bottom jaw. The incisors of a young horse are completely covered in enamel, but constant grazing soon wears the tips down and reveals the dentine. The incisors do not grow any longer to compensate for this wear, but the rate of wear is slow.

When a mouthful of grass has been cropped by the incisors, it is moved back in the mouth and chewed by the long straight row of specialised cheek teeth. Horses' cheek teeth, like those of all herbivores, look very different from the cheek teeth of carnivores. The teeth are long and the crown is flattish with ridges of enamel rising above dentine and cement. Instead of just fixing the root in its socket, the cement fills the grooves and crevices in the sides of the teeth.

The enamel ridges of the top and bottom rows of cheek teeth grind against each other in a sideways action and chew the grass very effectively; this is important since plant food can only be properly digested when the plant cell walls are broken, so that the cell contents are exposed to the animal's digestive juices.

Male horses usually have small canines in

the gap between incisors and cheek teeth. They seem to be of no help with feeding, but may be used when stallions bite each other during their fights for females.

Deer digestion is helped by their food being chewed twice. Deer use their incisors to crop grass but, unlike horses, they have incisors only in the lower jaw. They bite against a leathery pad in the upper jaw, and this may help to reduce wear on the incisors.

The lower jaw of a deer appears to have four incisors on each side, but the fourth incisor is in fact a canine which has become adapted for grass cutting rather than fighting. In the upper jaw, not only are there no incisors, but fallow and roe deer have no canines either. Red and sika deer have small upper canines rather like those found in male horses. Deer stags use antlers rather than teeth for fighting each other, and it is interesting that the only deer in Britain to have large, tusk-like canines are the Chinese water deer which do not have antlers.

Deer have 12 cheek teeth, and the enamel ridges run in new-moon-shaped crescents along their length. The top and bottom teeth together form a 'grinding mill' for effective chewing.

Chewing the cud While meat-eating mammals have lower jaws which only bite up and down, all the herbivores can move their lower jaws from side to side – a movement which is easiest to see when a cow or a deer is 'chewing

Above: A grey squirrel gnawing an acorn. As in all rodents, the actual gnawing is done primarily by the incisors of the lower jaw, while those of the upper jaw have the task of fixing the head in position while the lower teeth gnaw. To eat a harder nut such as a hazelnut, the squirrel holds the nut firmly with its forefeet and gnaws a groove across the top until a small hole is produced. Then it inserts the lower incisors in the hole to crack the shell.

Grinding cheek tooth

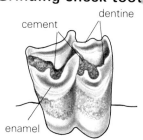

A long-crowned cheek tooth of a roe deer, showing typical structure of a herbivorous mammal. The enamel ridges act as rasps for grinding green vegetation

The teeth of grazers and gnawers

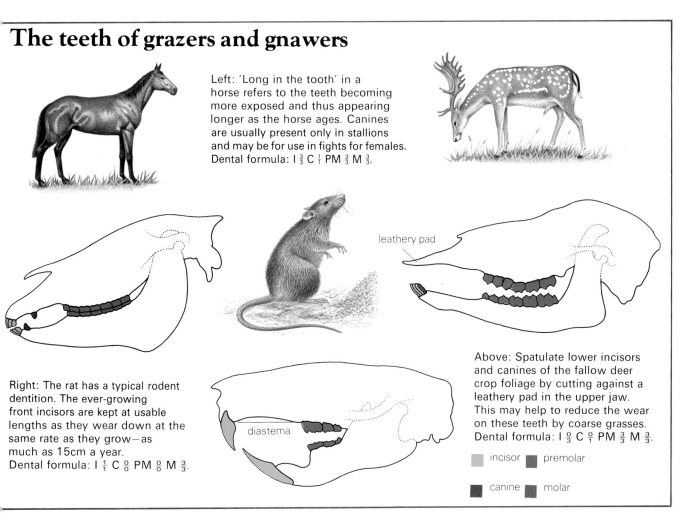

Left: 'Long in the tooth' in a horse refers to the teeth becoming more exposed and thus appearing longer as the horse ages. Canines are usually present only in stallions and may be for use in fights for females. Dental formula: $I\frac{3}{3}$ C $\frac{1}{1}$ PM $\frac{3}{3}$ M $\frac{3}{3}$.

leathery pad

Right: The rat has a typical rodent dentition. The ever-growing front incisors are kept at usable lengths as they wear down at the same rate as they grow—as much as 15cm a year. Dental formula: $I\frac{1}{1}$ C $\frac{0}{0}$ PM $\frac{0}{0}$ M $\frac{3}{3}$.

diastema

Above: Spatulate lower incisors and canines of the fallow deer crop foliage by cutting against a leathery pad in the upper jaw. This may help to reduce the wear on these teeth by coarse grasses. Dental formula: $I\frac{0}{3}$ C $\frac{0}{1}$ PM $\frac{3}{3}$ M $\frac{3}{3}$.

■ incisor ■ premolar

■ canine ■ molar

he cud'. When feeding, a deer is usually out in the open and exposed to danger, so it eats swiftly, giving each mouthful a quick chew before swallowing. When the deer is resting, safely hidden, it regurgitates each mouthful of food (the cud), and gives it a thorough second chew before it is swallowed again. Animals of this type are called ruminants.

The smaller herbivores, the rodents, rabbits and hares, have cheek teeth that are more varied than those of the larger herbivores. But they do not chew the cud. All the cheek teeth look alike and in the specialist grass-eaters, have enamel ridges across the grinding surfaces.

Many rodents, such as rats and mice, eat flesh as well as plants. Their cheek teeth do not have grinding ridges but low cusps.

No rodent, rabbit or hare has any canine teeth and the incisors are extremely specialised. True rodents, such as mice, rats, voles, squirrels and dormice, have only two upper and two lower incisors. These are curved and have enamel only on the front edge. The exposed dentine on the other side of the tooth wears away quicker and keeps the incisors always chisel sharp.

Rodents' incisors grow very quickly—a rat's incisor grows between 10 and 15cm (4 and 6in) a year—but wear away at the same rate. They have fewer teeth than most other mammals. Mice and voles have 16, the lowest number in British land mammals.

Right: The cutting incisors of a rabbit are chisel-sharp. Ridged cheek teeth grind the cropped plant's cell walls to a pulp. Rabbits need to eat 500g of vegetation daily to be in good health.

Below: Sheep grazing peacefully above the River Tweed, Peeblesshire, Scotland. Being ruminants, they give the grazed grass a quick chew before swallowing and later regurgitate the 'cud' to grind it thoroughly.

MAMMAL PREDATORS: THE HUNTING LIFE

Mammalian predators, both terrestrial and aquatic, are intelligent, adaptable and efficient. Each species has a different life-style, but all the members of the order Carnivora have teeth that are adapted to cutting and shearing a variety of prey.

ove: The otter preys on
w-moving victims,
ecially eels and coarse
es, but also
staceans, waterfowl and
h small animals as water
es and frogs.
e otter belongs to the
er Carnivora, which
ludes the weasel
posite page), fox, pine
rten, polecat, stoat,
dcat, and domestic dogs
l cats. Other British
datory mammals are the
y and common seals, and
ne whale species.

The mammals appeared about 200 million years ago when dinosaurs were only just beginning to be widespread and successful. For the first two-thirds of their long evolutionary history the mammals remained a relatively unimportant group of small, nocturnal animals. They fed mainly on insects and other small creatures, but when larger forms evolved, a few of their descendants adopted predatory, flesh-eating habits.

Most of today's predators belong to the single order, the Carnivora, which includes the superfamilies of the dogs and cats. The seals and sea-lions belong to a related order, the Pinnipedia. Then there are the carnivorous toothed whales in the order Cetacea, while in Australasia and South America there are some carnivorous marsupials.

Britain's carnivores Since wolves were exterminated in the British Isles in the 18th century the largest British land carnivore has been the badger. Although it is endowed with astonishing strength of jaw, the badger is not really a predator. It is almost omnivorous, feeding on roots, nuts, fungi, slugs, snails, frogs, voles, mice, rats, birds' eggs, worms and insects, including the larvae of wasps and bumble bees.

The largest British carnivore predators are otters, foxes and wildcats but, like many carnivores, they may also supplement their diet with insects, fruits and other foods.

Well-adapted bodies The bodies of mammal predators are adapted in various ways to make them efficient hunters. The wild cat, for instance, has several specialisations for hunting. Its shortened skull is large to hold the well-developed brain it needs to outwit its prey. When stalking prey that is difficult to detect by sight or smell, the cat may have to learn to associate the presence of food with obscure clues such as footmarks, or to lie in wait for prey that is still far away. Cats even learn to catch small birds by hiding motionless in long grass until the prey comes close enough to be captured with a quick dash. This kind of behaviour requires a large brain and considerable intelligence. The skull also contains powerful muscles so that the cat can

15

Above: Polecats frequently kill rabbits and they also take game birds and poultry. They shake their victims—a learned rather than an instinctive characteristic; young polecats do not always make a clean kill.

Left: The fox is mainly a solitary hunter, although it hunts for its family during the breeding season. It takes animals smaller than itself, biting them in the shoulder or neck and shaking them violently.

Below: The most common killing technique of the cat is a bite in the nape of the neck of its prey, driving the canine teeth into the spinal cord.

open its mouth wide, then snap the jaw together, stabbing the prey with its long, sharp teeth and driving the canine teeth into the spinal cord for the kill.

The cat's feet are also adapted for hunting. There are five digits in its front paw and four in its hind foot. They are armed with sharp retractable claws which are important weapons of offence and defence, while the body weight is carried on special pads. The cat walks on the 'palm' of its front paws and on the soles of its back feet–an unspecialised gait known as 'plantigrade'. In members of the dog family, which are adapted for chasing prey over long distances, the gait is 'digitigrade': like human athletes, dogs run on their toes.

Many predators have rather long bodies and carry much of their weight on their fore-limbs. The bodies of weasels, stoats, pine martens and polecats, especially, are long in relation to their total length; weasels, for instance, can easily run down tunnels after prey.

The teeth of carnivores are differentiated into small incisors, large canines used for killing prey, premolars and a somewhat reduced number of molars. The last upper premolars and the first lower molars on each side of the jaw are enlarged as the 'carnassial' teeth. In their most highly developed form, as in cats, these are sharp, flattened blades that sweep past each other with a scissor-like action, cutting meat and bone into fragments. Carnivores do not chew their food very much.

Many British carnivores are nocturnal. The eyes have a glistening layer or 'tapetum' behind the retina which, at night, reflects light back through the retina, giving each ray a double chance to stimulate one of the sensory rods. The effect can be seen after dark when the light from a torch or the headlamp of a car is reflected back from the eyes of a dog or cat. The pupils expand in the dark and contract in the sunlight.

Different hunting techniques Most carnivores, apart from the stoat, kill prey that is smaller than themselves. There is, in fact, a fundamental difference between the ways of hunting of the family Mustelidae (weasels, stoats, martens etc), the Canidae (dogs and foxes) and the Felidae (cats). Many carnivorous animals are solitary, but some species hunt in packs. Weasels and stoats, for instance, may be found hunting singly or in family groups.

Weasels hunt mainly among dense vegetation and are small enough to follow voles, mice and rats down into their underground tunnels. They also eat young rabbits. Pine martens prey on voles, mice, squirrels and birds. Stoats are exceptional in that they hunt hares and rabbits, which are much larger than themselves, as well as mice, voles, shrews and small birds. They will sometimes prance about to attract an inquisitive bird, then pounce on it and bite its neck.

In general, dogs hunt their prey by tracking

nd chasing, assisted by their excellent sense f smell, long legs, deep narrow chests and remendous endurance which enables them to ravel long distances before they attack their rey and tear it to pieces. Although cats, too, ave long bodies and powerful muscles which eact extremely quickly, they soon tire. They apture their prey by stealth, first stalking it, nen pouncing. They direct their attacks at ne head, whereas the Canidae usually attack om the rear. Unlike dogs, cats are equipped ith sharp claws and powerful forelimbs to vercome the defensive weapons of their ictims.

A cat stalks its prey using a series of dis- nctive movements. At first it crouches, linking towards the victim with its body lose to the ground. Then it pauses, in mbush, moving slowly and silently forward ehind cover until close enough to launch lethal attack. Wild cats often tear the heads ff larger prey such as rabbits to eat the rains. Smaller prey is frequently stored be- ore being eaten, the wildcat visiting its ache from time to time.

Marine predators Seals are marine carni- ores, distantly related to the terrestrial arnivora. They swim fast by flexing the hole body, using their hind flippers to ropel themselves. Their teeth are rows of val cones, although the canines are large. heir eyes are directed upwards, and the fish r squid prey is often caught from below and wallowed whole. The external ears are greatly educed, but the hearing is acute. The numer- us long hairs (vibrissae) on the muzzle are ery sensitive, enabling them to fish in deep ater and at night.

Many of the smaller toothed whales, such s the porpoises and dolphins, prey mainly on shes. Their elongated jaws contain numer- us peg-like teeth in long rows. These have st their function of chewing and serve only hold their slippery prey. The dolphin, for xample, has 40-50 slender, peg-like teeth ith which it captures agile fishes or squid. orpoises have teeth with lobed crowns so nat they can take bites out of their prey. The iller whale uses its large powerful jaws and tout teeth to feed on dolphins, birds, seals, nd even the flesh of large whales.

Prey escape Although prey animals are ften faster than their enemies, they are enerally less intelligent and adaptable. Con- equently the sick and weak often become the ictims of predators. Undoubtedly natural election sets its mark most distinctively on ne form and behaviour of animals in response oth to the capture of food and escape from redators.

Most prey species seem to take refuge in ight on the approach of a predator. The ffectiveness of this is often enhanced by the nimal following a zigzag course to avoid apture. This can be seen in creatures as ifferent as field-mice, voles and hares as well gulls and sandpipers.

Predators and prey

Predator attack strategy	Prey defence strategy

Fox hunts using all its senses, strong legs; bites and tears food.

Hare pricks ears at danger, can run at high speed away from predator.

Wildcat stalks prey crouching; pauses, attacks, drives teeth into spinal cord.

Hedgehog in open grass curls into tight ball protected by prickles.

Weasel hunts after rodents in their underground tunnels, kills with bite.

Woodmouse is nocturnal, secretive, camouflaged among dead leaves.

Otter kills prey with fierce bite, then uses front paws to handle it.

Rabbits show their white tails to warn others of danger.

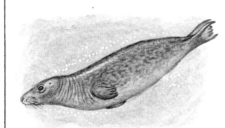

Grey seal swims fast after slippery prey, catches it using sharp teeth.

Fallow deer females show alarm by 'flashing' white rump patches.

FIERCE FERRETS

Ferrets have long been kept for hunting rabbits and controlling vermin. Though generally regarded as untrustworthy animals that will bite ferociously at the slightest excuse, ferrets are quite docile in the right hands.

Ferrets are the domesticated descendants of wild polecats. They have been bred by man for at least 2000 years and their exact ancestral species is disputed. Ferrets occur in two forms: the albino and the polecat-ferret. Albinos have pink eyes and pale creamy yellow (or occasionally pure white) coats.

Polecat-ferrets, on the other hand, have pigmented coats, their fur being dark brown or black and, in rare instances, a sandy red colour. As the name suggests, the polecat-ferret looks similar to the wild European polecat—a strong clue to its likely origin—and even shares the unusual 'bank robber's mask' head markings. In addition, both domesticated forms of ferret will breed with

the European polecat. The European polecat, if caught and tamed, can also be used with great success for ferreting.

Sinuous hunter The ferret is an active carnivore. When on the move it glides along sinuously, its body held rather low to the ground because of its relatively short legs. Like wild polecats, the ferret takes a very wide range of food, including rats, mice, voles, rabbits, eggs and birds. The word polecat is derived from the French 'poule chat' ('chicken-eating cat')—and ferrets do indeed have a penchant for chickens.

Many ferret owners feed their voracious charges on day-old chicks; the young ferrets do well on this diet, as long as it also includes

Above: An albino ferret—note the pink eyes. In both the albino ferret and the polecat-ferret the males are called hobs and the females jills. A hob is substantially larger than a jill, weighing 1-1.3kg (2-3lb); the jill rarely exceeds 600g in weight.

Below: A polecat-ferret on the prowl. This animal closely resembles the European wild polecat. Small populations of these animals exist in the wild in Britain.

ight: A polecat-ferret and
elow) the right way to
ndle a ferret. One of the
st records of domesticated
rrets comes from the 1st
ntury AD when the
storian Strabo described
ow a plague of rabbits was
pt in control by ferrets.
ie histories of rabbits and
rrets are interlinked: as
bbits were introduced
cross Europe, so too were
rrets. They were certainly
tablished here by Richard
s time, when a licence
as needed to hunt rabbits
ith them.

d meat from pigeons and rabbits. Powdered
ilk and pellet foods are useful substitutes.
Breeding The male ferret (hob) comes into
reeding condition in January or February.
is easy to tell because it then develops a very
rong smell, the stink glands producing a
eamy musk. Hobs must be separated at this
age because they will fight each other
rociously when kept in confined conditions.
he female (jill) comes on heat slightly later in
e year and stays in breeding condition until
ated. Jills do not fight together as much as
ie males, though it is advisable to separate
em before introducing a hob.
Ferrets ovulate only after copulation. This
known as induced ovulation and is a mech-
ism that ensures that ova are released only
ter mating and therefore are not wasted.
lating is by no means graceful; the hob
abs the jill by the scruff of her neck and
tes her sharply before carrying her off to
me secluded corner. Copulation is noisy and
ay last for over half an hour.
Pregnant jills do best if provided with a nest
clean hay or straw. During pregnancy they

always moult, losing much of their fur. They
are ready to give birth after about six weeks,
which is the same time as that required by the
wild polecat. Hobs may eat the newborn
young and are therefore generally separated
from the jills after mating. The jill herself may
even eat her young if she is stressed in some
way.

The kits Young ferrets are called kits. At
birth they are not much bigger than the top
joint of a human thumb. They are pink, hairless, blind and totally helpless and weigh
about 10g (about the weight of a 10p piece).
Their fur begins to grow after a few days and
it is then that the type of ferrets bred becomes
clear. Albino ferrets produce albino offspring,
but a polecat-ferret crossed with an albino
produces a mixture with a darker fur. Polecat-
ferrets also tend to produce offspring of
mixed colours.

Ferrets are prolific breeders; there are seldom fewer than four young in a litter, and six
is more usual. Twenty ferrets have been born
in one litter—and raised—but this is rather
exceptional.

At four weeks old the kits' eyes open. After
five weeks the youngsters are able to eat solid
food, such as minced fresh meat, and bread
and milk. A week later the kits attack almost
anything presented to them in the expectation
that it is food. Their sharp teeth have appeared
by this stage and can inflict serious wounds.
Soon after this the kits are usually separated
from their mother. Ferret owners wanting to
use their young animals for sport then ac-
custom the kits to being handled. To avoid the
usual furious biting onslaught a wise owner
feeds his young ferrets before attempting to
pick them up; they are less aggressive after a
meal.

The sport The sport of ferreting is as ancient
as the ferret itself, having been practised for
2000 years or more. The main quarry is the
rabbit, but some go for rats as well. Foxes are
too formidable a prospect for most ferrets,
but a few owners will try to match their ferrets
against them. Many millions of people have
practised ferreting; some have been notable,
including Ghengis Khan and the Emperor
Frederick II of Prussia.

Ferreting

The traditional ferreting
season for rabbits is
from September to March.
A warren with plenty of
rabbits is selected in
advance, such an area
being called a bury. Nets
are set over every burrow
exit in the bury, a purse
net being the type most
often used. It has draw
strings that close round
behind the rabbit when
it bolts into the net,
holding it firm. Two jill
ferrets and one hob is a
typical combination for
a small bury. The jills
do most of the work and
are put down into the
rabbit burrow first. It
may take quite some time
for the jills to move the
rabbits from the maze of
tunnels and galleries
they know so well. A
muffled thundering of
feet announces that the
rabbits are bolting for
the surface; they soon
rush headlong into the
awaiting nets. When all
the rabbits have bolted,
the jills return to the
surface where they are
picked up. Sometimes,
however, the jills kill
a rabbit underground and
then, after eating it,
curl up and go to sleep.
It is difficult to stop
this so, to locate a
feeding or sleeping jill,
the hob is brought into
action. It is put down
the burrow, quickly
locates the kill and drives
the jill off. The jill then
returns to the surface.
The hob, which has had a
piece of string tied to
its collar, is then
recovered by digging.

FERRET (*Mustela furo*)
There are two forms—the
albino and the polecat-
ferret.
Size Head and body
30-44cm (12-17in),
tail 13-18cm (5-7in).
Colour Albino is white or
creamy yellow, polecat-
ferret is dark brown, black
or sandy red (rare).
Breeding One litter of 4-6
or more kits a year.
Food Rats, mice, voles,
rabbits, eggs, songbirds,
invertebrates, chickens,
pigeons.

NOMADIC HUNTERS OF THE NORTH

Food is first in the short-eared owl's life – a life totally governed by the availability of field voles, its main prey. Not only is the size of its brood influenced but also its territory, lack of voles often forcing the owl into a nomadic existence.

The short-eared owl is one of the most widespread of the world's 133 owl species. Found throughout most of Europe and North America, the northern half of Asia and the southern half of South America, it has even made its way to a dozen remote oceanic islands, such as the Galapagos Islands, 965km (600 miles) west of Ecuador, and Hawaii in the very centre of the Pacific.

Despite this enormous range, the short-eared owl is not a common bird in Britain – barn, little, tawny and long-eared owls all have much larger populations. Although it has been breeding in Scotland, Wales and northern England for many years, it has only recently colonized the coastal marshes of East Anglia and Kent. Nevertheless, since it is primarily a day-time hunter, and since the population is augmented by migrants from the Continent in winter, it is not difficult to find. You may come across several of them together, roosting on the ground, or floating like giant moths over the wild and treeless terrain they tend to favour.

Bouncy flight Extensive tracts of moor, bog, heath, rough grass, dunes and coastal marsh are ideal habitats for the short-eared owl, quite unlike those of its relative, the long-eared owl which is a rarely seen, highly nocturnal forest dweller. Gliding just a couple of feet above the grass, with slightly raised, extraordinarily long, outstretched wings, you might well mistake one for a harrier, were it not for the large, round head which could only belong to an owl. Compared to the weight of the body, the wing area is very large and the resultant buoyant, rather bouncy, flight is characteristic.

When seen flying close-to, the striking appearance of this owl becomes obvious. The black-centred, pale yellow eyes are each highlighted by a ring of smoky black feathers which merge into the pale buffs and greys of the facial discs. Almost hidden among these feathers, like a secret weapon, is the cruelly hooked, razor-sharp beak.

The back is mottled and streaked with buff and brown, while the wings are a similar colour but with white spots. In contrast the underparts are pale, boldly streaked with brown on the breast but fading to fine, rather delicate streaks on the belly. Like other owls, the thick and muscular legs and feet are covered with tiny white feathers right down to the long, curved, needle-sharp claws. In flight the wings and tail are noticeably barred and there is a dark patch at the angle of the wing – the carpal patch.

Cunning hunters Short-eared owls use a 'glide, surprise and grab' hunting technique which makes them proficient hunters, each one able to catch several thousand voles a year. Using eddies and upcurrents in the wind, they often glide for considerable distances without a single flap, their soft, well-padded plumage ensuring totally noiseless flight, so

Above: In flight the short-eared owl is identified by its long wings which have a dark 'carpal patch' at the angle of the wing.

Opposite: This species is not often seen in trees, preferring to perch on posts or even on the ground.

Below: The owl's short 'ears', which can be raised or lowered at will, have nothing to do with hearing, but are thought to convey its mood – fear, excitement and so on – to other owls.

Round-up of British owls

The tawny owl is found among trees and the long-eared in fir woods; the short-eared owl favours open country, and the barn owl old buildings and farms. The little owl has a more general habitat, unlike the snowy owl which is limited to the Shetland Isles.

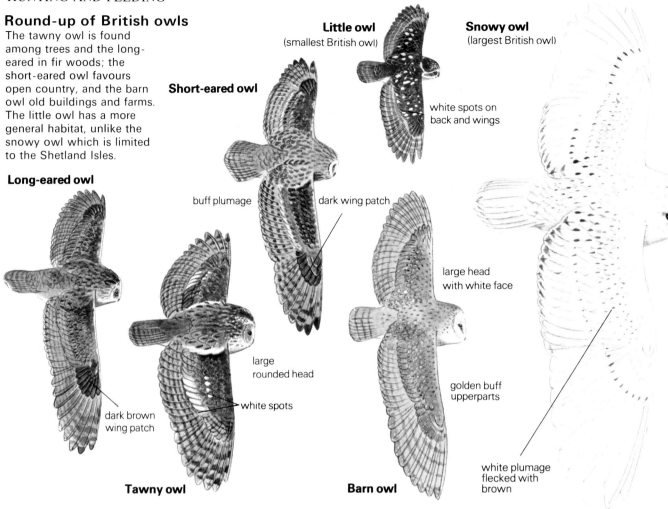

Little owl
(smallest British owl)

Snowy owl
(largest British owl)

white spots on back and wings

Short-eared owl

Long-eared owl

buff plumage

dark wing patch

large head with white face

large rounded head

golden buff upperparts

dark brown wing patch

white spots

Tawny owl

Barn owl

white plumage flecked with brown

Below: Young short-eared owls are a comical sight, covered in white and later grey down, quite unlike their parents. Fledging takes 20 to 30 days but they do not stay in the nest all this time. After only a fortnight they venture out and hide in the surrounding vegetation, even though they cannot yet fly. This behaviour makes it more difficult for predators to find them.

that the unsuspecting vole gets no warning.

Their prey-detection equipment is no less ingenious. The forward-facing eyes give superb binocular vision for accurate judgement of distances, while the discs of feathers surrounding each eye focus the slightest rustle on to enormous, highly sensitive ears, so that even in the gloom of dusk, when owls (and voles) are most active, they can pinpoint the position of their prey with ease.

Nomadic existence It is often thought that predators control the numbers of their prey. This is not true – the opposite usually applies, as is the case with the short-eared owl, whose own life is dominated by the field vole which forms most of its diet. Since vole populations

are far from stable, the fortunes of the ow and the strategies it adopts vary dramatica from month to month and from year to yea

Apart from hiding among long grass, th voles' only defence against short-eared ow is prolific breeding. During the summer th produce litters at the rate of five young eve seven weeks. As the youngsters can then selves breed when about six weeks old, vo populations often reach plague proportio (on average about once every four or fi years).

Evidently short-eared owls thrive durir these vole plagues, especially since the vol become noisy and may eat much of the gra that would otherwise conceal them. This ha two main effects: first, owls from many mil around flock, as if by magic, to the bountif food supply, and secondly, the owls capitali on the easy pickings by 'breeding like voles laying 10 or more eggs (14 is on record) ar sometimes having two broods in a seasor The glut is usually short-lived. In suc crowded conditions voles stop breeding ar this, combined with the heavy predatior results in a population crash. Consequentl in the year following a vole plague, any ow that have not moved on find the larde seriously diminished and may not breed.

The most dramatic demonstration of th nomadic nature of the short-eared owl com from Vancouver airport in Canada. Here, th neatly mown grass bordering the runway

bove: This female is
dopting an almost
orizontal stance – a
haracteristic peculiar to
ort-eared owls. Breeding
arts from April onwards
hen the female lays her
ther conspicuous white
gs in a hollow among
ll grass, heather, gorse or
ambles, where there is
me shelter. She is a good
other, incubating for hours
a time and leaving the
st only when absolutely
ssential. Throughout the
4 to 28 days of incubation,
d while the chicks are
ung and still need
ooding, her mate brings
od for the whole family.
heir diet consists mainly
field voles although other
dents, insects and even
nall birds may be brought
the nest by the male.

hort-eared owl (Asio
ammeus); resident bird
ined by migrants from
ontinent in winter. Found
ainly in Scotland, Wales
nd north of England where
favours open country.
ength 38cm (15in).

attracted flocks of roosting gulls and waders which became a serious bird-strike hazard to aircraft. In an effort to remedy the situation the authorities let the grass grow longer, hoping it would force the birds to roost elsewhere – it worked. However what the authorities didn't bargain for was the vast influx of owls which came to hunt the newly thriving vole population breeding in the long grass. Over 500 owls were trapped and taken elsewhere in only three years.

Family life In spring the male is seen displaying high over his territory, booming out his song at the same time. From a lofty position he twists his wings down and back to meet behind his tail and rapidly claps them together several times, meanwhile plummetting several feet towards the ground.

Following the courtship and mating procedure, the female lays her eggs in a sheltered hollow on the ground, at any time from April onwards. During incubation she rarely leaves the nest – her mate brings all the food needed for her and the young family.

While the owls can, to a certain extent, judge the amount of food available and vary the size of their clutch accordingly, they also have an additional safety mechanism which ensures that the maximum number of healthy young will fledge. The female lays eggs at two-day intervals and incubates right from the start, ensuring that the chicks also hatch at two-day intervals. Then, if the adults have

judged the food supply correctly there will be sufficient for all the family – from the oldest (and strongest) to the youngest – but if they overestimated the number of voles, only the youngest chick dies. The logic for this strategy is very simple: it is better to raise a few healthy nestlings than many weaklings.

Fledging takes 20 to 30 days depending both on the number of voles and the number of owlets – the more food there is to go round, the faster the owlets grow and the sooner they fledge. Initially the mother tears up food for the young, but before long one vole is just one mouthful. They cough up the indigestible bones, teeth and fur in a pellet about 5cm (2in) long and 2cm (¾in) in diameter. Analysis of these pellets shows that several small rodent species supplement the field vole diet, on the Isle of Man brown rats being particularly important. On the coast, particularly in winter, short-eared owls also catch birds such as finches and waders – even in flight – showing a surprising turn of speed and agility when necessary.

Today, when so many of our native birds are declining, it is good to report that short-eared owls are probably more common now than at any other time this century. One reason for this is that young forestry plantations, now a common sight in many upland areas, have proved to be an excellent habitat for them. While the trees are small and the grass is long, voles and owls thrive.

HUNTING HARRIERS

Three species of these large yet agile birds of prey occur in Britain, but in such small numbers that there is concern for their future.

Harriers are large, broad-winged, slender-bodied birds with long narrow tails. When seen in flight they are easily recognisable, flying buoyantly and gracefully, usually low over the ground, with dextrous turns and changes of direction as they quarter for food or make a half-pass at likely prey.

The three species of British harrier are separated by their chosen habitat. The hen harrier is a moorland bird, the marsh harrier a reedbed and marshland type, while Montagu's harrier—a rare summer migrant—has a strong preference for lowland heaths and arable fields. As the latter species is confined to land below 76m (250ft) in Britain, it doesn't overlap with the hen harrier.

Distinguishing our harriers As with most birds of prey, female harriers are larger than males, in this case by about 5cm (2in). Males, though, are more attractive. There are few more exciting sights for birdwatchers in Britain than a dove-grey male hen harrier sweeping over the dark expanses of a heather moor. The males are pale grey above, even paler beneath, with black wing tips and a white band at the base of the tail. The females are much darker, being brown above with a white rump conspicuous in flight.

Above: A female hen harrier drops down to her nest with prey for the young.

Right: A fluffy young hen harrier; both females and immature birds have banded tails and are often referred to collectively—and evasively—as 'ringtails'.

Opposite page: The head of a harrier is distinctive in shape, appearing strikingly owl-like from the front, with marked facial discs and a very small decurved bill. All species show a distinct neck ruff, in particular the hen harrier, as can be seen here.

Below: A female hen harrier at the nest. On their own territory some birds can be very aggressive, making spectacular diving attacks on intruders.

It was only in 1802 that a Colonel Montagu, studying harriers in Devon, realised that the smaller birds he saw were an entirely separate species from the hen harrier. Montagu's harrier, named after the Colonel, is a summer visitor which formerly bred, albeit sparingly, across the southern half of England and Wales but is now extremely rare.

In appearance and hunting methods it closely resembles the slightly larger hen harrier, but males can be distinguished by the narrow black centre lines on the wing and by the absence of a white rump patch. Balanced and delicate on the wing, Montagu's harrier flies even more lightly than the hen harrier, and its wings are distinctly longer and narrower. The female Montagu's harrier is very similar to the female hen harrier, the two being considerably more difficult to tell apart than the males of the species.

In former times, when great areas of reed bed covered the fenlands of East Anglia and other parts of the country, the marsh harrier was a familiar and widespread bird. Marsh

Identifying harriers

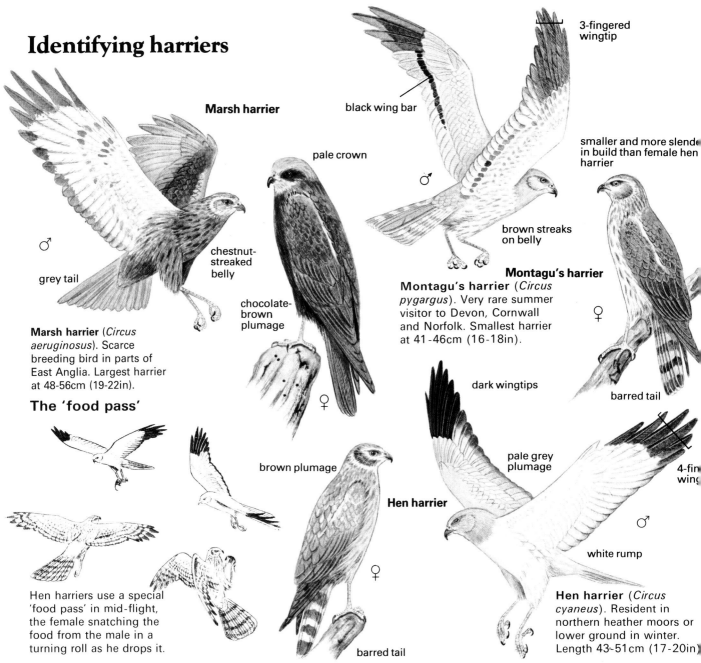

Marsh harrier

3-fingered wingtip

black wing bar

pale crown

chestnut-streaked belly

chocolate-brown plumage

grey tail

♂

Marsh harrier (*Circus aeruginosus*). Scarce breeding bird in parts of East Anglia. Largest harrier at 48-56cm (19-22in).

smaller and more slender in build than female hen harrier

brown streaks on belly

Montagu's harrier

Montagu's harrier (*Circus pygargus*). Very rare summer visitor to Devon, Cornwall and Norfolk. Smallest harrier at 41-46cm (16-18in).

♀

barred tail

The 'food pass'

brown plumage

Hen harrier

♀

barred tail

dark wingtips

pale grey plumage

4-fin wing

♂

white rump

Hen harrier (*Circus cyaneus*). Resident in northern heather moors or lower ground in winter. Length 43-51cm (17-20in)

Hen harriers use a special 'food pass' in mid-flight, the female snatching the food from the male in a turning roll as he drops it.

Above: The distribution of our three harrier species. After a disastrous decline in the 19th and early 20th centuries these birds have shown a small rise in numbers since World War II.

harriers are the largest of the family, distinctly heavier-looking and broader-winged than the others and consequently less buoyant and manoeuvrable in flight. Both sexes are predominantly brown, the male showing grey only on the tail and parts of the wings; the female is a dark-plumaged bird with a prominent creamy head and creamy shoulder patches.

Changing fortunes Our large birds of prey have been persecuted over the last hundred years or so in a systematic and comprehensive way. Harriers were no exception, and all three of our species fell victim to the ruthless control of predators in the name of game preservation in the 19th and early 20th centuries. The gun and the trap have thus been responsible for the wholesale removal of some of our finest birds of prey. Following this, the reclamation of heathland, fen and moorland for intensive farming has drastically reduced the available breeding areas suitable for these species.

In the early years of the 19th century the

hen harrier was a widespread breeding bi in tracts of wild heathland from the Orkne to the south coast counties of England. some areas it was extremely plentiful, a accounts of local carnage testify both to t number of birds and the ruthlessness of t killing; on two Ayrshire estates, for instanc 351 hen harriers are claimed to have be killed between June 1850 and November 185 By the onset of the First World War the h harrier was extinct as a breeding bird ever where except the Orkney Islands.

Only after the end of World War II, wh keepers had been away for several years, w it evident that a slight resurgence was taki place. The steady spread has continued, a there are now perhaps 600 pairs on moorla in Scotland, Ireland, northern England a north Wales. The bird is still illegally p secuted, however, especially by people wi grouse interests, because the hen harri definitely takes young grouse, but more because of the effect a hunting harrier has grouse – forcing them into concealment a us conflicting with an expensive sport on shooting days.

The marsh harrier has fared little better. was extinct in Ireland by 1917, by which time it had also temporarily disappeared from England and Wales. The end of World War II again marked a period of modest revival, centred on East Anglia, and by 1958 twelve to fourteen pairs were nesting. Since then numbers have risen steadily to around 60 pairs in 1989 and the marsh harrier is now spreading westwards across the southern parts of the British Isles.

There is little doubt that Montagu's harrier has always a scarce bird in Britain, being at the northern edge of its range here, although it, too, fell victim to gamekeepers and egg collectors in the 19th century, and has since suffered from destruction of its habitat. Nowadays it has the most tenuous of toe-holds here each summer, the beautiful dove-grey form of the male being a rare and sporadic sight over the rough commons and heathlands the quieter parts of southern England.

'Dancing' in the sky As the harriers start to re-occupy their breeding territories in spring they also begin to display. The courtship flights of all three harrier species are dramatic and exciting. The male marsh harrier performs high soaring flights above the chosen nesting place, followed by remarkable aerial evolutions, plunging with half-closed wings, sweeping high again, tilting, tumbling and

Above: A male Montagu's harrier and (below) a male marsh harrier. Throughout most of their European ranges these two species, and the hen harrier, have been in almost constant decline. Montagu's harrier is, without a doubt, one of the rarest and most threatened birds of prey in Europe, and the hen harrier and marsh harrier have patchy distributions with centres of population interspersed with areas that are now intensively developed and unsuitable for breeding.

looping in an ecstatic flight reminiscent of the wild gyrations of the lapwing. Montagu's and hen harriers, closely related and similar in many ways, also have spectacular diving displays. The males rise to 30m (100ft) or more and then, twisting sideways or somersaulting, plunge headlong earthwards, checking abruptly just above the ground and swinging up again to repeat the process.

At about this time, when the nest site is chosen, the male begins to feed the female, continuing to do so as she incubates the eggs for the four and a half week period. The male now carries out all the hunting, making use of a spectacular technique to pass food to his mate. As he approaches with prey in his lowered talons, the female rises from the nest to meet him. When she reaches him, flying slightly below, she rolls to her side or right over on her back, extending one long slender leg to snatch the food as he drops it, then rights herself so swiftly that the movement is often difficult to follow.

Growing up and feeding After hatching, the young birds stay close to the vicinity of the nest for five weeks, up to the time they fledge, being tended by the female first with food provided by the male but later on with items provided by both parents.

Harriers hunt in a low coursing flight, quartering the ground slowly and methodically, striking at their prey with dexterous turns and making full use of the long reach of their slender legs. Hen harriers prey mostly on voles and other small mammals, together with the chicks of such wading birds as lapwings and golden plovers, and on young grouse and other moorland birds. Montagu's harriers take a higher proportion of lizards, large insects and small birds, while marsh harriers prey on small amphibians and reptiles and a wide range of marshland bird nestlings, as well as on water voles and other small mammals.

By winter Montagu's harrier has moved far south to tropical Africa; many of the marsh harriers, too, move to southern France or the Iberian peninsula. Only the hen harrier – the most northerly of all the harrier species – winters here.

BULLFINCH: BEAUTY OR BEAST?

The bullfinch, one of our most beautiful garden birds, has a darker side, having earned a reputation as a wanton destroyer of buds on a variety of fruit trees.

The bullfinch is one of our most colourful garden birds, the male's rose-red breast contrasting strikingly with its blue-black chin, cap, wings and tail. In spite of all this colour, however, it is easy to miss a group of feeding bullfinches. Usually all you'll see is a brief glimpse of a white rump flitting along a hedgerow or darting off into the thick cover of scrub or woodland.

Efficient foragers Woodland, especially coniferous forest, is the bullfinch's preferred habitat, but it is a versatile bird both in choice of habitat and in the food it eats. Only the most open land, lacking in bushes and hedgerows, seems to be too bare. A bullfinch rarely moves more than a few miles from

Below: Both male and female birds feed the young. The nest—a platform of interwoven twigs—is easily recognisable, but take care not to visit it too often as you may alert eager predators.

me territory and is expert at seeking out the
st food available in its local patch – even
the extent of choosing between different
rieties of fruit trees. In gardens and orch-
ds it eats the buds of numerous bushes and
es, especially those of forsythia, apple,
ar and plum. The short, stubby bill is
ally suited to this food; it can strip the hard
ter husks off seeds and buds with very little
uble.

Adult bullfinches are vegetarians, though
ey feed their nestlings on large quantities
insects and spiders, which are predigested
d then regurgitated for the chicks. As the
ung grow, the parents start to include seeds
their diet, increasing the amount gradually,

Half-a-tree-a-bird-a-day

Bullfinches eat buds at a horrifying rate. Calculations on fruit farms
show that one bird can eat half the buds of a pear tree in a single day.
In fact, this only takes about $1\frac{1}{2}$ hours' feeding at a comfortable pace.
Rates of 10 to 30 buds per minute are common, depending on the size
and type of bud. Fortunately, most bullfinches depend on the seeds and
buds of wild plants and only turn to fruit buds as the best alternative
when wild supplies have failed.

At present there is no effective bullfinch deterrent which is economically
viable. Assessing the cost of bullfinch damage is difficult, even when it
is confined to single trees. Damage to plums and damsons is long-term,
affecting the growth of the tree and, in subsequent years, the crop. Other
fruit trees, notably pears and apples, can withstand substantial bud loss
without loss of crop and, though damaged, often produce larger fruit.

e male offers his mate a beak-
of twigs as part of the
urtship display; bill caressing
another part of their ritual.

til by the time the young leave the nest they
e fed almost entirely on seeds. Throughout
e summer and until late autumn bullfinches
t a huge variety of seeds – anything from
nute grass seeds to the ash keys which
ng in inviting bunches and are one of the
llfinch's favourite food.

From December onwards bullfinches eat
e and shrub buds; these contain next year's
f and flower growth and are very nutritious.
like other finches, bullfinches don't have
search ground covered by leaves or snow to
d fallen seeds or berries. They husk buds
the tree, leaving a scattering of litter which
ds some people to think that they are
ndals – destroying but not eating the buds.
any garden plants and commercially grown
es and bushes, cultivated for their early
wering or fruiting capacity, produce large
wer buds that swell early in the year when
wild equivalents – hawthorn and black-
orn – are much smaller. Because of the
mage done to orchards in southern Eng-
nd, the bullfinch has been removed from
e protected bird list in some counties and
any are now trapped or shot.

Busy breeding season The bullfinch is one
the many birds which overproduce young
ch summer to ensure that some survive
nter to breed the following year. This is
rhaps one of the main reasons why trapping
d shooting, even on a large scale, does not
em to have affected the British population.

Above: The juvenile bird does not have the glossy black cap of the adult, nor the rose-red breast. By the end of the year, however, this bird's pale bill will have darkened and it will have a thick, waterproof coat of feathers to protect it through the winter.

Previous page: Male bullfinch in all the glory of full spring breeding plumage.

Bullfinch (*Pyrrhula pyrrhula*); length from beak to tail 15cm (5¾in); distribution widespread in woodland, plantations, hedgerows and gardens; absent from Isle of Man. Resident.

Most pairs of bullfinches rear two broods of about four nestlings a season; some pairs even manage to fit three broods into a nesting season lasting from late April to August or even September, despite the fact that over half the broods started do not survive. Efficient predators such as jays, magpies, stoats, weasels and cats often find even the best concealed nests and eat the eggs or nestlings. For this reason the bullfinch builds its nest – a distinctive platform of twigs bearing a cup of fine roots lined with hair – in a thick, prickly, inaccessible bush or hedge. The pale blue eggs, dotted with reddish spots at the blunt end, are conspicuous. However, the hen bullfinch with body feathers in a combination of pink, grey, buff and brown, is well camouflaged for sitting on the nest.

Only the hen builds the nest and incubates the eggs. Incubation starts in earnest when the last egg is laid so that they all hatch together – usually on the thirteenth day. Both parents feed the young. While the nestlings are being fed, visits to the nest are kept to a minimum. The parents develop special cheek pouches in the summer and cram them with food to bring back to the young. They sneak silently into the bush together so predators don't follow them to the hidden nest. Because the cheek pouches hold so much food, the youngsters need feeding only every half-hour or so. The young spend 12-18 days in the nest. After this the adults abandon them

and start a new nest.

At this stage you can identify the you[ng] bullfinches by the absence of black on t[he] head but from July onwards each bi[rd] moults, replacing all its fluffy juvenile bo[dy] feathers.

Serenades and songs Bullfinches sing m[ost] often during the breeding season. Not ma[ny] people have heard the song because it is ve[ry] quiet – a soft, pleasant mixture of short, cle[ar] piping notes and hoarse wheezes which t[he] cock seems to reserve for his mate. Wi[th] feathers fluffed, head bobbing up and do[wn] and tail cocked to one side, he serenades h[er] to secure the firm pair-bond necessary f[or] successful breeding. More frequently you c[an] hear the short, plaintive, carrying whis[tle] which is used to contact others of the sa[me] species. This happens particularly in wint[er] when several birds – possibly a family part[y] may flock together where food is to be foun[d.] The call has many variations and is sometim[es] repeated three or four times as a second ty[pe] of song. The finely tuned ear of the bullfin[ch] can almost certainly recognise individuals [by] their particular accent – something whi[ch] must be particularly useful when recen[tly] fledged young are still being cared for by th[eir] parents. From March onwards, except wh[en] the hens are incubating their clutch of eg[gs,] you can often see bullfinches in pairs. It see[ms] from the evidence of ringing that some pa[irs] may well mate for life.

AN OUTSIZE GULL: THE GREAT BLACK-BACK

The great black-backed gull is the largest of our gulls, and also the most rapacious. Besides fishing for itself, it eats fishing industry scraps and plunders rubbish tips. It robs other birds of their catch, but is just as likely to eat the birds themselves; and sometimes it even preys on its own species.

Above: A great black-backed gull calling. The calls are a help in identifying the birds. Though of a similar type to the calls of the herring gull and lesser black-back, the great black-back's call is much deeper in tone and harsher. The most characteristic calls, usually produced near the nest in the breeding season, are a gruff, barking 'aouk' and a throatily gutteral 'uk-uk-uk'. During the winter months they are relatively quiet. The gull in the photograph is one of a pair nesting in an isolated spot, not in a colony. These pairs choose high eminences on cliffs or on the tops of rocks for nest sites, and the male always has a number of perches nearby, each commanding a good view. From here he barks a warning to his mate if intruders threaten to come too close.

cause of its enormous size—a head and ulders taller than gulls of any other species nding nearby—and because of its plumage, ich is pure white with striking jet-black gs, an adult great black-backed gull is one the easiest seabirds to identify. In flight, broad black wings show a conspicuous te trailing edge, and their slow and steady immensely powerful beat is another ture separating the great from the lesser ck-backed gull. The latter has a faster gbeat, and is distinctly smaller, being y 53-56cm (21-22in) long in comparison h the maximum of 74cm (29in) for the at black-back.
urther distinctive features of the great

black-backed gull are the massive head and the beak, which is sometimes about 7cm (3in) long—powerful enough to tear carrion or the thick skins of other seabirds. Often during the summer months a pair of great black-backs stand side by side near their nest, and it is then possible to separate the two sexes with some ease, as the female is noticeably smaller and slighter in build than the male.

The younger generation Apart from their distinctively large size (a feature useful only when other species are nearby for comparison), young great black-backs are much harder to identify. Great black-backs rarely breed before they are five years old, so there are four different immature plumages, one in

31

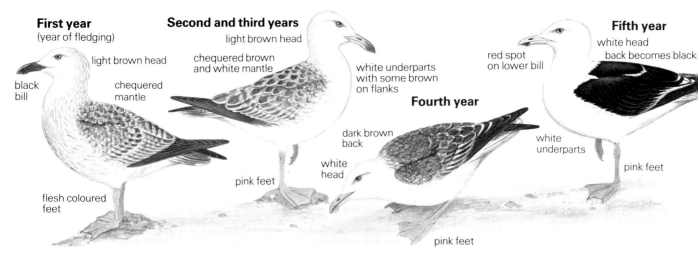

First year
(year of fledging)

light brown head

chequered mantle

black bill

flesh coloured feet

Second and third years

light brown head

chequered brown and white mantle

white underparts with some brown on flanks

pink feet

Fourth year

dark brown back

white head

pink feet

Fifth year

white head

back becomes black

red spot on lower bill

white underparts

pink feet

each of the years preceding breeding. The resulting variety is confusing enough, but in addition the birdwatcher has to bear in mind that each of these plumages is roughly similar to one of the immature stages of both the herring gull and the lesser black-back (although these two species resemble each other more nearly than they resemble the great black-back).

In their first full year (from soon after hatching till the following summer) young great black-backs differ from the other young gulls in having whiter heads and underparts, and in having a more clearly marked chequered mantle (upper back). In the second full year, this contrast between a dark

Great black-backed gull
(*Larus marinus*); our largest gull; breeds on rocky coasts; winters at sea or inland. Length 74cm (29in).

Below: The bulky nest is situated at the top of the cliffs. Two eggs are the normal clutch, but in this case only one has hatched— the other lies crushed, the victim of some accident. Note the unconsumed squid at the edge of the nest: this was probably found as carrion, but proved unsuitable for feeding to the chick.

chequered mantle and pale head and belly intensified. As they age further, the man and wings of young birds become almost dark as those of adults, although they brown and not jet black, and there are s dark bars on the tail and a broad black ba at the tail tip.

Colonies and single nests The breeding si of great black-backed gulls are located alc the rocky coastlines of northern and west Britain, most of the Irish coastline, and rocky islands in these western waters. Th are strikingly few breeding pairs on the e coast of lowland Scotland, or on the ent eastern English coast, or again on the sol coast from Kent to the Isle of Wight, althou non-breeding pre-adult birds may be s anywhere round our coasts in summer.

In some areas, especially where they numerous, great black-backs breed in sm scattered colonies, either of their own spec or interspersed among herring gulls a lesser black-backed gulls in mixed colon Over much of their breeding range, on other hand, it is common to find single pa breeding in isolation, choosing the high promontory on the cliffs or the top of a rc as a site for their bulky nest.

Evidence of a varied diet Around the ne the remains of previous meals can often found. Sometimes these take the form o sizeable 'midden' (refuse heap) of carcase: rabbits and seabirds, but usually there plentiful castings, or pellets, of undiges remains that the birds regurgitate. Exam ation of these has shown that great bla backs have a very varied diet, including ma species of fish, molluscs and crustacea some caught by plunge-diving into shall waters. Some of the remains are those deep-sea fish, and it is likely that these w obtained by scavenging at nearby fish wharf or behind fishing boats out at sea.

Attacks on seabirds Studies of the fc remains of great black-backed gulls h shown that they sometimes rely heavily on larger forms of prey: besides rabbits, t especially favour other seabirds. Most incl the occasional seabird in their diet, but so pairs seem to specialise in preying on nea

consumed, leaving an inside-out skin, with head and wings attached, as characteristic evidence of the predator responsible.

Spreading inland Although it remains the most maritime of our gulls, being found far out to sea, the great black-back is undergoing a change in its winter distribution. Adults, and especially immatures, can be seen close inshore anywhere round our coasts in winter, often near fishing ports or sewage outfalls. Inland, too, the birds are rapidly widening their range, and there are few refuse tips that do not attract some great black-backs during the winter months. When it comes to scavenging, they may not be as nimble as the smaller gulls, but more than make up for this by depriving other birds of their scraps – by sheer, brutal bullying power.

With their large, sharp beaks and strong muscles, they can even open the carcases of dead sheep or stranded dolphins. Wherever either carrion or human food waste is to be found, the great black-back is among the foremost competitors to consume it. Thus for birdwatchers in the eastern half of Britain, the best place to find this, the largest of our 'seagulls', is inland, on the nearest refuse tip.

Growing numbers In 1969-70 Operation Seafarer, a breeding season survey of our seabirds, showed the great black-back, with around 20,000 pairs (three-quarters of them in Scotland), to be the scarcest of the 'everyday' gulls. Despite this, the increase in numbers and spread in range since the middle of the 19th century has been considerable. In the north of its range, this is thought to have been due to warmer weather which has encouraged breeding and improved the rate of breeding success during the present century.

For the majority of our seabirds in this age of pollution and interference, an increase in numbers would always be welcomed. In the case of the great black-back, however, any welcome should be tempered with caution. This elegant and powerful gull, thriving on man's waste, is always ready to prey on other seabirds. When the supply of unnatural bounty falls short of requirements, the result can be a serious fall in numbers for some of our most attractive seabird species.

Above: With such large wings, their flight appears slow and ponderous, but great black-backed gulls are surprisingly fast in the air. They can outpace and seize in mid-air such birds as puffins and storm petrels.

Left: A chick pecks its way out of the egg. For this task it is equipped with a specially tough extension to its upper beak, which you can see as a white ridge. As soon as its down has dried, the newly hatched chick is able to walk and scamper about. The down is greyish-fawn with black camouflage markings, making the chick inconspicuous in the nest until it rushes out to greet a homecoming parent. By pecking at the red spot at the tip of the lower part of the beak, it stimulates the parent bird to regurgitate the meal that it is holding in its crop. The chick accompanies these agitated pecks with a series of piercing, wheedling cries.

Below: A great black-back with its catch, on the quayside.

bird colonies and can wreak considerable struction. The eggs and young of any sea-rd that nests in an exposed site are vulner-le, including other gull species and occasionally even neighbouring great black-cks, seized in a cannibalistic attack.

Of the adult seabirds caught, many are of ecies that are ungainly on land, such as the ffin and the Manx shearwater, which seem pecially helpless. Young shearwaters, erging from the safety of their burrows to ercise their wings prior to fledging, are rticularly vulnerable on moonlit nights. It s been estimated that in the mid-1950s a pulation of 200-250 pairs of great black-cked gulls on Skomer, an island off Pem-okeshire, accounted for a total of more than 00 shearwaters and puffins. Fortunately ese two species breed in huge colonies (over 0,000 pairs on Skomer), so they can ually – at least for a while – survive this rnage.

Once the prey has been caught, it is casionally swallowed whole in mid-air. ore commonly, it is despatched on the ound with a few hammer-like blows from e powerful beak. Seabirds such as Manx earwaters and puffins have thick, tough ins, which the gulls deftly remove. A sharp p of the beak at the throat and tail, a flick the powerful neck, and the body comes ar of the skin. A couple more bites sever e wing bones, and the carcase is then

FISH:THE FIVE SENSES

The sensory organs of a fish equip it superbly for survival – good vision, an excellent sense of smell, hearing, and pressure detectors all help it find food, avoid predators and recognise its own kind.

Because fishes live in water, a medium alien to man, people find it difficult to judge how well a fish's senses work. In contrast with, say, a bird like a chaffinch, which we know from everyday experience can sing and thus hear, as well as see, our appreciation of a fish's senses is almost non-existent. We cannot hear them make noises, and therefore cannot assume that they are able to hear, nor can we easily prove that they see well, or that they see in colour. It is also difficult to guess how sensitive they are to flavours.

However, scientific examination of fish sense organs shows that fish are well-equipped to cope in their watery habitat; indeed, the sensitivity of some organs is far greater than that of many other animals.

Looking through lidless eyes One of the noticeable features of a fish is its eyes – large, bulging, dead-looking organs that lack the eyelids of mammals.

The anatomy of a fish's eye is basically the same as in all other back-boned animals: it is spherical, with a tough, protective outer cover in the front; there is a hard, crystalline lens surrounded by an iris; and at the back of the eyeball there is the retina, layers of light-sensitive cells with rich blood and nerve supplies. The lens of a fish's eye is a

Most of our freshwater fishes, such as the carp (above), are thought to be able to distinguish colours. The two pairs of nostrils you can see on each side of the carp's head are not concerned with breathing but with the linked senses of taste and smell.

The stone loach (below) is well equipped with sensory barbels which it uses to find food. It stays close to the bottom of rivers and brooks and is mainly a night feeder.

perfect sphere (a human eye lens is oval cross-section); it is also absolutely clear a positioned close to the outer covering of t eye. Images of the fish's surroundings a transmitted, without distortion, on to t retina. In general, the fish can see for considerable distance without difficulty, b if it needs to see some close object clear then special muscles move the lens within t eye to attain perfect focus.

Many of the individual cells that make the retina are of the type known as cone they are sensitive to bright illumination a colour and there is every reason to belie that most fishes can distinguish colours we This is not true of deep-sea fishes, or on that are most active at night or live habitual in murky waters.

Smell and taste link-up The senses smell and taste in fishes are interlinke Fishes have two pairs of nostrils on ea side of the head, but they have nothing to c with breathing as in mammals; they lea to two chambers (nasal sacs) one on each si of the head, each of which is filled wi sensitive sensory organs. In fishes that re heavily on their sense of smell – the eel, f instance – these organs are very elaborat Eels can detect one thousandth of a gram crushed worm in 267 million litres of wat (about 58 million gallons).

The organs that give fishes their sense taste are specially enlarged cells scattere in the mouth, on the lips, on the barbels, a even on the lower head and pelvic fins some fishes. A carp tastes its food by touchi it with its barbels or its lips – it does not ne

Sight and pressure senses in fish

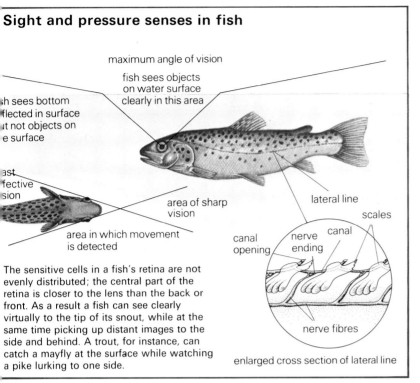

maximum angle of vision

fish sees objects on water surface clearly in this area

[fis]h sees bottom [re]flected in surface [b]ut not objects on [th]e surface

[le]ast [ef]fective [vi]sion

area in which movement is detected

area of sharp vision

lateral line

canal opening

nerve ending

canal

scales

nerve fibres

enlarged cross section of lateral line

The sensitive cells in a fish's retina are not evenly distributed; the central part of the retina is closer to the lens than the back or front. As a result a fish can see clearly virtually to the tip of its snout, while at the same time picking up distant images to the side and behind. A trout, for instance, can catch a mayfly at the surface while watching a pike lurking to one side.

another fish sensory system difficult for man to understand since we totally lack such a sophisticated sense.

What we see as a line on the fish's side is actually a canal with openings along its length; within the canal are special sensory cells that can detect changes in pressure. As a fish swims beside its fellows in a school, the changes in water pressure caused by the flexing bodies are detected by these cells. Then, as the school nears an obstruction in the river bed, the pressure waves are deformed; this change is detected, as also are the changes in pressure caused by an attacking predator. The effect must be something similar to a continuously registering radar system, alerting the fish to movements of many kinds in its immediate surroundings.

Sensitivity to electricity Sense organs that can detect the minute electrical charges of living muscle are a feature of some fishes, notably skates and many sharks. These fishes are known to have a system of pores particularly on their undersides which can detect minute electrical charges. The skates certainly produce their own electrical fields, and probably use them to recognise individuals of their own species on the sea bed. These modest electrical abilities are developed to an extreme in the electric ray (an uncommon British sea fish) which uses its powerful electric current–up to 220 volts at 8 amps in a big fish–to stun prey.

[t]ake the food into its mouth to find out if it [e]dible.

The sense of taste plays a large part in [fin]ding food. If you watch a pouting or a cod [in] an aquarium you can see them swimming [clo]se to the bottom with their chin barbels [an]d long pelvic fins brushing the sand and [co]nstantly searching for food.

Grunt 'n' groaners Many fishes make [sou]nds, using a variety of methods. For [ins]tance, the herring blows bubbles from its [sw]im bladder, other fishes grind their teeth [or] like the cod, haddock and the gurnards, [gru]nt and groan using their swim bladders to [am]plify the noises made by special muscles.

[Li]fe in the sea is, in fact, far from the [sil]ent world' of popular belief. Fishes of the [car]p family have a distinctive bony connec[tio]n between the swim bladder and the inner [ear] which probably helps them to hear more [acu]tely. It is also fairly certain that a large [roa]ch crunching up pond snails with its [thr]oat teeth makes a noise that can be easily [hea]rd in the immediate vicinity by other [fish]es, particularly by other roach. Schooling [fish], such as herring or sprats, are surrounded [by] a 'noise shadow' as they swim; this ['sh]adow' is caused by the movement of [hu]ndreds of beating fins and flexing muscles. [Th]e more advanced noise-makers, such as the [ha]ddock, grumble and drum as they move [aro]und in a school on the sea bed. The [ad]vantages of fishes making noises, and [be]ing able to hear well, are that a school can [ke]ep together–even when they cannot see [on]e another in the sunless sea. The fishes in [a] school also communicate about potential [foo]d or predators in their surroundings.

Pressure detector The lateral line, which [is s]een in most fish as a line of pores opening [on]to the scales on the side of the body, is

Below: The pike, a fish that relies mainly on its good eyesight to catch its prey, has relatively simple sense organs in its nasal cavity. By contrast, the eel has an exceptionally well-developed sense of smell.

DASHING DACE
OF FAST WATERS

One of our smallest, sleekest members of the carp family, the dace is also among our most successful freshwater fishes. On a summer's day you may see one leaping out of a river, eager to catch any insect that has strayed too close to the water.

Above: A young dace. The dace, and its close relatives the chub and the ide, are river fishes.
Dace are widely distributed in rivers across England, and in central Wales in the Dee catchment. Dace have also been reported on the borderlands of Scotland, though they were undoubtedly introduced there, and they also occur sparsely in the south of Ireland, being found in the River Blackwater in County Cork—again as an introduction.

The fresh waters of northern Europe are dominated by fishes of the carp family. Most are slender bodied with modest-sized scales on the body but not on the head. They have a single dorsal fin, which contains no sharp spines, and a slightly forked tail. Cyprinids live in schools, actively swimming in search of food or shelter. The dace is in many ways a typical member of the family, for it is an active schooling fish that lives mainly in open water in rivers.

Distinguishing the dace Its closest relatives in British waters are the chub and the ide or orfe, an introduced fish often seen in its golden-coloured ornamental form. The dace is rather more slender than either of the other two and has a narrow pointed head. Its scales are moderately small, with between 48 and 51 scales in the lateral line. Both chub and ide have broad heads and heavy muscular backs, and different numbers of scales along the lateral line, chub having 44 to 46 scales (which are thus larger than in a dace of comparable size) and the ide having 56 to 61 much smaller scales.

The most important distinguishing featu[re] however, is the shape of the outer edge of t[he] anal fin (and to a lesser extent of the dors[al] fin). In the dace it is concave, while the ch[ub] has a distinctly convex or rounded free edge [to] the fin. The ide has a flat dorsal fin and [a] slightly concave anal fin.

All these features are the kind of characte[r] that can be used to distinguish a fish in t[he] hand. It is much more difficult to be su[re] about the identity of fish in the riv[er] However, if you see a small school of fishes [in] a river in shallow water, swimming rapid[ly] and keeping close formation, then the chanc[es] are that they are dace. The presence of t[he] school may be betrayed by the quick gleam [of] silver as light catches the side of a fish turnin[g] but the flash is always brilliantly silver w[ith] none of the golden glint or the spark of red f[in] that comes from a school of roach.

Where to look Dace are essentially river fis[h.] Small specimens up to 13cm (5in) long live [in] small streams (sometimes almost narr[ow] enough to jump across). Typically they a[re] brooks with wider shallow stretches inte[r]spersed with deeper pools at the bends in t[he] stream. In upland areas small dace can [be] found where rocks narrow the beck into [a] series of pools and small torrents.

These little waters are important nurse[ry] streams for the dace, which share this habit[at] with juvenile trout and grayling, and you[ng] minnows. However, young dace are not co[n]fined to such tiny streams. At a length of 2[0-] 25cm (8-10in) they dominate the smaller cle[an] rivers where the flow is moderate, and fishes [of] this length and up to their maximum size [of] 30cm (12in) live in large rivers. Dace are n[ow] one of the most abundant freshwater fishes [in] the upper tidal Thames and very lar[ge] numbers are caught by anglers there. T[his] shows, in addition to the cleanliness of t[he] er today, that dace thrive in a large river, n one with heavily silted water like the ames, provided there is a continuous flow water.

Spawning time The dace spawns earlier in year than do most members of the carp nily. The precise date varies with the local mate and the severity of the weather, but it ually takes place when the water tempera- e reaches about 7-8°C (45-46°F). In rivers southern England this means that spawning ually begins in the second half of March, t in the north it may not take place until rly April. A very cold winter or a cool udy spring may delay the spawning.

Spawning occurs mostly at night, the ools gathering in gravelly shallows at the il' of a riffle where the water runs quickly er a stony bed. The eggs are yellowish and out 1.5mm in diameter. Being slightly cky when first laid they adhere to the fine at of algae covering the gravel, or they fall tween the stones themselves. As the water nperature is relatively low when the eggs are d, development is slow and in a normal ring they do not hatch for between 25 and days.

The number of eggs produced by the female ries with her size (as it does in all fishes). males about 15cm (6in) long–the length at ich they begin spawning–produce around 00 eggs, while those of 25cm (10in) may ed as many as 18,000.

Success story Despite the low number of gs laid and their long period of lying protected on the river-bed, the sheer mbers of dace in our rivers show them to be ery successful species. This is probably due their spawning much earlier than any of eir carp family relatives and in a different rt of the river (most of their relatives awning in deeper water). This means that as on as the water begins to warm up in the ring and the populations of crustaceans and her invertebrates begin to build up, the ung dace are in a favourable position to ke advantage of this food. But they are often a knife-edge: a late spring, or heavy rains llowed by frosts, might mean that as much 90% of the young dace die within a week of tching.

The diet of the adults is relatively un- ecialised except that they eat large numbers insect larvae. In winter they tend to feed on ddis-fly larvae and even molluscs, but in mmer they eat mayfly larvae and adults, ackfly and midge larvae, and a very small oportion of algae and water plants.

During the summer dace are at their most sible, leaping at the surface of the water in rsuit of newly hatched mayflies or caddis es, and ever on the lookout for the hatching aquatic insects. Anglers take advantage of dace's surface-feeding activities by fishing r it with a fly and are frequently successful r, although the dace is rather a small fish, it ves good sport on a fly rod.

The dace group

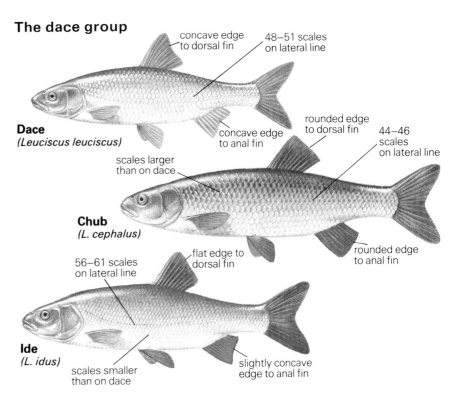

Dace (*Leuciscus leuciscus*) — concave edge to dorsal fin — 48–51 scales on lateral line — concave edge to anal fin

Chub (*L. cephalus*) — scales larger than on dace — rounded edge to dorsal fin — 44–46 scales on lateral line — rounded edge to anal fin

Ide (*L. idus*) — 56–61 scales on lateral line — flat edge to dorsal fin — scales smaller than on dace — slightly concave edge to anal fin

Above: The dace and its close relatives are best distinguished by the shape of the edge of their anal and dorsal fins. The colour of the lower fins may vary from yellow to orange in both dace and chub, and is reddish in the case of ide.

Right: In summer dace leap out of the water in pursuit of food.

Below: The dace has a very acute sense of smell, aided by the nostrils in front of its eyes.

Rising to feed

JOHN DORY: A STEALTHY PREDATOR

The John dory, a flattened, disc-shaped fish, is a slow swimmer: the secret of its hunting success is its quick-acting, protrusible jaws.

The John dory is probably the most distinctive of all British sea fishes–the lugubrious expression on its face being memorable. Its body is flattened from side to side but is at the same time deep; the head is large, with big eyes placed high on the sides of the head. The most obvious feature, however, is the huge mouth, with the bones of the upper jaw very mobile so that the whole top half of the mouth swings forward to form a protrusible scoop.

Unusual appearance The edges of the body are armed with large hooked spines. These are most noticeable along the belly where they form strong spiny scales, and along the bases of the dorsal and anal fins where they are simply spikes. While the second dorsal fin and the main part of the anal fin are relatively small and low, the rays of the first dorsal fin are large, strong spines, and the first rays of the anal fin are detached and are conspicuously large. The dorsal spines bear long streamer filaments. The pelvic fin, too, has very long rays.

In colour, the dory tends to be unremarkable except that on each side, more or less in the middle, it has a conspicuous black blotch about the size of the eye, surrounded by a

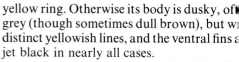
Above: The position of the dory's eyes gives binocular vision at close quarters. This specimen has unusually yellow lower fins (below).

yellow ring. Otherwise its body is dusky, of grey (though sometimes dull brown), but w distinct yellowish lines, and the ventral fins jet black in nearly all cases.

The dramatic eye spots on the sides of t John dory have led to a popular associati with the biblical story of Peter taking t tribute money from a fish's mouth. The da marks on either side of the fish were thoug to be the thumb and finger prints of t Apostle. A similar legend involves the ha dock, which also has dusky thumb-prints its sides, but neither fish occurs in the Sea Galilee, the scene of the miracle. The story however, sufficiently strongly associated wi the John dory for it to be known as St Pete fish in some parts of Europe, even in Scandi avia where it is not abundant.

Method of moving The dory is not a power swimmer. Dories are usually seen in grou keeping station under moored boats floating objects, by making gentle undulatio of the dorsal and anal fins. They also li among kelp and near rocks, although from t frequency with which they are caught in traw they must also live over open sandy bottom In British seas the species is only rea

common on the southern and western coasts, roughly from the Isle of Wight westwards to the Isles of Scilly and then along the Welsh and Irish coastlines. However, it does occur further east and north than this with moderate regularity, and is fairly frequently captured in the North Sea. Since it is not a particularly powerful swimmer, there is little doubt that at times, and perhaps from choice, the dory simply drifts in the sea's currents.

How the dory hunts The dory's weak powers of swimming, and its slow deliberate movements, can become a positive advantage to the fish when seeking food. Perhaps surprisingly, it eats fishes in large numbers, and it also captures cuttlefishes. Its food comprises almost any of the fishes common in the area in which it lives, and its method of catching these is by stealth.

From head-on, the very deep but narrow body of the dory is hard to see, and when hidden in cover the fish is almost invisible. The narrowness of the head also permits the dory to see objects close in front of its snout, and its forward binocular vision is helped by the mobility of its eyes in their sockets. Having sighted prey approaching, the dory keeps head-on towards it, slowly edging closer by means of gentle movements of the fins. When still some way away (the distance depending on the size of the dory) the jaws are shot forwards with incredible speed and the prey is swept into the mouth with the in-rushing water.

The remarkable efficiency of the dory's way of catching food is seen by the variety of fishes which have been found in its stomach. Herring, pilchard, pout, pollack, wrasses and gobies are all active swimmers which have been caught by the dory's stealth. Sometimes they eat large numbers of fishes—there is a record of a foot-long dory which contained twenty-five small flounders and three sea scorpions. This was evidently a fish which was

The dory and its jaws

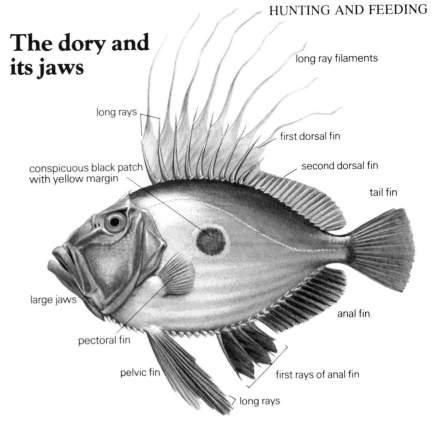

long ray filaments

long rays

first dorsal fin

second dorsal fin

tail fin

conspicuous black patch with yellow margin

large jaws

anal fin

pectoral fin

pelvic fin

first rays of anal fin

long rays

How the dory catches prey

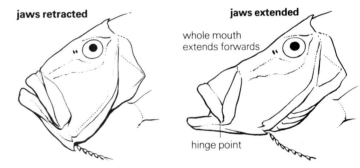

jaws retracted

jaws extended

whole mouth extends forwards

hinge point

Below: The dory is normally found inshore, in depths of 10-50m (6-30 fathoms). It grows to a size of some 40cm (16in) on average.

Above: In one quick lunge, both jaws shoot forward while water rushes into the mouth, carrying with it the helpless prey.

using its excellent vision to spot food hidden on the sea-bed, and was probably swimming along in a head-down position—a posture they frequently adopt—while scanning the sea-bed.

Late summer spawning In British waters the dory spawns during August. The eggs are small, about 2mm in diameter, and pelagic. They develop slowly: it is known that in the Mediterranean they take 12-13 days, so in our colder waters they may take three weeks to hatch. Within two weeks of hatching, the post-larva is recognisable as a dory; the large head and deep body are more or less the same proportion as in the adult—even a 6mm long fish is 3mm deep. At this stage, and for the next few months, they live in the upper 30m (16 fathoms) of the sea, and are more or less at the mercy of the tidal currents. In the English Channel those that are swept inshore join local breeding populations, while those reaching the North Sea do not breed.

STUDYING THE WAYS OF STARFISHES

Starfishes crawl at a steady pace across the sea-bed, scenting and tracking down prey animals in a sinister fashion. Their activities are fascinating to observe, but there is also a practical reason to study their behaviour: they can devastate oyster beds, and in man's view this brands them as pests.

Above: Starfishes starting to swarm on a mussel bed in the North Sea—these are *Asterias rubens*. The white lines on the rock resemble pavement cracks, but this is natural substrate.

Below: A solitary *Asterias rubens* sets off to feed. One ray detects a nearby mussel bed and takes the lead; the other rays are about to begin moving in the same direction.

Starfishes belong with the sea-urchins, sea-cucumbers, brittle stars and feather stars to a group of animals known as echinoderms. To understand their behaviour one has to appreciate that there are radical differences which separate echinoderms from other animals. An echinoderm has no head, nor does it possess a centralised brain. It lacks eyes, although the tips of the 'arms' or rays of starfishes have light receptors known as optic cushions, that form no image but simply detect light. The form of its skeleton differs from that of almost any other animal group. An echinoderm also possesses a unique locomotory system of tube-feet.

How starfishes walk A starfish's body consists of a number of limbs called rays, arranged round a central mouth. The mouth is

rrounded by a nerve ring, from which rves run off into each ray. Starfishes often ve five rays, though *Crossaster papposus* ually has from eight to 13 and *Luidia ciliaris* s seven. The rays do not walk as legs do, but ey play an important part in locomotion cause they bear the numerous tube-feet on eir undersides, and these walk by taking tiny ps, each in the same direction. The tube- t are arranged in two rows of pairs, with a oove between the rows leading along the ray m the tip to the animal's mouth at the ntre of the underside. They are driven by eir own muscles and also by the fluid essure from within the animal.

Starfishes crawl at a slow, steady pace– terias, for example, can cover several ntimetres in a minute. Any of the rays is pable of taking the lead, and as a direction comes established the tube-feet on all the her rays begin stepping and help propel the imal in the same direction. If accidentally erturned, starfishes have a 'righting re- onse': one of the rays turns over at its tip til the tube feet gain a purchase, and then adually pull the rest of the animal back into upright position.

Starfishes have a well-developed sense of ell, enabling them to detect the presence of od or enemies. *Asterias rubens*, for example, n sense from a distance many animals ch as oysters, common mussels or scallops, l of which it eats. *Crossaster papposus* does t have such discriminatory powers at a stance, but when in contact with another imal it can make the distinction's necessary r its own survival. When it touches another ember of its own species, for example, it sets f in the opposite direction, but when it uches *Asterias rubens* it attacks and eats it.

Feeding behaviour Starfishes are generally rnivorous, and are in fact specialised and ficient killers, capable of interesting be- viour, for they have exploited one parti- lar evolutionary avenue to an advanced gree. Their bodies are just the right shape to rap round a mollusc or part of another arfish, holding the mouth in direct contact th the victim.

Bivalves are very suitable prey animals: ey cannot move about very much, and while eir hard shells protect them from many all predators, the starfish can clamber on to e shell and attach some of its suckered tube- t to each valve. It then begins to pull them en. This steady tension tires out the ductor muscles that hold the shells shut, owing the attacking starfish to prize them ghtly apart. Alternatively, the bivalve may ed to open its shells deliberately for its own ysiological requirements. Either way, a ght gape is all the starfish needs to insinuate e fine folds of its stomach, which it turns side out through its mouth and into the ell of the bivalve. Once this is in contact with e live tissue of the victim, digestion begins d the prey dies. When digestion is complete,

a well-cleaned empty shell is all that remains and the starfish withdraws its stomach folds and makes off.

Starfish swarms At certain times some kinds of starfish become strongly gregarious and appear in swarms, often of over 50 and some- times several thousand strong. There is good reason for investigating this swarming behav- iour, for some starfishes can devastate shell- fish beds. It is because of this economic sig- nificance, therefore, that the study of starfish behaviour has become a scientific priority.

Starfishes that behave in this way all belong to species that prey on animals which some- times occur in great abundance, such as mussels in beds or corals on reefs. Attracted to the plentiful prey, the starfishes switch from a dispersed, solitary life to a concentrated, gregarious one. *Asterias rubens* abandons its normal tendency to seek dark places if, as often happens, the mussel bed where a swarm develops is in shallow, well-lit water.

Studies with *Asterias rubens* give rise to an

Above: The common sunstar (*Crossaster papposus*) usually has between eight and 13 rays, but the one shown here has 14.

Below: A specimen of *Stichastrella rosea* regrows a lost ray. If damaged in an attack by a predator such as a bird or a fish, a starfish can usually regenerate lost rays. This differs from the regeneration of limbs by crabs or lobsters, which have specially fragile places in their limbs where the breakage occurs and heals rapidly. Virtually any piece of a starfish ray can be regrown if lost, but if the nerve ring surrounding the mouth is damaged this may prove fatal. The nervous system seems to play an important role in regeneration.

interesting conclusion. One feeding individual produces a chemical effluent that repels neighbouring starfishes of the same species until, after a certain amount of exposure to the effluent, starfishes begin to find it attractive. This change in response, from repulsion to attraction, results in a change in the behaviour of the starfishes and, in conditions of plentiful food, leads to the formation of swarms.

How starfishes breed Starfishes do not need to mate, for fertilisation can be carried out at a distance. The sexes are separate in almost all species—males simply release sperm to be carried away on sea currents, and females similarly release eggs. This process is known as spawning, and in British waters it typically occurs in May and June. Fertilisation then takes place by chance encounters of eggs and sperms, after which the egg quickly develops and hatches into a microscopic floating larva.

The larva develops and grows, until it metamorphoses into a very small starfish only a millimetre or two across, which is known as a juvenile. A year after hatching it may be, say, 10cm (4in) across, but it can grow more rapidly and the largest *Asterias* starfishes in British waters are around 50cm (20in) across. Such magnificent specimens may be seen on the west coast of Britain from the Channel Islands north to Scotland where the warm waters of the North Atlantic Drift (the so-called Gulf Stream) provide good conditions for growth.

Above: An *Asterias rubens* feeding: its hunched stance resembles the spawning posture of *Marthasterias glacialis* (right). An underside view of *Asterias* with the remains of its prey is seen below.

British starfishes generally do not swarm breed, though feeding aggregations may be an advantage for breeding because of the close proximity.

Burrowing starfishes While most starfish live on rocks, some are sand dwellers a these can be efficient burrowers. Burrowi enables them to escape detection by p dators, as well as to hunt for molluscs that in the sand. These starfishes differ in t development of their tube-feet from oth starfishes. *Astropecten irregularis* and *Lui ciliaris* are examples: unlike the rest, they ha no suckers on their tube-feet, for these are n useful in their shifting habitat. Individu tube-feet can lift sand particles up on to t back of the starfish, which thus gradua burrows down as more sand is lifted upwar These tube-feet are also well adapted f walking over the surface of the sar Burrowing starfishes also eat various surfa dwelling animals, emerging from the sand order to capture them. In evolutionary ter these starfishes are relatively primitive.

SEA-BORNE MARAUDER

The Portuguese man o' war is not a single animal like the jellyfish which it resembles, but is an animal colony, made up of four types of individual called polyps.

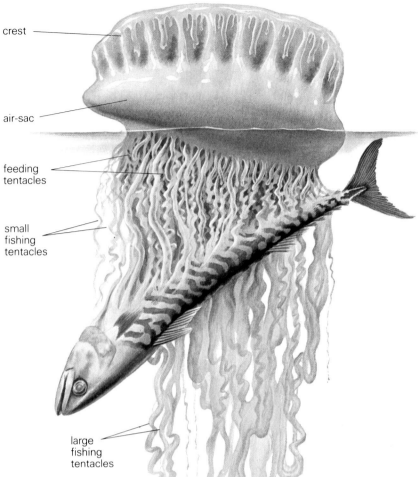

crest

air-sac

feeding tentacles

small fishing tentacles

large fishing tentacles

The Portuguese man o' war lives in warm open seas, but is sometimes washed up on the southern and western shores of the British Isles. This surface-dwelling coelenterate measures up to 33cm (13in) long by 13cm (5in) wide and its longest tentacles hang down 3m (9ft) or more.

At no time in its life cycle does it depend on shallow water or attach itself to the sea bed – unlike its close relatives the seafirs, and, more distant ones, the jellyfish (see pages 42-3).

Four polyps Although superficially it resembles a jellyfish, the Portuguese man o' war differs in one important respect: it is an animal colony, not a solitary individual. The body is composed of a 'society' of four types of individuals called polyps.

The most conspicuous polyp is the single bag-like float called the air-sac. This gas-filled individual is the only part that can be seen above the water. At the top is a crest which catches the wind so the colony may be blown about.

Trailing traps Three other types of polyp hang from this float by short stalks. The long coiled tentacles containing powerful stinging cells, which make the Portuguese man o' war so dangerous, belong to the fishing and defensive polyps known as dactylozooids. They lack mouths and cannot feed; but they trail their long tentacles in the water like a drift net to trap and immobilise prey before transferring it to the mouths of the feeding polyps.

These feeding polyps, which hang in bunches, are called gastrozooids. They have a mouth with which to ingest prey, and a single tentacle to assist this. Their gastric cavities make connections with the other polyps in the colony and pass them food.

Reproduction The final type of polyp is the gonozooid. It produces medusae called gonophores which remain attached to the parent polyp. The gonophores produce eggs and sperm which are released into the sea and unite to form a larva. Still in the open water the larva develops and eventually founds another floating colony. At no stage in the animal's life cycle does the man o' war depend on the sea bed.

Like its distant jellyfish relatives, the Portuguese man o' war (*Physalia physalis*) moves at the mercy of wind and current. Though it lives in the open sea, it does occasionally get washed ashore if persistent winds blow from the south west. It can, however, regulate how much it is affected by the wind by deflating or inflating the air-sac. In rough weather it raises its tentacles and spreads them near the surface to increase stability. It also submerges the upper surface of the air-sac under water to stop the sun drying it.

The Portuguese man o' war relies on the strength of its stinging cells and tentacles to overwhelm prey such as surface-swimming fish, including young mackerel (above). Certain small fish such as *Stromateus* swim among the tentacles and appear resistant to the stinging cells. These fish, as well as some turtles, feed on this creature's tissues.

The name Portuguese man o' war may have been originated by early ocean navigators who were reminded of Portuguese war ships (caravels) by the animal's float polyp.

Left: If specimens are washed up on beaches, the float polyp is often broken off from the rest of the animal colony. Do *not* touch even a dead specimen because its stinging cells can still inflict severe wounds.

HOW INSECTS EAT

Insects are a diverse group – and this is reflected in their diets, for together they have exploited nearly every feeding opportunity that exists.

With over a million known species, and at least another five million awaiting discovery and description, insects are easily the largest group of living organisms in the world. They are also the most diverse group, and this is particularly apparent from their mode of feeding and their diet.

Chewers and suckers Two broad feeding categories can be recognised among insects: the chewers and the suckers. The former – the chewers – have jaws which can bite and rasp at food. They include the plant-feeding species which leave holes providing clear evidence of their presence, and predators, which kill and rapidly dispose of their prey with bites. Examples of such chewers are grasshoppers – attackers of vegetation – and dragonflies which hunt and kill.

The second category, the suckers, have a tubular stylet or proboscis which they use to extract liquid food from living plants, animals, dung or rotting flesh. These insects insert their mouthparts either by pushing between crevices or by piercing and sucking at sap, juices or body fluids. Such a feeding method leaves little trace, and is seen in aphids (plant-suckers), and mosquitoes (blood-suckers).

Life-cycles and diets Insects can be further divided into two categories according to their

Above and left: The adults and larvae of the common wasp have different diets. While the adults feed on nectar, the juices exuding from rotting fruits, and the honeydew produced by aphids, the larvae are carnivorous, relying on small invertebrates supplied to them by the worker wasps.

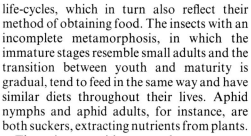

Below: Cabbage aphids are equipped with sucking mouthparts so they can extract nutrients out of a plant's phloem.

life-cycles, which in turn also reflect their method of obtaining food. The insects with an incomplete metamorphosis, in which the immature stages resemble small adults and the transition between youth and maturity is gradual, tend to feed in the same way and have similar diets throughout their lives. Aphid nymphs and aphid adults, for instance, are both suckers, extracting nutrients from plants.

Those insects with a complete metamorphosis, in which the transition is less gradual, however, have larvae which feed, almost immobile pupae which do not feed, and adults which may or may not take in food – and if they do their diet is nearly always totally different from that of the larvae. Both beetles, which are mostly chewers, and butterflies, which are mainly suckers, fall into this category.

Sucking and chewing, then, are the two principal ways of obtaining food, and immature insects may or may not utilise the same resources and feed in the same way as adults.

Frothy froghopper One sucker with an incomplete life-cycle is the froghopper, also known as the meadow spittlebug. The nymphs of this species cause the small blobs of foam, often called cuckoo spit, which are found on vegetation in May and June. Soon after hatching from the egg (which overwinters among vegetation) the froghopper nymph pushes its stylet into new plant tissue until it locates the xylem – the water-conducting vessels in plants. It then extracts from the plant large quantities of water which pass through its alimentary system, before being pumped

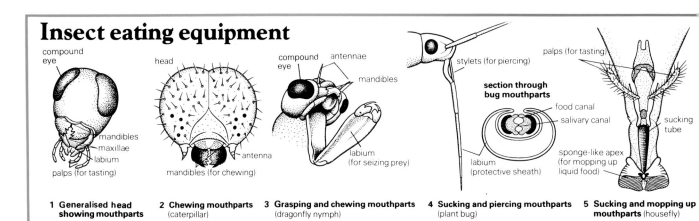

Insect eating equipment

- compound eye
- head
- mandibles
- maxillae
- labium
- palps (for tasting)

- head
- mandibles (for chewing)
- antenna

- compound eye
- antennae
- mandibles
- labium (for seizing prey)

- stylets (for piercing)
- **section through bug mouthparts**
- food canal
- salivary canal
- labium (protective sheath)

- palps (for tasting)
- sucking tube
- sponge-like apex (for mopping up liquid food)

1 Generalised head showing mouthparts

2 Chewing mouthparts (caterpillar)

3 Grasping and chewing mouthparts (dragonfly nymph)

4 Sucking and piercing mouthparts (plant bug)

5 Sucking and mopping up mouthparts (housefly)

Above: The emperor dragonfly, in common with all other dragonflies, is a hunter and a killer. Equipped with jaws that can bite and rasp at solids, it rapidly overcomes its victims by out-flying them and then delivering a few fatal bites. You are most likely to see the emperor dragonfly in the sunshine or around nightfall hunting for smaller dragonflies and insects around ponds and lakes from June until early September. It is our largest hawker dragonfly.

into foam just as it leaves the anus. The nymph lives immersed in this foam which probably protects it from predators.

The plant's xylem contains small amounts of nitrogenous nutrients in solution, and it is these that constitute food for the developing froghopper nymph. As the nymph grows, so the foam blob becomes larger, until the nymph eventually moults and emerges as an adult. It then leaves the foam, which quickly dries up. Adult froghoppers feed less often than the nymphs and do not remain on the same plant.

Sugar-tapper The cabbage aphid is also equipped with a sucking stylet which it pushes into the plant's phloem, where the energy and nutrient supply is located. The resources the phloem are altogether richer than t xylem so aphids are able to extract lar amounts of sugar. This sugar solution pass through the aphid's body and is excreted sugary honeydew, the stickiness of which noticeable on the leaves of trees in d summers.

Cabbage aphids are restricted to cabbag and related plants, so when there is a hea infestation they are a considerable drain the energy and nutrient reserves of a pla They remain on the same plant, continua tapping the nutrient flow, and move aw only when the supply dries up.

A moth's diet The elephant hawk-moth is insect with a complete metamorphosis; t larvae feed in a totally different way from t adults. When fully grown, the caterpillars the elephant hawk-moth are 9cm (3½in) lo and decidedly chubby. By day they r motionless at the base of rosebay willowhe stems and related plants, but at night th climb the plants and consume enormo quantities of leaves, defecating almost equa large amounts of frass (caterpillar droppin at the same time. Elephant hawk-mo caterpillars must consume this vast amount the food is neither particularly nutritious n digestible.

In winter the nutrients and energy acquir by the caterpillar during the previous autu are used to power the metabolic processes t turn the large, fat caterpillar into a strea lined pink and black moth. The adult flies dusk, and feeds by unwinding its coiled-proboscis and inserting it into strong scented, tubular flowers from which it suc up sugary nectar. It does this while hovering front of the flower; as soon as all the nectar extracted it moves on to the next flower.

Nectar-feeder and predator Adults of t common wasp feed on nectar and other liqu food, such as the juices which exude fro rotting fruit or the honeydew produced aphids. Unlike the elephant hawk-mot however, they also have to obtain food f their larvae which develop in the nest.

Once a wasp colony is well-established contains thousands of cells, each with

typical insect's mouth
is surrounded by 3
rs of appendages: the
ndibles for biting, and
accessory jaws—the
xillae and the labium.
terpillars (2) have well-
veloped mandibles,
ile dragonfly nymphs
have enlarged labia for
zing prey. Plant bugs
have modified
uthparts for piercing
d sucking, and
useflies (5) have fleshy
uthparts.

ght: The elephant hawk-
th is another species
ose adult and caterpillar
d in different ways. While
chubby caterpillar
low) feeds on vast
antities of leaves, the adult
icately sucks in nectar
ough its long proboscis
ich it inserts in tubular
wers.

ght: The foam you see on
nts in May and June is
duced by froghopper
mphs. Soon after hatching
m its egg the nymph
rces the plant tissue and
racts large quantities of
ter from the plant's xylem
ater-conducting vessels).
liquid then passes
ough the nymph's
estive system and out
ough its anus in a bubbly
m-like substance. The
mph then lives in this
m, which probably
tects it from predators.

voracious larva which must be fed by the workers. The workers are fierce predators and scavengers, and attack and kill caterpillars, flies, butterflies and spiders.

Cannibalistic ladybirds The seven-spot ladybird is a more typical predator than the common wasp. In spring the females lay little clusters of bright yellow eggs near, or among, aphid colonies. Upon hatching the tiny ladybird larvae rush for the nearest aphids and start devouring them. Provided there are plenty of aphids to consume, the larvae grow quickly and soon form orange and black pupae attached to leaves and stems. If the aphids become scarce, the larvae attack each other—an example of true cannibalism. On becoming adult the ladybirds continue to feed on aphids, although if the local food supply fails they embark on long distance flights in search of better pickings.

Parasitic fly maggots The bluebottle look-alike, *Protocalliphora sordida*, is an unpleasant looking fly, the adults of which feed on flower nectar although their maggots are parasitic. Female flies lay their eggs in the lining of birds' nests during the incubation period of the eggs. Here the fly maggots hatch, usually at the same time as the nestlings, and periodically attach themselves by means of a sucking disc to the bellies of the young birds. The maggots pierce with their mouth hooks and suck the blood, growing rapidly, but spend most of the time hidden among nest material. As many as one hundred maggots may exist in a single nest.

Froghopper, aphid, moth, wasp, ladybird and parasitic bluebottle are just examples of the varied ways in which insects find and utilise food—they illustrate the remarkable diversity that exists within the insect class.

Left: The wood tiger beetle (*Cicindela sylvatica*) grow up to 17mm (⅔in) long, an is found mainly on heathland. It is especially fond of burnt areas where is well camouflaged.

Above: *Cicindela hybrida* grows up to 15mm (⅝in) long and inhabits sand dun

Above: *Cicindela germani* is no more than 10mm (⅜i long and is found only on the Isle of Wight.

Above: Green tiger beetle (*Cicindela campestris*) in flight, with wing covers raised well out of the way of the wings. This species reaches 15mm (⅝in) long.

TIGER BEETLES: HANDSOME HUNTERS

Your first encounter with a tiger beetle is likely to be a startling one – a rustling or whirring sound rushing past your ear. The flight of a tiger beetle is fast and erratic and difficult to follow and, when the insect does land, it blends so well with the vegetation that it is almost invisible.

Tiger beetles are so-called because of their fierce predatory habits. They belong to the same family (Carabidae) as ground beetles but, unlike most ground beetles, are active only in the sunshine. The group is on the edge of its range in Britain, with just five species existing. Only one of these, the green tiger beetle, is at all widely distributed. The others are very local insects.

Five species, or only four? The green tiger beetle is a very handsome creature, with a ground colour ranging from bright green to almost black. There is a distinct metallic sheen on the pronotum and the wing cases (elytra) carry a variable pattern of cream spots. The legs and margins of the wing cases

are coppery red. The insect lives mainly on heathland and in other sandy places and occurs in most parts of the British Isles. Like the other tiger beetles, it is active in spring and summer.

The wood tiger beetle is blackish brown with a bronze or purple sheen and yellow spots and stripes on the wing cases. A rare insect in Britain, it is most likely to be found in a broad belt stretching from Devon to Surrey.

Our other tiger beetles are even rarer than the wood tiger beetle, and have not even received common names. *Cicindela germanica* looks like a smaller version of the green tiger beetle, but its body is much narrower and

Above *Cicindela maritima* reaches 12mm (½in) in length and lives in sandy coastal areas.

Larvae that lie in ambush

Larval tiger beetles are carnivores, but instead of roaming in search of prey like the adults, they lie in ambush. On hatching from the egg, the larva enlarges its burrow, using its huge jaws to loosen the soil and its broad flat head to throw the excavated material away. The tunnels are periodically enlarged as the larva grows and when complete may be 30cm (12in) deep. The larva anchors itself at the top of the shaft and waits for a meal to arrive. (It is held in place by sharp spines that dig into the wall of the burrow.) The mouth of the burrow is plugged by the larva's large head and thick thoracic shield. If the victim walks right over the waiting larva, the larva simply flicks its head back and impales the prey on its jaws, but otherwise it shoots the front part of its body out of the lair at great speed and grabs the victim as it passes. The larva's diet consists mainly of ants, but caterpillars and other insects are also eaten. If the prey struggles, the larva drags it to the bottom of the burrow before beginning to eat it.

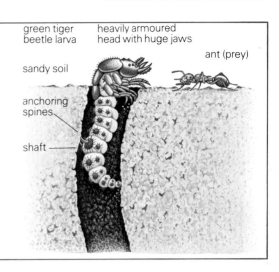

green tiger beetle larva
heavily armoured head with huge jaws
ant (prey)
sandy soil
anchoring spines
shaft

re cylindrical. Once found from Devon to mpshire, it now appears to be confined to Isle of Wight.

C. hybrida resembles the wood tiger beetle t is usually lighter in colour, with a yellow e and larger yellow marks on its wing cases. nhabits coastal sand dunes in North Wales d north-west England from Cheshire to mbria. C. maritima also lives on coastal nes, but occurs further south than hybrida. has been recorded from most coastal inties from North Wales round to East iglia. The two species are very much alike, t maritima may be distinguished by the ominent right-angled bend in the central low band on its wing cases. Some ento ologists consider maritima to be just a riety of hybrida, thus reducing our com ment of tiger beetles to just four species.

Built for speed Tiger beetles fly well on rm days and take to the air at the slightest turbance, although their erratic flight does t last long and they soon drop to the ground ain. They are most at home on the ground, ere their long spindly legs enable them to ove with great speed. They are, in fact, iong the fastest runners in the insect rld, and have been timed at speeds of about cm (2ft) per second.

Ground hunters Tiger beetles hunt entirely the ground, finding their prey by sight. e beetles thus favour rather open habitats ere they can spot their prey easily with ir large eyes. Sandy heaths provide just the ht conditions for them.

The prey consists of a wide variety of ier insects, including large numbers of ts. Tiger beetles can detect such prey from listance of about 15cm (6in), but they do t dash in immediately to catch it, for their o speed can be maintained for only a few itimetres. Having sighted its prey, the etle trundles towards it until it is within out 8cm (3in). Then comes the final sprint, ting a mere ⅛th of a second. The huge, irply-toothed jaws take a firm hold and ish the victim to death.

Burrow builders Although they are sun ing insects, the tiger beetles do not like to too warm, and on the rare occasions when

the ground becomes uncomfortably hot, they spend the middle of the day in their burrows. They also retire to the burrows at night. Female tiger beetles dig short burrows in which they lay their eggs, normally choosing undisturbed and untrampled ground and laying one egg in each burrow.

Jaws and legs are all used for digging the burrow. The soil is loosened by the jaws, pushed back under the body by the front legs and kicked away by the hind legs. The burrow is not much longer than the beetle itself and is excavated remarkably quickly.

Larval life Larval tiger beetles, when they hatch from the egg, enlarge their burrows and live in them, lying in wait for any prey that passes. The larvae of C. hybrida and the other dune-living species dig sloping tunnels in steep banks, while the wood and green tiger beetle larvae excavate vertical shafts in flat ground.

Instead of the adult's large compound eyes, the larva has six simple eyes (ocelli) and can probably pick out prey by sight at a distance of about 5cm (2in), provided it is moving. The larva may also rely on scent and vibra tions to tell it that its prey is approaching.

By late summer the larva has reached a length of about 2cm (¾in) and is ready to pupate at the bottom of its shaft. The pupal stage lasts for only a few weeks, but the fully developed adult remains at the bottom of the burrow throughout the winter.

Sneaky parasite

You might imagine that the tiger beetle larva, tucked safely into its burrow and wielding vice-like jaws at the entrance, would be quite safe from attack, but this is not in fact the case. The female of a small ant-like creature called *Methoca ichneumonides* manages to avoid the larva's snapping jaws. She gets down into the burrow where she stings the larva's abdomen and lays an egg on it. *Methoca* then leaves the burrow, first filling it with soil before flying away. Her offspring feeds on the young beetle. The sting paralyses the larva until the *Methoca* grub completes its growth.

Below: Green tiger beetle laying an egg in a burrow. Sandy heaths are ideal for these beetles in that they are well-drained and therefore relatively warm, and easy to burrow in.

Above: A lycosid spider carrying a cocoon. In spite of the size of her burden, the female seems to be able to trundle about in search of prey without difficulty.

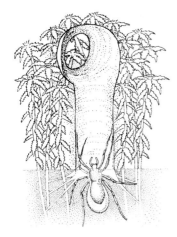

Above: The marsh spider, *Pirata piscatorius,* builds a vertical silk tube among sphagnum moss. It emerges to catch prey from the open upper end of the tube, and shelters underwater at the lower end among the moss stems.

THE HUNTER AND THE HUNTED

Wolf spiders are active hunters, preying on insects and sucking their juices for food. In turn, they themselves fall victim to small spider-hunting wasps.

Some insects, and other arthropods, are fierce predators which hunt down creatures smaller or weaker than themselves for food. This is not always a one-way system, however. Some of these hunters are themselves attacked by equally ferocious predators. The lives of wolf spiders and spider-hunting wasps (pompilids) cross in this way: the spiders prey on small insects such as flies and are in turn preyed on by the wasps.

Speed and surprise Wolf or hunting spiders catch prey not with a web like our familiar garden spiders, but by the speed, strength and surprise of their attack. They run down chosen victims in much the same way as a wolf—hence their name. They belong to two families, the Lycosidae and the Pisauridae; in Britain there are nearly 40 species of the first and just three of the second. M[...] of these spiders are a drab brown or g[...] colour and can be distinguished from ot[...] spiders (mostly web-spinners) by the patt[...] of their eight eyes. These are arranged [...] three rows–four eyes in the front row a[...] two in each of the other rows. Most w[...] spiders are 5-10mm ($\frac{1}{4}$-$\frac{1}{2}$in) long, and e[...] the largest never reach more than 20m[...] ($\frac{3}{4}$in).

Wolf spiders are ground hunters a[...] frequent woodland, meadows, heathland a[...] marshland. Some are associated with spec[...] ised habitats, such as the swamp spid[...] *Dolomedes fimbriatus,* or our five *Troch[...]* species which favour heathland and [...] under stones or heather, only coming out [...] search for prey after dark. Our two m[...] numerous species, *Pardosa amentata* a[...] *P. pullata,* occur almost everywhere.

The keen sight of the wolf spider enable[...] to spot moving prey from a distance o[...] metre (3ft) or more. It lurks in the und[...] growth, then rushes out to chase and ov[...] power the victim with a bite from its fan[...] Some species, such as the pale-bodi[...] dark-ringed *Arctosa perita,* dig a burrow [...] the ground to hide in, and pounce on victi[...] as they pass by.

Mating and breeding Courtship amo[...] wolf spiders is carried out by means of vis[...]

...nals. A male in mating condition stands in ...nt of a female and waves his long palps as ...sending a message by semaphore. Some ...cies wave the front legs, while others ...rate the whole body. The female faces the ...nalling male and repeats his movements to ...dicate that she is ready to mate. At the end ...this display, the male climbs on top of the ...nale and injects into the genital opening of ... female the sperm that he has previously ...nsferred to a special organ at the tip of ...ch palp.

The female spider lays her eggs on a silk ...t and wraps them up in more silk to make a ...und cocoon. A lycosid female attaches the ...coon to the tip of her abdomen, while a ...saurid carries it, held up by her fangs and ...pported by strands of silk, beneath her ...dy. The newly-emerged lycosid spiderlings ...mber straight on to their mother's back ...d are carried around for several weeks until ...y disperse. In contrast, a female pisaurid ...aches her cocoon before the spiderlings ...erge and spins a sheet of silk over it. The ...ung spiders remain in this nursery tent, ...h their mother on guard, until they are ...le to fend for themselves.

Small but deadly Wolf spiders are hunted by ...nale solitary wasps – the spider hunters.

... attack and overcome a large hunting ...der is quite a feat, but these tiny wasps ...ch as the red-and-black-banded *Anoplius* ...cus and the grey *Pompilius plumbeus* – are ...le to sting the spiders and paralyse them ...h their venom. The thin-waisted wasps can ...rve their abdomen round the spiders and ...ng them on the more vulnerable underparts. ...e female pompilid catches spiders – par...ularly *Arctosa* and *Trochosa* – during the ...nmer, to feed her future young. After ...ting, the female wasp searches among the ...dergrowth for a spider. Her excitable ...haviour as she rushes about with wings ...ivering makes her very noticeable. Once ...ught, spiders are quickly immobilised. ...seems that the spiders – panic-stricken by ... colour, scent and lunging, darting be...viour of the attacking wasp – make little ... no attempt to fight back.

The wasp carefully hides its paralysed prey, sometimes in a shallow grave, while she digs a nesting burrow in the soil with her legs and jaws. Her long legs are equipped with stout bristles and spurs which help in raking the earth. When the burrow is complete – it consists of a straight or slightly curving shaft with a cell at the bottom – the wasp hauls the spider into it, dragging it backwards down the hole. All this hard work is not always rewarded, however. Since the wasp hunts first, then digs the nest, there is a period during which her prey is left unguarded. Many wasps return to the prey repeatedly while digging, but even so it may be stolen, often by other hunting wasps.

Paralysed provender When the spider is in position at the bottom of the burrow, the wasp lays a single egg on it, then seals up the opening of the nest with earth. When one nest is complete she repeats the whole procedure for the next egg, laying 10 or more eggs a season.

The egg hatches in two to three weeks and the larval wasp feeds on the spider which, in many cases, is still living but in a state of helpless paralysis. Having fed up on the meal provided, the larva develops into a pupa and overwinters in this form, emerging as an adult the following spring. Some *Anoplius* species hibernate in adult form.

Young lycosid spiderlings travel on their mother's back until they are old enough to fend for themselves. They descend by scrambling down their mother's legs, then run up tall grasses or other foliage. At the top each youngster rises into the air, attached to a long strand of silk and is carried along on the wind. This – called ballooning – helps the young spiders to disperse; they may be carried only a few metres, or several miles. Once they land, they start their own life of hunting.

Deadly attacker

Anoplius fuscus is the commonest pompilid wasp on sandy soils in southern England, but is rare in the north and does not occur in Ireland.

Females, already fertilised from mating the previous summer, emerge in April and start nesting almost at once. They hunt by sight and smell and usually manage to immobilize their chosen victim with one well-aimed sting.

Female spider-hunting wasp, *Anoplius fuscus* (21mm long).

Anoplius fuscus searches among stones or vegetation until it encounters a spider. At this stage the wasp's antennae are highly curled.

Anoplius fuscus curves its abdomen right under the spider so that its sting can reach the vulnerable underparts and penetrate easily. At the same time, the wasp flutters its wings rapidly.

Courtship, mating and raising young

No animal lives for ever, and most live for a very short time. The average lifespan of a robin is one year, a badger lives about 15 years, while a worker bee lasts about a month. If a species is to survive, it is essential that it produces and raises offspring.

To survive in a natural environment, a species not only has to produce at least as many surviving offspring as dying adults each year, it also has to be capable of withstanding changing conditions. The way that animals are able to maintain sufficient inherent variation to allow survival is by sexual reproduction. This ensures that offspring are not just clones of their parents, but inherit varying characteristics so that some do well while others do not.

Selection of the most suitable mate is vital, and in many species elaborate courtship rituals have developed to ensure that the fittest and strongest males have first choice of the available females. For some animals, merely finding a mate is difficult, especially if the species is rare or solitary. An extraordinary array of stimuli and responses has developed, including audible ones such as bird song, scent such as the production of pheromones in moths, or visual ones such as the luminescence of the female glow-worm seeking a mate. Such devices can be highly effective – for example, a male emperor moth can sniff out a female from up to two miles!

Once courtship and mating are over, the young are produced. What happens next varies enormously. Many birds and mammals, for example, nurse their young towards a stage when they can fend for themselves. Others, including many fish, such as cod and salmon, produce huge numbers of offspring of which only a few will chance to survive. Other parents play no part in the upbringing of their offspring, but give them a good start in life – the jelly-covered masses of frogs eggs have enough food to start them off.

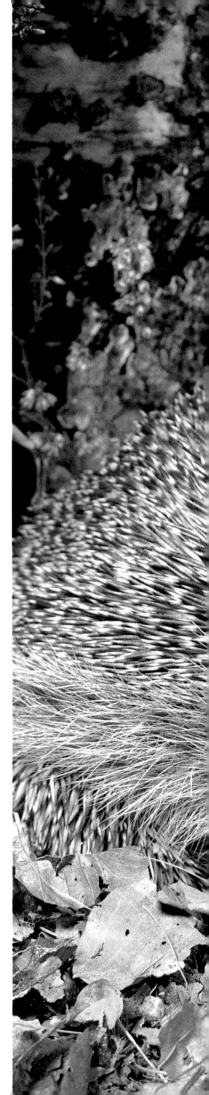

Left: A black-necked grebe in breeding plumage takes two chicks for a ride. The chicks are vulnerable to predatory fish such as pike, and soon learn to climb on to the back of one parent and hide among the feathers while the other parent dives to catch their food. Often all that can be seen is a tiny striped head poking up between the wings.

Left: A female hedgehog with her litter. After mating, the male plays no part in breeding, the female raises the litter of four or five babies on her own. About one month after birth, the young are led out out of the nest on feeding excursions. After this, they are old enough to fend for themselves.

MAMMAL COURTSHIP: LOOKING FOR A MATE

Courtship among mammals is often an elaborate ritual which minimises aggression and gives normally solitary species a chance to find a mate. For all animals it is an opportunity to identify the condition and ability of potential partners and to perpetuate their genes by reproduction.

The long winter nights of the British countryside are often interrupted by high-pitched screams that can travel for a mile or more, sending chills down the spine of most people. However, these cries, made by vixen foxes, carry a particular message to other foxes: they herald the vixen's presence, warning others to keep away and informing dog foxes that a potential mate is nearby. They are a noisy affirmation that winter is the foxes' courting season.

The right species, the right time For invertebrates (such as insects), and lower vertebrates (such as fishes), and birds, courtship is a means of establishing the species of the partner; each individual performs a series of

actions which, unless they obtain the correct response, prevent the occurrence of what would be a biologically useless mating. These animals, the peacock for example, often have elaborate visual displays.

In mammals, however, the need for such displays is lessened, perhaps because scent provides much of the necessary information about the species, sex and readiness to mate of the partner. Courtship, as a preliminary to mating, appears instead to ensure that when the female has reached the point in her sexual cycle when mating is most likely to result in pregnancy, a sexually excited male is there, ready to pair with her.

Since there is usually only one period of the

Above: A fallow deer buck calling during the rut in October, and a doe. Some mammal species are solitary throughout the year, apart from a brief period when they meet to mate. Others, such as the fallow deer, are gregarious and, with the exception of the adult male, spend much time in herds. Male mammals put most of their reproductive energies into mating, with selection favouring those which are good at finding and competing for females. Females, on the other hand put most of their reproductive energies into parental effort, with a period of lactation when the young are directly dependent on them for food in the form of milk.

ar which is best suited to the birth and owth of the young of many species, it is important that mating occurs at the right ie. Many British mammals are solitary for ost of the year, often occupying a territory iich they may mark with scent to warn off ruders, so reducing competition for food. ent marking probably also reassures the ner that it is on home ground. When food scarce and widely dispersed, individuals iy themselves be at low densities, ranging er large areas. This reduces competition food, but it makes it more difficult for an imal to find a potential mate. To overcome s, mammals may alter their behaviour ring the mating period, ranging more dely or using special scents or calls, such as it of the vixen fox referred to earlier.

The female usually becomes attractive to male considerably earlier than the period en she is sexually receptive to mating. This ows her to evaluate a number of courting iles to find the best mate for her–the ongest, or the most compatible, or the best le to obtain food during the difficult time er the birth, or a combination of all these ctors.

The reproductive efforts of the female go iinly into bearing and then feeding and ring for the young, while those of the male into finding and mating with the female. iles can have many more young during their etime than females since they can mate with eral females, whereas once a female has en successfully mated she cannot mate iin during pregnancy and lactation. These ferent levels of investment in the young, d the different reproductive potentials, are idamental differences between the sexes, d are probably responsible for the behav- ir changes they show during courtship. The ection of mates which results from com- tition between courting males may also be eason for the evolution of a period when female is attractive, but not receptive.

Early stages Initially, at least, courtship is ially a one-sided affair, with the male mak- all the advances and being evaded or re- ised by the female. The pursuit of the female the male is thus a common part of court- p behaviour. In the hedgehog, for example, male follows the female, attempting to ff at her genital region, but she repulses n by butting and biting. He retreats, but ntinually renews his efforts to approach r, snorting and hissing in a threatening way. is may continue for 20 minutes or more fore the female runs a short distance, lowers r spines (since these would otherwise be rmful), and lies down with hindlegs out- etched behind for the male to mount and pulate with her.

This process of pursuit may be prolonged er a number of days, as is often the case in carnivores. When a female fox is in heat xually attractive), her smell attracts the le long before she is ready to accept him.

He may therefore attend the female for a long period, and since he is strongly inhibited from biting her at the time, he does not retaliate in the initial stages when she repulses him. He simply follows her around and tries to sniff her genital region. As she comes more fully in to heat which, presumably, he detects by smell, she ceases to repulse him and may even invite copulation by standing in front of him in the mating posture.

Elaborate affairs Courtship among carni- vores, though prolonged, is not a sophisti- cated affair as it is with some other mammals, such as squirrels. The male red squirrel may follow the female, or may actively chase her. The female accelerates if the male approaches too rapidly, but if he shows signs of giving up she may pause to wait for him, or may even move back towards him. As he approaches, the male makes a special call which closely resembles the cry of the young when trying to maintain contact. This probably helps to in- hibit the female's aggressive tendencies–a necessary prerequisite for close approach by

Above: Red deer fighting. The mating success of a stag depends on its fighting ability, the strongest animals having the largest harems and hence the opportunity to sire the largest number of offspring. Fighting, however, can be costly: an individual stag may damage his antlers, break a leg or become blinded by an antler point.

Below: A rabbit scent- marking–releasing pheromones from its chin gland to mark out its territory. This is one way the dominant buck can inform others of his presence.

With solitary mammals there may not much opportunity for comparing potent mates, but with social species this is clea an easier task, and many species have a peri of conspicuous inter-male competition. T 'boxing' of male hares in spring is an obvic example. Another is the male red deer, whi is a polygynous animal (having more than c female partner); the male red deer has distinct rutting season when a number males compete for a harem of females, ma moving to areas favoured by hinds and roun ing up as many as they can hold, to defe against challenging males.

Each autumn the Scottish Highlands sound to the barks of rutting red deer.

the male.

Before the final approach and mating the male squirrel performs an elaborate tail display. He stops a short distance from the female, turns broadside on to her and waves his tail horizontally a few times; then he moves round in a wide circle. Finally, with the hairs erected as fully as possible, he brings his tail down over his back in a slow, deliberate movement, remaining like this for up to a minute. Such elaborate visual displays have only evolved in diurnal species where vision is important.

In nocturnal species, such as most carnivores, courtship is less elaborate and the senses of smell and hearing appear more important than sight. Mustelids, such as the pine marten and otter, frequently scent-mark and urinate as part of the pre-mating procedure; and it is probable that hormones released by the female as she comes into heat result in the formation of particular smells which signal her sexual condition to potential mates. Small rodents may also use scent in this fashion: experiments with captive bank voles have shown that unmated females in the presence of males (but not in actual mating contact) will be induced into breeding condition, but in the absence of males this will not happen. Similar effects have been found in other rodents, such as the house mouse.

Assessing the prospect Judging the capability of a male to be a good mate and parent is obviously important for a female if she is to improve her own reproductive potential without prejudicing her chances of survival. This means she must compare potential mates before allowing one to be successful. At the same time, of course, the male may be doing the same thing and moving around many females. However, he may be less choosy than she is.

Above: A dog fox courting a vixen. Her courting calls are heard in winter.

Right: Hedgehogs mate after a lengthy courtship ritual in which the female bites and butts the male while he snorts and hisses.

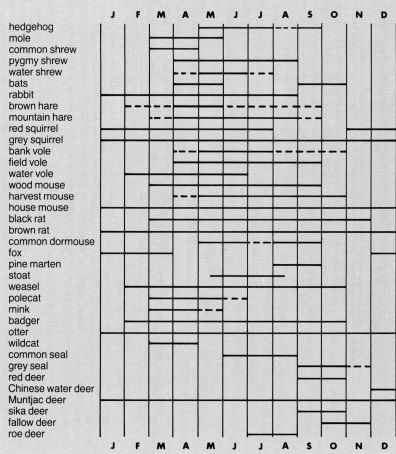

Main mammal mating seasons (excluding whales)

	J	F	M	A	M	J	J	A	S	O	N	D
hedgehog												
mole												
common shrew												
pygmy shrew												
water shrew												
bats												
rabbit												
brown hare												
mountain hare												
red squirrel												
grey squirrel												
bank vole												
field vole												
water vole												
wood mouse												
harvest mouse												
house mouse												
black rat												
brown rat												
common dormouse												
fox												
pine marten												
stoat												
weasel												
polecat												
mink												
badger												
otter												
wildcat												
common seal												
grey seal												
red deer												
Chinese water deer												
Muntjac deer												
sika deer												
fallow deer												
roe deer												

iduals assess each other's fighting potential rough roaring. The original harem holder ars at the challenger, slowly at first but then an increasing rate. If the defender can roar a faster rate, then the intruder usually reats. The stags which roar well are those in od physical condition, so this is a good lication of fighting ability. At the peak of e rut harem holders may roar at intruders roughout the day and night, and since they not feed much during this time, they show steady decline in body weight. Weaker in- viduals may lose the ability to roar loudly d they are more vulnerable to losing their nales to another, stronger male.

If a challenger matches or outroars the fender of a harem, he approaches and both gs engage in a parallel walk. This probably ables them to assess each other more sely, and if one is clearly stronger than the her the contest may end here. However, if e match is still relatively equal, a serious ht ensues, in which stags interlock antlers d push against each other. The contest is timately decided on strength–often related body weight–and skilful footwork. These borate assessments of ability help to reduce e number of escalated fights, and so mini- ise the harm which can be caused to the mbatants.

Scientists think that the 'porpoising' be- viour of common seals in late summer and tumn is a sexual display prior to mating ich may involve assessment of potential ates as with the red deer, except that simple onogamous (having only one mate) pairing an individual male and female occurs here. ey bob up and down in the water, often ping right out as they travel along the rface at speed. They may also circle around, metimes on their backs, and even turn mersaults in the water. This display is found a number of seal species, particularly the rp seal of North America and Greenland, t variations of this behaviour may also be en in the common harbour seal.

Although it has not been tested, we may eculate that the ability to porpoise and ase around in the water may reflect the ility of that animal to be a good mate and rent. Such species as the common and grey al, which spend much of their time in the en sea, often dispersed widely as they for- e for food, need the opportunity to locate otential mates. To achieve this, both species me to land for pre-breeding assemblies.

Behaviour on land differs a little between onogamous species such as the common al, and polygynous species, such as the grey al. Bull grey seals acquire a territory either land or in the sea adjoining a breeding ach. Cows enter this territory but are not tively gathered by the bull in the way that d deer hinds are gathered by the stags; once ithin the territory, however, the bull will pend much energy defending his potential ates from intruders.

Courting grey squirrels

The male grey squirrel approaches the female, flicking his tail back and forth and stamping his feet as he follows her along the branch. The female moves off, but the male immediately goes after her.

The female finally turns to face the male and growls at him. He displays for a moment, calling and waving his tail in a circle, before he makes his final approach to mate with her.

Left: A boar badger setting his scent or 'musking' the sow. Courtship and mating can occur at any time between February and May, but the fertilised eggs do not implant into the wall of the female badger's uterus until about mid-December.

Below: Grey seals mating on North Rona in autumn. Male grey seals are polygynous and acquire territory on the beach or in shallow water. They defend their potential mates from intruders.

REPRODUCTION IN BRITISH MAMMALS

Some mammal species produce up to seven litters annually, whereas others bear just one litter, and often only one offspring. Many are born blind, naked and totally dependent on their mothers for weeks, whereas some soon learn to cope alone.

Above: A British saddleback sow suckling her piglets. A well-nourished sow is able to breed when she is seven months old and has about 10 young in each litter. They take milk from their mother for up to eight weeks.

Like most other animals, mammals tend to give birth to their young when food resources and weather conditions are at their most favourable. In the British seasonal climate this is in summer, so it is not surprising that 80% of British mammal species concentrate their breeding activities particularly from April to September.

Ante-natal differences The gestation peri (the period when the embryo develops insi the mother – usually from conception birth) varies considerably between species. is shortest in the small rodents and inse ivores – from two to four weeks – and long among some of the ungulates such as the deer, where it may extend to eight months.

In some species there is a delay followi the period of mating (when the sperm of t male is inserted into the oviduct of the femal and the development of a fertilised e (embryo). This is called delayed fertilisatic

In bats, sperm may be stored over winter the male or the female. Males produce spe in summer and may store it for use during t mating season the following spring. If t male has already mated the previous autum it may be stored in the female's uterus a oviduct, and a vaginal plug develops to pi vent further copulation until the egg fertilised after ovulation. This usually occu about seven weeks before birth, but it vari between species. In the little pipistrelle it six weeks, whereas in the larger noctule it weeks.

Other British mammals show a variant of [thi]s process known as delayed implantation. [He]re the egg is fertilised but remains free in [the] uterus and does not develop until it is [im]planted in the uterus wall. The period of [del]ayed implantation is usually quite long (as [mu]ch as 10 months in the stoat), or variable [(9] months as in the badger). Normally it is [aro]und 3-5 months, as in, for example, the [gre]y and common seals, pine marten and roe [dee]r. This delay in gestation means that both [ma]ting and birth can occur at convenient [tim]es of the year, irrespective of the length of [ges]tation. It generally occurs in species with [sin]gle litters each year, and may have evolved [wh]en ancestors of present-day forms found it [dis]advantageous to bear multiple litters each [yea]r.

The length of gestation dictates the number [of] litters a mammal may have each year. If it [is] just two to four weeks and conditions [rem]ain favourable, a female can have many [litt]ers successively in one season. A rabbit, [for] example, can have up to seven litters, each [com]prising up to seven young (as the season [pro]gresses the size of litter tends to get [sm]aller). Young rabbits become pregnant [wi]thin about four months of birth. On the [ot]her hand a red deer, or the grey or common [sea]ls, have just one offspring annually, while [the] sperm whale bears a single offspring only [on]ce every three years.

Embryo failure Although one or more mat[ing]s may result in a number of developing [em]bryos, it is common for a proportion of [the]se to fail. The timing of this mortality [va]ries according to species. In the mole, with [an] average of four embryos, 6-20% of the [em]bryos may be re-absorbed, probably de[pe]nding on the body condition of the female. [If f]eeding conditions are poor, more embryos [ma]y be re-absorbed, or abort, than if the [fem]ale finds plenty of food. In the hedgehog [the] loss of embryos before birth is usually [sm]all (less than three per cent) but about 20% [of] young may die before weaning.

Other environmental conditions besides [foo]d availability may result in loss of [em]bryos. In the rabbit, for example, mortality [ma]y involve entire sets of embryos and if the [po]pulation is breeding at high densities up to [60]% of litters may be lost in this way, pre[su]mably the result of increased stress under [cro]wded conditions.

Post-natal care Mammals differ from most [oth]er animals in that the young are fed on [mi]lk secreted by the mammary glands. This [me]ans the mother must spend at least some [tim]e with her young, and for their part the [yo]ung are dependent upon her at least for a [pe]riod until they are weaned, but often for [lon]ger than this. Maternal care, however, [us]ually also involves the mother in protecting, [cle]aning and keeping warm her young, and in [so]me cases the mother plays an active part in [int]roducing them to solid foods.

When the young are born they must either be sufficiently advanced to be capable immediately of independent movement and of keeping warm by bearing fur (precocial) or, if they are more or less naked and blind (altricial), they must be protected in some form of nest or refuge. In the British Isles almost all species in the former group are ungulates (deer and goats) or pinnipeds (grey and common seals) or whales. The two hare species are exceptions which contrast with the closely related rabbit in being born fully furred in a scrape (form).

All precocial young are born furred and with functional eyes and ears, but they may vary in their ability to follow their parents. Some, such as whales and dolphins, immediately follow their mother, initially rarely being separated from her. Most, however, spend much of their time resting in the one spot where immobility and cryptic coloration

Above: The young of the mouse-eared bat, now almost extinct in Britain, and (below) a roe deer kid. In bats, delayed fertilisation occurs when the sperm may be stored over winter in the male or female. Other British mammals have a period of delayed implantation when the egg is fertilised and does not become implanted in the uterus wall or start to develop for several months—about three to five months in the case of the roe deer. This is a relatively uncommon process, although it occurs across a variety of mammal families.

Left: A wood mouse suckl▊ her young in the undergro▊ nest. Wood mice have litt▊ of five to six young from March to October, depending on the availabilit▊ of food. They develop the▊ juvenile coats after about ▊ week, their eyes open at about two weeks, and the▊ are weaned after about 18 days.

reduce their chances of being discovered by a predator. Thus the young of deer and hares spend their first few days (usually up to ten days) concealed among vegetation where potential predators have great difficulty in finding them.

Although the fawn chooses the lying-out place, the mother dictates the feeding time. She may call as she approaches and adopt a characteristic posture. After a mutual nose-sniffing session the mother may lick the rear of her young, who then starts to suckle at her udder. As it grows, the fawn spends less time lying-out alone and starts to follow its mother.

Most species with precocial young have small litters of either one (deer, seals, whales) or two or three (hares). Those with altricial young generally have much larger litters. In small rodents such as mice and voles, in insectivores such as shrews, in small mustelids such as weasels and stoats, and in rabbits, there are generally four to eight young in a litter. In larger carnivores, such as the pine marten, badger and fox, and in squirrels, there are three to five in a litter. Bats are rather unusual in having a single young born blind and either hairless or with only sparse

fur. It clings to its mother for much of the first few weeks. She rarely flies with her young unless disturbed, but when she is feeding she will leave it for periods in a nursery crêche after it is about one week old.

For those mammals which bear blind and helpless young a refuge must be found–a cave, the roof of a building or a hollow tree, or–more usually–a nest or den. All small rodents, such as mice, rats and voles, build

Below: Carnivorous mammals (the hunters) deposit their young either below ground in a burrow as do the fox and badger, or above ground in a den among rocks or the roots of a tree, as do the pine marten, stoat, otter and wildcat–and the polecat, the growing young of whi▊ are shown here.

Shelters for mammal young

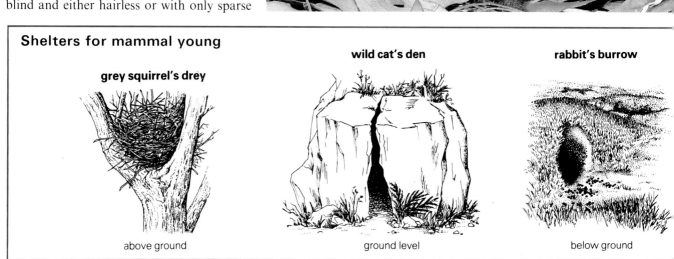

grey squirrel's drey

above ground

wild cat's den

ground level

rabbit's burrow

below ground

...ts which may comprise leaves and grass or ...n paper, string and other man-made ...tructable materials. Some species, such as ...water vole and wood mouse, generally ...ld a nest below ground; others, such as ...common dormouse and harvest mouse, ...struct a ball of grass or leaves at the base ...vegetation or slung from grass or reed ...ms. The mother rabbit builds her nest of ...ss or moss underground in a small burrow ...a side-branch of the warren itself and, ...ring the two days before she gives birth, ...es it with fur from her belly.

...Once born, the young are initially con-...ntly attended by their mother who pro-...es food in the form of milk, and warmth. In ...st species she remains with her young for ...first 24 hours but then makes forays out ...obtain food for herself. Some species ...nd more time with their young than others. ...us, for example, a vixen fox remains in ...endance all day and most of the night for ...first three weeks of her cubs' lives. The ...bit, however, visits her young only once ...htly and suckles for about five minutes ...y. When the young are alone they keep ...rm by huddling together. If a nest is dis-...bed, the mother often picks up the young ...e by one (usually by the scruff of the neck) ...d takes them elsewhere. She may then have ...build another nest or, as in the case of the ...and grey squirrels, an alternative nest is ...erally available and simply requires lining ...h soft fur and moss.

Growing up As the young develop and their ...s and ears open they become more re-...nsive to objects other than their mother. ...ell probably plays an important part in the ...ther-infant bond, although high-pitched ...eaks or squeals, sometimes in the ultra-...ic range, may also summon the parent in ...e of distress. An intruder–a potential ...dator or a member of the same species–is ...ven off aggressively by the mother and in ...case of some carnivores, notably the wild ...., the young may also react by hissing ...spitting.

...Although the young of precocial species ...tinue to suckle for a long period (some-...es as long as a year) despite their rapid

Above: A rabbit doe lying across the nursery hole of the burrow while her young feed. Baby rabbits are born 28 days after the eggs have been fertilised; they do not go out from the nest until they are about 18 days old.

Below: A grey seal cow suckling her very young pup. An older pup with its mother is further down the beach. Seal pups are precocial–capable of independent movement and of keeping warm from birth.

ability to feed themselves, they do feed on other items as well. Altricial young, how-ever, depend entirely upon their mother's milk for most of the lactation period. This period may be as short as two or three weeks, as in most mice and voles, or two or three months, as in most carnivores (four months in the wild cat).

In most rodents the young become inde-pendent soon after weaning, but for carnivor-ous species there is a slow transition to solid foods which at first are brought to the nest by the mother and may be partially digested by her. Later, usually slightly before weaning, the young start to make their own forays from the nest accompanied by their mother who may then capture prey in their presence. The young play a great deal with each other and practise capturing food. If they lose contact with their mother they generally call anxiously and she returns immediately. As they become increasingly independent, she in turn becomes more aggressive towards them and finally, just before she gives birth to the next litter, the parent-offspring bond is broken, and the young begin to live lives of their own.

Although the bond is broken for most mammals at this stage, in some of the social carnivores–notably the badger–the young may remain in the same social group as their mother for several years and may rear their offspring with her subsequent litters.

A NEST FOR EVERY SITUATION

A bird's nest can be just a scrape in the ground or an intricately woven cup, but it must protect eggs and shelter young from predators and bad weather.

Above: The eggs of the oystercatcher—perfectly camouflaged against the pebbles on the beach—need no extra protection.

Below: Nest and eggs of a red grouse; the long grass helps to hide the nest, but the eggs are protected mainly by the camouflage coloration of the hen.

Nests are the places where birds lay their eggs. But nests are not exclusive to birds: reptiles, fish, various insects, worms and other animals all make structures called nests. All these creatures make a nest for one good reason— to protect its contents. Eggs are fragile and need protection from breakage; they need warmth to develop and must not be exposed to bad weather; the eggs (and the young emerging from them) are particularly vulnerable to predators and must be guarded by the nest's construction and concealment.

Although a bird's nest always contains the eggs, it may not always house the developing young. Most small song birds, and some larger birds such as crows, owls and birds of prey, hatch out naked, blind and helpless and remain in the nest until they are ready to fly. Ducks and waders, on the other hand, hatch with their eyes open, with a covering of down and well-developed legs, and can scamper about or swim as soon as they have dried off.

Early in spring, or even during winter with larger birds, the male establishes his territory. Usually, within that territory there will be a number of suitable nest sites. With some birds, like the wren, the male does the bulk of the construction work on several nests, before the pair finally settles on one and puts the finishing touches to it. In the same way, the male lapwing will make several scrapes (by shuffling his feet and belly to produce a saucer-shaped depression in the soil) bef the final site is selected and a dried gr lining added.

With many other birds, it seems that female plays the major role in selecting actual site, and subsequently in building nest. The male, however, does not idly wa his female dash back and forth with beakf of nesting material. He still has the vital of guarding the territory, which demar continual alertness. The biological co plexities of the breeding season beco apparent: both birds must get themsel into the peak of condition—which means lc hours of feeding—but at the same time ter tory must be secured and patrolled *and* nest built.

Ground nests The simplest nests are th where the eggs are laid on the ground. Oft in such circumstances, protection from p dators comes with the site; for examp guillemots nest on inaccessible sea c ledges. For others, such as the oystercatc or ringed plover, birds which nest on beach, the camouflage colours of the e; provide the necessary concealment. Ma wader nests look very simple—just scrapes the ground—but they are in fact structu and in some cases ornamented; one n contained over 1000 small pebbles, as well twigs and pieces of shell.

Other waders, ducks and gulls make ne which are a further development of the sim

The basic structure of cup nests is the same, even when the size varies from the few centimeters in diameter of finches' nests to the one metre or more of those made by the heron and golden eagle. An outer framework of stout grasses, small roots, twigs or branches is lodged in a suitable tree fork or similar place. Gradually smaller and more flexible materials are tucked and woven into this structure, until the central cup is ready for lining. This nest is typical of the majority of perching birds–called passerines–which includes most small birds of farm, wood and garden. Where such birds extend their breeding range high up mountains or well to the north where there are few trees, similar nests are built on or close to the ground.

Domed nests are elaborations of the cup nest; additional protection is given by roofing over the structure and making a side entrance. Willow warblers build low-level grass nests of this type, while magpies construct high level, much bulkier versions. The most attractive examples are the long-tailed tits' cobweb-and-lichen, flask-shaped nests which are amazingly flexible to accommodate the

und type. They gather dead vegetation, sam and jetsam into a mound and make a ression at its centre. The structures made ducks and waders are usually at a low el, but the black-headed gull makes a lt-up nest on the flat terrain of estuarine marshes or moorland bogs, where the er level may rise suddenly and inundate -lying eggs.

Game birds are also ground nesters and lay ir eggs in grass-lined hollows. The hen tects her clutch from predators by her own iouflage colouring and will not budge n the nest unless it is absolutely necessary. ne birds do not have a strong scent, so dators like foxes find it hard to detect a grouse or ptarmigan hen on a nest.

he floating nest is the next logical development. The little grebe's nest, loosely anchored nearby vegetation, can rise and fall with floodwaters and naturally survives far ter than those of the coot or moorhen, ch are fixed firmly in the reeds or on a -hanging bough. For specialist swimmers the grebes, which have legs set well back a torpedo-shaped body, walking is awkd; floating nests are easier to get on and

up nests The cup is a practical shape for iy purposes: the eggs cluster naturally in bottom safe from disturbance and, if the t is well constructed, safe too from the eyes orying predators. Often the cup is lined i dried mud, fine grasses, moss, fur or hers, which provide excellent insulation the eggs; this also enables the incubating ale to slip off occasionally to eat or drink. s insulation becomes more important n she has to help gather food for the ng.

Above: Song thrush with young on nest. The cup shape of the nest stops the eggs rolling out and keeps the chicks safely in.

Right: Up to 12 chicks can be stuffed into the tiny, stifling, dome-shaped nest of the long-tailed tit. The nest is built of moss and cobwebs and is lined with countless feathers.

Nest boxes in the garden

One of the major problems for birdwatchers who wish to observe nesting behaviour is that birds try to make their nests as inconspicuous as possible. A nest box in your own garden gives you the opportunity to watch nesting birds at close quarters and in comfort. You can buy or make suitable boxes, or even put out an old kettle or an oil can.

Position the box high enough up a tree or the side of a house or shed so it is well out of reach of marauding cats (or children), but so that you still have a clear view. Make sure the box is not in direct sunlight or beating rain—you don't want the nestlings to overheat or drown. If you want to put up several boxes, position them at least 18m (60ft) apart, so different families do not disturb each other.

Once the box is in position, watch carefully to see which species of birds take an interest in it, and what nesting materials they use. The birds do not usually object if you want to look inside the box to check progress, but don't disturb a female sitting on eggs; watch for her to leave, then look but don't touch.

growing brood, and the better known dried leaf constructions of the wren. The male wren may build in any sort of crevice, from a tangle of ivy to an old jacket pocket in the garden shed.

Cavity nests Several birds, notably the owls, jackdaw and stock dove, nest in natural or man-made cavities such as hollow trees and church belfries. The house sparrow is a notable exploiter of cavities in buildings (although fully capable of building an untidy, domed nest outdoors). You might think these nests would be safer than other types, but this is not the case. The tit family are cavity nesters, but are vulnerable to attack from mice, woodpeckers and weasels.

Right: Suspended securely between reeds, the nest of the reed warbler is well hidden from predators and is so shaped that the eggs will not fall out even though the reeds sway in the wind.

Below: The great spotted woodpecker uses its strong beak like a hammer and chisel to excavate a nest hole high up the trunk of a tree where few predators will venture.

Other species, such as the woodpecke kingfisher and sand martin, excavate th own cavities in wood or the soil. Wo peckers, which make a speciality of hamm ing and chiselling out nest cavities in t trunks, are equipped with an extra pad cartilage tissue situated just between the of the beak and the nasal bone that acts a shock-absorber, preventing the birds fr developing a splitting headache.

Soil excavation is done with the feet a (sometimes) the beak. In sandy soils, so species produce metre-long tunnels ending a nest chamber. The Manx shearwater a puffin – both seabirds – are also tunnel neste Both use natural rock crevices or oust rabb from burrows in the cliff-top turf.

Suspended nests Perhaps the most sophi cated nests of all are the suspended ones. the British Isles, the best examples are woven mossy hammock nest of the tiny go crest and the basketwork nest of the r warbler which incorporates supporting r stems. This structure must withstand only the movement of the reeds in high win but also (as the reed warbler is a comm foster parent) the massive weight of a yo cuckoo.

Exceptions to the rule In general terms i possible to group nest types and relate th broadly to groups of birds and their habita but there are always exceptions. One exam is the woodcock, which is a wader and wo therefore be expected to nest on the seash or in swampy moors and marshes; in fac scrapes its nest on the ground in deep wo land. Another exception is the goldeneye duck, and therefore likely to nest on ground beside water – which actually nest holes in trees, often high above the groun

Avian architecture

House martin: mud nest
shaped like a quarter globe
with a slit entrance, just
below the ceiling or eaves.

Magpie: large nest in upper
branches of a tree.

Greenfinch: cup shape,
well camouflaged, close to
ground in brambles or
thicket.

Long-tailed tit: neat dome
of grass and mosses, with a
side entrance.

Goldcrest: woven from
mosses, hanging from a
branch like a hammock.

Song thrush: mud-lined
nest, often in middle
height of tree.

Collared dove: sprawling
twig nest, often on a roof or
other man-made structure.

Buzzard: the nest is
reoccupied each year and
new sticks are added to its
bulk.

Spotted flycatcher: in the
base of a broken branch, with
a clear view.

Wren: small nest in any
convenient place, such as the
roots of a fallen tree.

Great crested grebe: a
floating nest woven among
reeds as a mooring.

Meadow pipit:
inconspicuous nest hidden in
a tuft of grass.

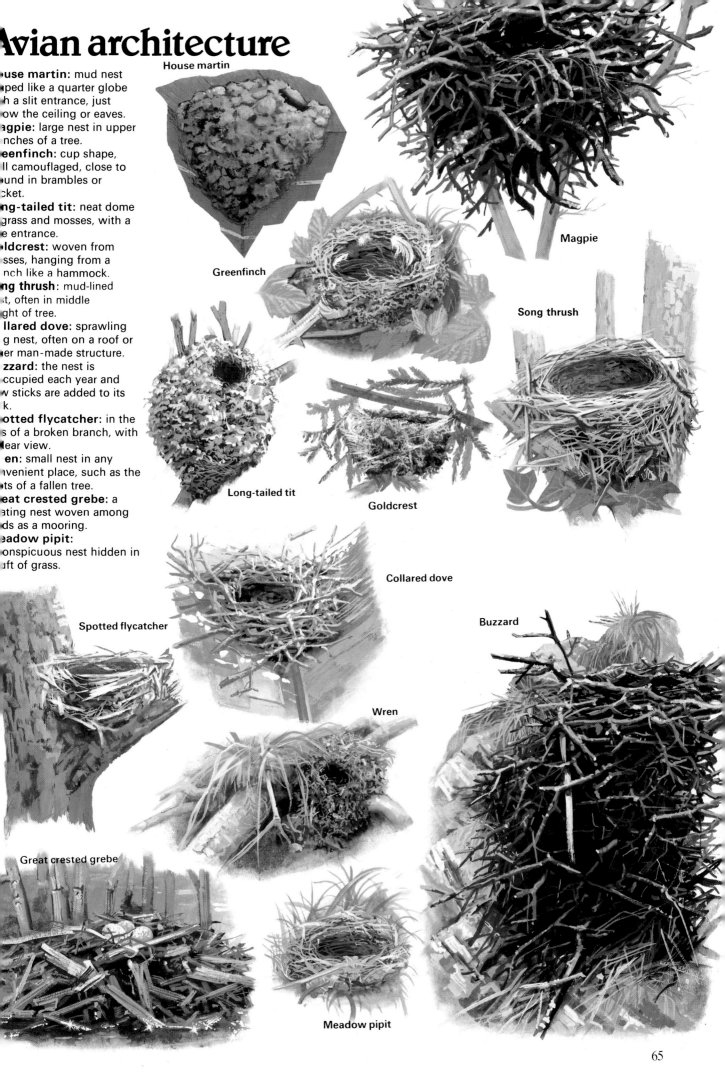

House martin

Magpie

Greenfinch

Song thrush

Long-tailed tit

Goldcrest

Collared dove

Buzzard

Spotted flycatcher

Wren

Great crested grebe

Meadow pipit

BREEDING FOR SUCCESS

rds have an intriguing variety of egg colours, laying times, clutch sizes and nest designs, rising from the endless search for ways to ensure survival of the young.

ong way back in time, perhaps over 140 lion years ago, the fossil record shows t the first truly bird-like creatures de- oped as an offshoot of the reptiles. Unlike mmals, birds continue to use the reptiles' thod of reproduction—the fertilised ovum eloping inside an egg that is incubated side the body of the adult until it is ready atch.

t is not easy to assess whether laying eggs better or worse method of reproduction n the mammalian system, in which the ing develop inside the mother until birth. h method has shown its advantages and idvantages, and as the 'egg method' has ured for over 100 million years, it must

be regarded as a success in evolutionary terms.

Eggs of all shades One striking feature of eggs is their intriguing range of colours and markings. Often it seems easy to attribute some advantage to the colouring–the black-speckled, sand-coloured eggs of terns or of the ringed plover, for example, are ideally camouflaged, for these birds nest on sand, among fragments of seaweed or on shingle beaches. The eggs of hole-nesting birds such as stock doves, woodpeckers and owls, are generally white: no doubt this helps the in-cubating bird to locate the eggs in the dark nest, and so avoid trampling on them. In addition, it seems natural that eggs so well

Above: A very large clutch of mallard eggs–a normal clutch is seven to eleven. By laying huge clutches, ducks compensate for the loss of young to predators and bad weather.

Opposite: A pair of kestrels at their nest. The male (left) visits the female with food–here, a vole–while she does most of the incubating.

Below: A pair of reed warblers engaged in courtship feeding.

hidden need no colour camouflage. Birds that nest in crowded colonies need to recognise their own eggs, and this may be the explanation for the wide variety of ground shades (the basic colour of the egg) and black squiggles found on the eggs of guillemots in their cliff-ledge colonies.

There are, however, unexplained anomalies. For instance, each egg in every clutch laid by the red-backed shrike is a different colour: this has made them so attractive to egg collectors, from Victorian times to the present day, that the species has been plundered almost to extinction in England. Another anomaly is the dunnock: few birds are so well camouflaged as this species, its colours matching the undergrowth in which its nest is built. But once the sitting bird has flown what could be more glaringly conspicuous than the clutch of bright sky-blue eggs? Quite the opposite of being camouflaged, these must be positively eye-catching to predators such as jays and magpies.

Feeding for fitness For many birds, breeding success must depend heavily on the good physical condition of the pair. The whole breeding cycle must occur during a period when plenty of food is available. Well before the time for laying, the male needs plenty of food to give him the strength to perform his lively song and active display in order to attract a mate. He also needs all his strength to establish and hold a territory against rival claims.

The female must also get into first-class condition for the hardships of the breeding season. Courtship feeding, in which the male fetches caterpillars or other delicacies for his mate, has true practical importance: producing eggs requires a great deal of energy, and the female needs every scrap of food she can get. The female blue tit, for example, stores up so much food in her body that she increases in weight by half as much again during the fortnight before egg laying begins.

Nests of many kinds One advantage of laying eggs is that the mother does not have to carry heavy young within her body. But it gives rise to more problems in turn. First, eggs are fragile and need protection from break-

age. Secondly, they need correctly controlled warmth and insulation from the harshness of the weather. Besides this, the eggs, and in most cases the young, are static and may be vulnerable to a number of specialist or opportunist nest predators. Birds have derived solutions to all these problems from a single feature – the nest.

The simplest 'nests' are merely places where one or more eggs are laid directly on to the ground. The eggs may be protected by their own camouflage or by the sheer inaccessibility of the nest site – a cliff ledge for example. In some waders and many ducks and gulls, the art of nest building is a little more elaborate: nearby vegetation is gathered into a heap to help insulate the eggs and offer some protection against change in the water level. The grebes have a subtle variation of this method: their nests are 'rafts' of vegetation that float on the water, rising and falling with the water level, and moored in place with pliable stems of long foliage.

The cup-shaped nest built by most small and medium-sized birds offers protection in a variety of ways. The eggs naturally cluster

Left: Cuckoos practise a form of parasitism in their unique method of breeding. They do not build nests or look after their young, but lay their eggs into other birds' nests. The young cuckoo hatches first and ejects its potential 'brothers and sisters' from the nest. Here a dunnock is seen looking after a young cuckoo, thinking it is its own offspring. The commonest hosts are meadow pipits, dunnocks and reed warblers.

Opposite: Another unusual breeding method is practised by the short-eared owl: the owl lays its eggs at intervals of two days or more, and starts to incubate as soon as the first egg is laid. The eggs hatch at similar intervals, so that in a clutch of seven there may be a two-week difference in age between the oldest and the youngest chick. There is some flexibility in the size of the owl's brood, although it is achieved in a manner that we find distasteful: should the food supply diminish, the oldest may eat the youngest, and so on, until the family is reduced to a more viable size.

The helpless and the active young

Nidiculous (altricial, nest-loving) species of birds hatch naked, blind and helpless: these include most songbirds and some of the larger species, such as eagles.
Nidifugous (precocial, nest-fleeing) species hatch with eyes open and a covering of down, and can soon run and feed themselves; these include ducks, gulls and waders.

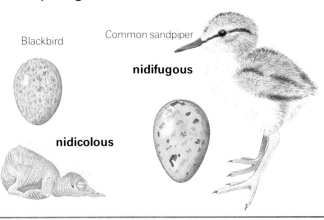

Blackbird

Common sandpiper

nidifugous

nidicolous

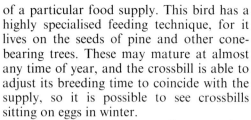

of a particular food supply. This bird has a highly specialised feeding technique, for it lives on the seeds of pine and other cone-bearing trees. These may mature at almost any time of year, and the crossbill is able to adjust its breeding time to coincide with the supply, so it is possible to see crossbills sitting on eggs in winter.

The nesting brood The nestling stage is a time of considerable risk. The young are noisy and inexperienced, and may easily draw the attention of a predator. Parent birds have to spend almost all the daylight hours in ceaseless attempts to keep the young well-fed. In consequence the young are vulnerable to cold weather, heavy rain or hailstorms.

Birds clearly take great pains through spring and summer, and the young have to undergo many hazards before the lucky few that survive fly away and join the adult population. Many eggs and young are lost in the process, so the breeding patterns may seem highly wasteful; but their success can be judged by the variety and the numbers of birds that surround us in their many different habitats.

ether in the base of the cup, where they well insulated from cold and partly hidden m the eyes of predators.

ven better protection from prying eyes is en by domed nests, more complex struc- es made by small birds such as wrens and g-tailed tits. Tree holes also give good all- nd protection, and are used as nesting s by many species of birds, including owls, odpeckers and pied flycatchers. Wheatears well concealed in their nests in cavities ong rocks and in walls, as are puffins in ir underground burrows.

iming it right In the course of evolution, umber of patterns of breeding have arisen t specifically take advantage of certain umstances. The blue tit and great tit ulations in Britain are a case in point. e majority of these birds depend on ter moth caterpillars as a supply of food their young. These caterpillars occur in rmous numbers, but only for a month or in early summer. To take the best advan- e of this annual event, the blue tit or great lays its eggs all in one clutch, between 5 16 in number. Laying is timed precisely hat the young will hatch and grow to their st demanding size when the caterpillars fully grown.

n contrast to this, almost a literal case of eggs in one basket', the majority of small medium-sized garden birds produce two three clutches, and may even lay more in a d summer. Their clutches are smaller, h only four to six eggs. This method allows m to exploit a moderate food supply oughout the summer, rather than a short- d glut in June.

he crossbill has a variable breeding time ich, like that of the tits, is linked to the time

Above: A ringed plover's nest, superbly camouflaged on the shingle—so well that you may not notice it even when you know it's there! This nest is no more than a place where eggs are laid directly on to the ground, but in some of these 'scrapes' the ringed plover may make a scant lining with a few strands of seaweed or other plants.

Right: The chaffinch conceals its eggs and brood within an elaborately constructed nest. The lichens that it uses to make the outer layers of the nest may also camouflage the nest if it is built on a branch that is also lichen-covered.

THE DUNNOCK: HOW UNLIKE A SPARROW

The inconspicuous dunnock has one of the strangest and most complex courtship and mating arrangements among common birds, in which two males share one female. One male is always dominant over the other, although both may mate with the female.

our second most numerous farmland [...] species–they are outnumbered only by bla[...] birds.

Social life Recent research has shown t[...] the social life of dunnocks is far from ordin[...] –indeed, it is absorbingly complex. In win[...] dunnocks tend to remain in approximately [...] same areas in which their breeding territo[...] were located during the previous spri[...] Throughout this range, groups of dunno[...] congregate at particularly good feeding ar[...] When birds do meet at the favoured area, [...] heaviest birds are dominant over the ligh[...] ones, and since males are heavier t[...] females, the former tend to survive the win[...] better.

Separate or sharing Both males and fem[...] possess territories in the breeding seas[...] When feeding on the ground in dense ve[...] tation it is very difficult to see, and therefor[...] evict, an unobtrusive intruder, and so intr[...] ions occur frequently. They are in fact [...] frequent that the minority of male territo[...] are effectively shared, in the full knowledg[...] the owner. Within this sharing relationsh[...] one bird is dominant over the other: [...] dominant bird is usually the older of the tw[...]

Pairs and trios During the breeding seas[...] some dunnocks associate in pairs, one m[...] and one female, but others, possibly [...] majority, form larger groups, usually of th[...] birds. Trios consist of one female and t[...] males, with the two males sharing the sa[...] territory. One of the males, usually the ol[...] and heavier and called the alpha male, [...] dominant over the other, called the beta m[...] The alpha male asserts his authority over [...] beta male, especially over sexual relati[...] with the female, but the subordinate bet[...] nevertheless tolerated within the territory a[...] does occasionally manage to copulate with [...] female, especially later in the breeding seas[...]

Trios occur generally in the best habit[...] where the dominant alpha males have la[...] territories. Since the beta male helps [...] territorial defence, the dominant bird deri[...] some benefit from the beta's presence i[...] large territory that might otherwise be di[...] cult to secure. This may, at least in p[...] explain the alpha male's tolerance of [...]

Male and female dunnocks look very alike. Most of the plumage is a warm brown with black streaks, while the head and breast are noticeably grey and the crown, back of the neck and ear coverts are washed with brown.

Dunnocks belong to the insect-eating family of accentors, which accounts for their very sharp bills, contrasting with the stout, seed-cracking bills of true sparrows. Dunnocks inhabit a wide variety of scrub and similar vegetation, and spend most of their time feeding on the ground, never far from thickets to which they can retreat whenever danger threatens. Their ability to occupy a wide variety of habitats which occur commonly in Britain has enabled them to become

Above: The dunnock's presence is often betrayed by its call: a piping, often somewhat insistent and vibrant 'tseep' of mournful quality. The song is a thin, high-pitched warbling.

Right: A dunnock nest in a yew hedge: a fairly typical site both for the type of vegetation and for the location. There are usually four or five eggs, and the hen takes sole charge of both nestbuilding and incubation. The pair usually rears two broods in a season.

sociate, but the presence of a second male in close proximity to the alpha's mate does present problems.

While it may be helpful to receive assistance with territorial defence, the alpha male must to ensure that all of his mate's eggs have been fertilised by him and not by the beta male, for he does not want to waste energy feeding someone else's chicks. The alpha male overcomes the danger that his mate may have been fertilised by the beta male in a most intriguing way.

Mating dance Part of the pre-copulatory display of dunnocks involves the female stooping forward, vibrating her wings and tail, fluffing out the feathers around her posterior like a can-can dancer, and exposing her cloaca to the male. At this, the male pecks at the female's cloaca for a minute or two before he copulates. During this pecking, males have sometimes been seen to eject a small fluid droplet which, on microscopic examination, has proved to be a mass of sperm. The male seems to be trying to ensure that the female's sperm store is empty before he copulates, in an attempt to guarantee that only his own sperm is available to fertilise her eggs.

The female encourages the beta male to stay in the territory. When she can get away from the attentions of the dominant bird, she solicits matings from the beta male and this seems to lead to his assistance at a later stage in the breeding cycle. For in trios where the beta male has copulated with the female, the subordinate male helps to feed the nestlings, whereas if the beta male does not mate, then he offers no assistance. Where this assistance is given, broods are more successful than in the absence of any help.

Why be subordinate? But where does the advantage lie for the beta male, to work so hard in the breeding season for so little reward? The answer may be that, being so low in the social hierarchy, he may be incapable of establishing and maintaining a territory single-handed. Without any territory he would be unable to breed, but by helping a more dominant bird he is able to live in a good territory and stands a chance, albeit limited, of making some contribution to the next generation.

The unexpected in bird life Most popular bird books readily show the more noticeable peculiarities that have evolved in birds' structures. Examples of these are the filter-feeding bill of the flamingo, the cone-opening mandibles of the crossbill and the bizarre head ornaments of the ruff. Popular field guides fail, however, to illustrate the peculiarities of behaviour, and these may go unnoticed for many years. Only recently has the peculiar social behaviour of the dunnock been discovered—and this is one of our commonest birds! Perhaps some of our other common and apparently ordinary birds have exciting aspects of behaviour yet to be revealed to us.

The dunnock or hedge sparrow

spotted plumage

juvenile

warm brown plumage
black streaks
grey head
grey throat and underparts

adult

Mating behaviour

wings and tail vibrate

dominant male pecks cloaca of female

female displays with fluffed feathers

stooping posture

intruding subordinate male

dominant male driving subordinate male away

female displaying

dominant male mates with female

Dunnock (*Prunella modularis*). Resident; Britain's only member of the accentor family. Length 14cm (5½in).

Above and right: Three phases of the mating behaviour of dunnocks. The middle phase, where the dominant or alpha male asserts his authority, is not an uncommon one, for trios are probably more frequent than pairs.

Below: Both parents feed the chicks, and if the beta has mated he helps too.

An adult female common yellow ophion (*Ophion luteus*). It is about 2cm ($\frac{3}{4}$in) long, with a wingspan of about 3cm ($1\frac{1}{4}$in). During the day this ichneumon wasp often rests on a leaf, becoming active at night. Its habit of entering houses, attracted by artificial light, and its wasp-like appearance can alarm some people. Although it has no sting, it can inflict a painful jab with its ovipositor if handled.

THE ENEMY WITHIN

Parasitic ichneumon wasps are the deadly enemies of other insects. They pass the larval stage of their lives feeding inside the living bodies of caterpillars and other larvae.

It is not strictly accurate to call ichneumon wasps parasites. For a true parasite, the host must remain alive as long as possible, for if it dies the parasite will also die. The case of ichneumons is rather different. The parasitic relationship lasts only as long as the larval life of the ichneumon. At the end of the larval life, the host is killed. Thus, the host caterpillar is doomed to a premature death as soon as the female ichneumon implants her eggs inside it. For this reason, ichneumons and other insects with this particular mode of life are called parasitoids.

Living larders If you inspect fences near growing cabbages in July and October, you may often find the caterpillars and newly-formed chrysalids of the large white and small white butterflies. Here and there you might

see a dead caterpillar surrounded by num ous little grubs or oval yellow cocoons. Th are the early stages of a small ichneum wasp, *Apanteles glomeratus*, which is extre ely useful to Man. This tiny black wasp la 30-100 eggs under the skin of a half-gro large or small white butterfly caterpill When the minute larvae hatch, they live a grow in their victim's body, feeding on blood and fat but avoiding all the vi organs, until the caterpillar prepares pupate a couple of weeks later. Then ichneumons devour the whole of the cat pillar's interior, killing it in the process. T fully fed ichneumon larvae finally eme through the caterpillar's skin and spin th cocoons around the withered remains.

You may see the adult ichneumons flitti about among cabbages in summer, searchi for host victims. Once the female's eggs ha hatched the parasitized caterpillar, which being eaten from within, often appears sm ler than other, healthy caterpillars. It a seems to be 'lazy'–sitting exposed on a le while others conceal themselves in hidi places. Occasionally, collectors of butt flies and moths who take home caterpillars the hope of rearing specimens are d appointed to find that they have been bree ing ichneumons instead.

Night-fliers Ichneumons of the *Oph* genus are very common, especially the yell ophion (*Ophion luteus*). These yellowi

wn insects fly at night and are often
acted by artificial light, appearing in
ses in the summer. They are parasites of
larvae of some of our larger moths such
the puss moth, the broom moth and the
amore moth.

he female ophion implants a single egg in
chosen victim. Most ichneumon wasp
ales have long ovipositors (egg-laying
ans), but ophions are unusual in having
rt ones. Another ichneumon, *Pimpla*
igator, a large species, has a short, spike-
ovipositor and is one of the species which
ists in keeping cabbage white butterflies in
ck.

ine wood parasite The largest British
neumon wasp, *Rhyssa persuasoria*, fre-
ents pine woods and plantations, searching
the host of its parasitic larva, the giant
od wasp or horntail. The larva of the giant
od wasp bores into the trunk of pine trees
into felled timber stacked in the open. You
see the female *Rhyssa*–easily identified by
extraordinarily long ovipositor–flying
ut searching pine logs and trunks in June
July. How she locates a wood wasp larva
ough several centimetres of wood is still a
stery, but the antennae are certainly used
searching, and the sense of smell may also
involved.

When the female *Rhyssa* finds the larva she
looking for, she raises her abdomen and
es into the wood with her long, slender
positor. The sheaths on either side of the
positor do not enter the wood but are
sed vertically upwards. When the tip of
ovipositor reaches the wood wasp larva,
egg is passed down it. In the process the
is elongated out of all recognition, but it
ains its oval shape as soon as it is extruded
to the skin of the victim. The female then
thdraws her ovipositor and flies off in
rch of another host.

When the egg hatches, the larva remains
tside the body of its host throughout its
, apparently sucking blood through the
n. The effect is just like that of an internal
rasitoid. When the *Rhyssa* larva is fully
wn its host's body is just a shrunken bag
skin.

Man's allies The ichneumon wasp is a
eful ally of the forester because the large
nnels made by the wood wasp ruin valuable
ber. Parasitoids like *Rhyssa* are used as
ents in the control of insect pests and are
rticularly effective against pests which have
en introduced into territories outside their
tural range. *Apanteles glomeratus* was the
st parasitoid species to be shipped from one
ntinent to another and be successfully
ablished. It was exported from England to
e United States of America to combat the
troduced large white butterfly which was
using serious damage to brassica crops.
is species of ichneumon is still one of the
st effective enemies of the destructive
tterfly.

Britain's largest ichneumon

Rhyssa persuasoria, with its blue-black body
colour, white spots and red legs, is a
spectacular-looking insect which frequents
pine woods. It has a head and body length
of 3cm (1¼in). The female has a bristle-like
ovipositor which adds nearly 4cm (1½in) to
her length. The ovipositor consists of a
slender organ adapted for boring through
pine wood and egg-laying, and is protected
on either side by a sheath. Males do not have
an ovipositor.

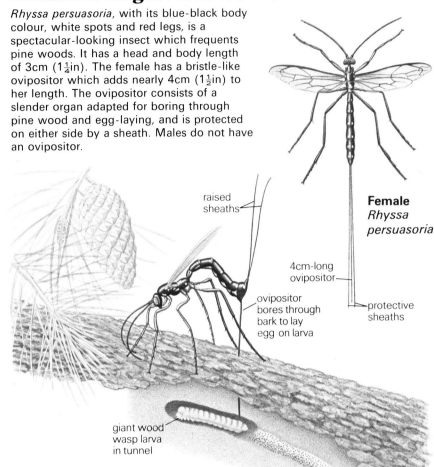

raised
sheaths

Female
Rhyssa
persuasoria

4cm-long
ovipositor

ovipositor
bores through
bark to lay
egg on larva

protective
sheaths

giant wood
wasp larva
in tunnel

A wood wasp, *Sirex noctilio*, was established early this century in pine plantations in
New Zealand. In 1928–9, more than 1000
mature *Rhyssa* larvae were extracted from
infested pine trunks in England and sent to
New Zealand.

Operations of this kind exploit the principle
that when an insect pest of agriculture or
forestry is introduced to a new territory, it
becomes more numerous and harmful than it
is in its native region because its particular
natural enemies are likely to be absent. The
parasitoid can then be introduced to great
advantage, and is likely to be more effective
than usual because its own natural enemies
are also absent.

Above: Scots pine branch
cut away to show *Rhyssa*
ovipositing on wood wasp
larva.

Below: A caterpillar of the
large white butterfly
festooned with the larvae
of the ichneumon wasp
Apanteles glomeratus. The
larvae are spinning cocoons
around the caterpillar, which
at this stage is nothing
more than a bag of empty
skin.

HOW INSECTS FIND THEIR MATES

Insect communication between members of the same species is directed principally towards sex. Before mating, partners must locate and recognise one another – not a simple matter since they can be separated by distances as great as two miles.

Above: Peacock butterflies have distinctive colouring on their upper wings so that partners can identify one another before mating.

Opposite: Glow-worm females have luminous tails which they swing from side to side to attract males.

Most insects live solitary lives, widely dispersed in a mixed habitat which is usually shared with other similar species. In order to reproduce, the prospective partners – male and female – first have to find and recognise each other. This is done by using either one or a combination of the senses – sight, sound or smell.

The allure of scent The sense most frequently involved is scent, normally emitted by the more passive female and detected by the active male. The scent, known as a pheromone, is chemically unique for each species so the male does not waste time pursuing females of another species. After mating the female usually ceases to secrete the pheromone.

The sex pheromones of moths have been closely studied, and field experiments show that males flying upwind can find females at remarkable distances. Two miles and more have been reported in tests using marked males released at increasing distances from the 'calling' female. The pheromones are produced in minute quantities – at such large distances they must be diluted to extremely

small concentrations. Tests on the gy moth have revealed that the male respond just one tenth of a thousand of a millic of a gram of pheromone.

Colour identification The sense of s probably works in a similar way in a g many other insects, but some of the la day-flying species use their eyes to locate recognise partners.

Butterflies are the most obvious exam their bright colours having developed recognition during the course of evoluti They are usually displayed on the upper w surface; by closing their wings over the b butterflies can change their appearance fr vivid conspicuousness to that of withe leaves or pieces of bark.

The males of many butterflies establis territory and wait, resting on a leaf or ground for females of their own species tc past. When one arrives the male flies up intercept and tries to persuade her to desc on to his perch. If an intruding male of same species appears the first male flies and drives it away; some males intercept butterfly which appears regardless of species. Before mating, final recognitior established by perception of a pheromone

Dragonflies use their sight to con almost all their activities. The males strongly territorial and fights between riv frequently result in torn wings and amputa legs. The females roam more widely than th partners. When a female enters a ma territory – which is usually on or near wat the male flies up to her and attempts to ma She normally accepts him if she has mated already.

Night-lights Nocturnal insects can cc municate visually only if they are lumino In Britain the one common species to fall i this category is the glow-worm (*Lampy noctiluca*) – a beetle. The female reaches m urity when she still resembles the form o larva, and rests among the grass at nig displaying the brightly luminous organ tha situated on the underside of her abdom The male, a fully developed beetle, but o slightly luminous, flies about and is guided the female by her bright greenish-yellow lig

Pest control

In America, where gypsy moths have become tree-pests, experiments are being undertaken to see if their pheromones can be used for pest control – a glass rod dipped in a solution of female pheromones is placed near the male's antennae. His response to the test indicates that scent organs can detect only female pheromones of the same species.

Scent organs

The female emperor moth (near right) emits pheromones from scent organs which are situated at the rear of her abdomen. These pheromones may be detected from as far away as 3km (2 miles) by the male (far right), whose elaborately feathered antennae are designed to increase the area available to detect mere molecules of pheromone.

Left: Communication between male and female grasshoppers is vocal—the male doing most of the 'talking'. He has two distinct songs. One is loud, calling the female to his side but also challenging other male grasshoppers to keep their distance, while the second occurs when the two partners are together. This is a quiet gentle chirping, conveying a message quite distinct from that of the normal loud song. Female grasshoppers are also capable of singing, normally in reply to the male's call, but theirs is a quiet, subdued song. Both sexes create these sounds by rubbing their hind legs (which carry a row of stridulating pegs) against the forewings.

overlap on to the back, one bearing a ridge and the other a row of pegs or teeth; sound is produced by rapidly moving the wings, and is again distinct for each species. Curiously, in crickets the right wing overlaps the left, and in bush-crickets the left overlaps the right. Both these groups of Orthoptera differ from grasshoppers in having their hearing organ on the tibia—the fourth segment of their fore legs. Females and males both possess these hearing organs, although only the latter stridulate.

The other vocal group of insects is the cicadas—members of the 'bug' order, Hemiptera. One species only, *Cicadetta montana* occurs in the British Isles, and is restricted to Hampshire. Only the males have a song which again serves to attract the females and is created by the vibration of a stretched membrane at the base of the abdomen.

In warmer countries, where cicadas are more common, their songs are a familiar sound at dusk and can be extraordinarily loud.

There are no 'fire-flies' in Britain, but in some countries where they are abundant, different species are distinguished by differing codes of flashes and flight patterns that enable each insect to find its appropriate partner.

Insect song Communication by sound is common among the Orthoptera–grasshoppers, crickets and bush-crickets. All produce their songs by stridulation, a sound which can be imitated by stroking your finger-nail along a comb.

Grasshoppers have a row of minute, evenly spaced pegs on the inner side of the femur of each hind leg which they stroke against prominent veins on their forewings. Each species has a characteristic arrangement and number of pegs which produce a unique song that can be distinguished by other grasshopper species, and by the human ear. The singing is done mostly by the males and serves to attract the females, who reply to his call, despite having weaker stridulating pegs. Grasshoppers' hearing organs are situated on each side of the base of the abdomen.

Crickets and bush-crickets stridulate in a completely different way. Their forewings

Courtship rituals

In some insects, when an encounter has been brought about by location and recognition the male has to perform a courtship display before the female will accept him as a sexual partner. This is the case with many

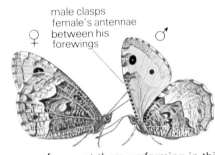

male clasps female's antennae between his forewings

butterflies—the casual observer can often spot them performing in this distinctive manner. The courtship ritual of the grayling butterfly, in particular, has been closely examined. The female initially emits a pheromone which the male detects with his highly sensitive antennae, helping him to confirm visual identification—the distinctive colouring on her forewings. Having established that the female is the same species, he flies up and intercepts her flight. If she is ready to mate she alights on the ground with the male, taking up a position facing him. The male then proceeds to open and close his wings several times, eventually clasping the female's antennae between them. In this way he transfers scented scales—androconia—from his wings to her scent organs (the olfactory receptors), thus stimulating her to proceed with mating. This scent is an aphrodisiac and quite distinct from the pheromone by means of which recognition was originally established.

THE ANTICS OF SPIDER COURTSHIP

...ider courtship can be a complex and lengthy affair
...s the smaller, more submissive male may spend an
entire day attempting to approach, excite and
seduce the female who, initially, is more likely
...regard him as a potential meal rather than a mate.

Courtship is a ritualised form of behaviour preparatory to mating, and it is only very rarely that animal species mate without such preliminaries between the sexes. The courtship of spiders includes behaviour which is decidedly advanced compared with most other invertebrates. Much of it involves signals for identification but the spiders also exhibit types of behaviour which might be described in anthropomorphic terms as extrovert, seductive, devious or pre-emptive. For the male spider this interaction is essential if he is to avoid being mistaken for prey. For the female, a considerably larger individual, it helps to pacify her predatory instinct and provides the stimulation necessary for copulation.

Sperm induction In most species it is the male that actively seeks the female, although the female may have made some effort by emitting chemical signals (pheromones) into the air or on to silk drag-lines trailed behind her which help the male to track her down.

On becoming adult, the male spider usually loses interest in prey, leaves his web or retreat and spins a tiny sperm web. On to this he ejaculates a drop of semen which he draws into organs in his palpi. He then goes in search of a partner and attempts to inject the semen into her genital apertures.

The entire exchange of information between the two sexes can be highly complex, with successive or simultaneous actions and signals including pheromones, sounds, vibrations, visual effects and tactile stimulations. For each species the combined effect is unique so that individuals can find a suitable mate from their own species.

Courting on a web Spider courtship techniques may be broadly grouped depending on whether they are those of web-builders, clear sighted hunters, or poor sighted hunters. Among the web-builders (families Araneidae, Theridiidae and Agelenidae) courtship usually involves the male jerking and vibrating the web threads by tugging with his legs and drumming with his palps and, when the female has permitted his approach, stroking her body. The males are not always successful though, and in the case of the garden spider

...ove: Courtship is not easy
...a male garden spider. On
...casions he has been
...tched for an entire day,
...eatedly tweaking the web
...d advancing towards the
...ale, only to be met each
...e by a fierce onslaught.
...inging down out of the
...y on a thread fixed to
...ne nearby vegetation he
...n pauses, climbs up and
...s again and again until
...ntually he succeeds in
...xing her on to the mating
...ead where she at last
...comes submissive.

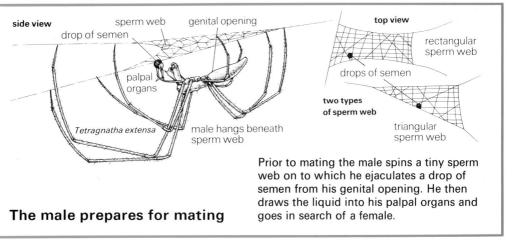

side view — sperm web — genital opening
drop of semen
palpal organs
Tetragnatha extensa — male hangs beneath sperm web

top view
rectangular sperm web
drops of semen
two types of sperm web
triangular sperm web

The male prepares for mating

Prior to mating the male spins a tiny sperm web on to which he ejaculates a drop of semen from his genital opening. He then draws the liquid into his palpal organs and goes in search of a female.

battle-scarred males are sometimes seen towards the end of the mating season with only three legs left.

Males of the ubiquitous *Meta segmenta* wait in the outskirts of the female's web until she is busy with an insect before approaching. Hours may pass without either making a move, but as soon as an insect is caught in the web and the female begins to feed the male advances and strokes her with out-stretched legs. They grapple, then break, and while she returns to the meal he trails a mating thread over her ready to begin his vibrations which, if he is lucky, will eventually interest her in mating.

Many web-spinners have stridulatory

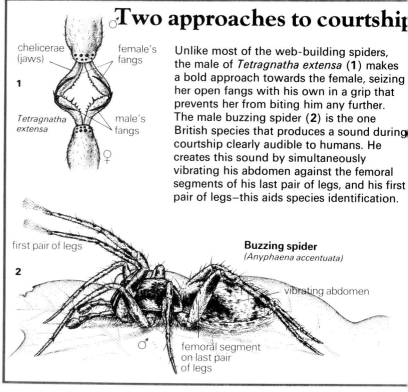

Two approaches to courtship

Unlike most of the web-building spiders, the male of *Tetragnatha extensa* (**1**) makes a bold approach towards the female, seizing her open fangs with his own in a grip that prevents her from biting him any further. The male buzzing spider (**2**) is the one British species that produces a sound during courtship clearly audible to humans. He creates this sound by simultaneously vibrating his abdomen against the femoral segments of his last pair of legs, and his first pair of legs–this aids species identification.

Buzzing spider
(Anyphaena accentuata)

Left: The male *Xysticus* spider binds his partner down with silk, but she can break free, so the purpose may simply be to improve stability during copulation.

Below: Look carefully at this picture and you will see a pair of *Tetragnatha extensa* spiders. The male (right) is gripping the female's fangs (left) with his own so that she cannot bite him.

organs on their body which produce acous signals unique to each species. *Zygiella notata*, a species common under the eaves sheds, is one such example and so is the sm *Dictyna arundinacea* and the house spid *Tegenaria parietina* and *Tegenaria atrica*.

Visual performers Among clear-sight hunting spiders the males often perform visual display before approaching the fema Wolf spiders (Lycosidae) and lynx spid (Oxyopidae) wave their palps up and dow or vibrate them. The common wolf spide courtship involves an elaborate semapho type display in which the male stands as tall possible and holds his black palps out sid ways, alternately raising one and loweri the other as he slowly advances on the fema

By far the most extrovert courtship displa are performed by the jumping spiders (Salt idae), known for their highly develop eyesight. In a most elaborate dance the ma perform various antics and show off th colour pattern to the best effect. A fi example is the male jumping spider *Aeluril insignitus*, which, in contrast to the drab coloured female, has a black and wh abdomen. Holding his body at an angle w the rear end touching the ground, the ma lifts his first pair of legs (which are black with striking bright yellow segment) as hi overhead as possible and then down aga Repeating this hypnotic movement he a vances towards the female with jerky steps, long as she is not hostile.

The large semi-aquatic raft spider has lycosid-like courtship, the male stretching his palps and rapidly vibrating his front le but he often waits until the female is eati something before advancing.

In the much more common *Pisaura*

Luring the female with semaphore

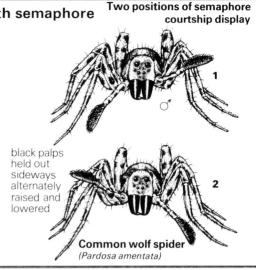

Two positions of semaphore courtship display

Clear-sighted hunting spiders perform elaborate visual displays during courtship. In the case of the common wolf spider (left) the male embarks on a semaphore-type display in which he holds his black palps out sideways, alternately raising one and lowering the other. He repeats these movements as he slowly advances towards the female until she either moves back or drives him away. If he persists however, she should become excited.

black palps held out sideways alternately raised and lowered

Common wolf spider
(Pardosa amentata)

bilis the male first catches an insect, wraps it [in] silk, and then hands it to his partner before [att]empting to mate. The great arachnologist, [W] S Bristowe, describes how the male *Pisaura* [so]metimes cheats by wrapping up the empty [carc]ase of a fly, or even by running away with [the] wedding gift at the end of the mating [cer]emony.

Courting in the dark Short sighted hunting [spi]ders (families Dysderidae, Gnaphosidae [an]d Thomisidae) tend to walk about in a [gro]ping fashion with their forelegs stretched [ou]t ahead, and frequently their courtship is [ext]remely brief. Unable to introduce them-[sel]ves by web vibrations or visual signals, [the]re is an immediate and frenzied interplay of [leg]s when the sexes meet, the male attempting [to] reach the mating position while still using [tac]tile stimulation.

[M]any such species, like the woodlouse [spi]der, spend much time in closed silken cells [an]d this is where the male usually finds a [fem]ale. On arriving at the silken cell the male [sp]ends some time making an introduction by [pro]bing the silk with quivering legs. He then [te]ars open the cell with his large fangs, places

Above: *Meta segmenta* males only approach the females when they are busy feeding.

Below: A jumping spider, the most extrovert of seducers.

his first two pairs of legs through the hole and walks in. The female meets him, brandishing her gaping fangs, but as he taps and strokes her body with extended legs she quietens down.

In the rather large and fierce *Drassodes lapidosus*, the male reaches maturity earlier than the female and then takes possession of an immature female by enclosing her in a silken cell and mating with her immediately after her final moult, before she gains full strength. *Micrommata virescens* and several of the crab spider males seize the female by a leg and hold on until her struggle ceases or the counter attack becomes too dangerous for them to proceed.

Competing males Encounters between male spiders are frequent, especially where population density is high, as with wolf spiders on the woodland floor. When two male wolf spiders meet in the presence of a female they assume specific threat postures and may begin to fight. A dominant male (established in previous fights) is likely to be the winner and it is he who turns his attentions to the female, circling around her and waving his palps in a courtship ritual.

Home and territory

Many animals have no permanent home at all, others have several homes, while some have a fixed home only for certain periods of the year – when raising their young, or hibernating, for example. The character of these homes varies enormously, from massive structures such as the extensive underground setts developed by badgers, to the bare scrape on a rock surface on which a seabird lays its eggs and rears its young.

Species such as the badger have a system very much like people, with a clearly defined home and a much wider area (the range) in which they search for food or a mate. Some species defend a feeding territory and will not tolerate intrusion by others, even of the same species. Their territory may be based around the home, or may be nothing to do with any permanent structure, especially out of the breeding season.

Territorial behaviour is not confined to mammals and birds: many invertebrates also maintain a territory – like the male dragonfly patrolling a stretch of riverbank or pond-side.

Many species aggressively defend their territory in the breeding season, but become sociable and highly mobile for the rest of the year. Migrant seabirds and waders that breed in Britain may defend a tiny area of land for a few months while they rear their young, but then spend the rest of the year travelling throughout the world, often in the company of large numbers of their own species.

Thus homes, territories and home ranges exist when they have a purpose, changing or disappearing as the need itself changes or disappears. Inevitably, the existence of a home or territory to be defended gives rise to an interesting range of aggressive displays and these are amongst the most fascinating aspects of animal life.

Left: Lapwings perform a series of dramatic freefalls, raking their wings back to speed their descent, in an attempt to defend their territory. The frenzied dives are accompanied by a 'whooshing' sound caused by the air passing over their wing feathers and by screeching calls used to intimidate intruders.

CHECKLIST

This checklist is a guide to the animals featured in the following section. Each species has been chosen for its particular concept and defence of home and territory. The animals listed in **bold** *have their own chapter.*

Badger
Black-tailed godwit
Bombardier beetle
Caterpillars
Cicada
Death-watch beetle
Deer
European otter
Fox
Gannet
Great tit
Grey seal
Hedgehog
Ladybirds
Lapwing
Marine turtles
Mole
Native ponies
Perch
Pied wagtail
Rabbit
Redshank
Robin
Sea-urchin
Sheep
Shelduck
Spiders
Stickleback
Squirrels
Wading birds
Wild cat

Left: The common dormouse is the only British rodent to hibernate. It sleeps for half the year, curled tightly in a ball with its chin resting on its stomach and its tail curled over its head. The winter nest is built on or below the ground, usually under dead leaves or among tree roots.

MAMMAL TERRITORY AND HOME RANGE

Mammals maintain and defend territories in which they can live, feed and breed. But territories are only a small part of a much larger area – the home range – in which they pursue day-to-day activities.

me range' means 'normally used area' – animal's usual stomping grounds, over ch it travels regularly in the course of its . Few mammals attempt to defend the le of their home range: they select a ritory' within it. This territory is usually rved for the use of one animal (and etimes its mate), excluding others of the e species.

ests, food and harems Most animals try defend their own nest sites against elcome visitors, so the nest area resents a part of the territory. In addition, s usually assumed that territory is nded to provide an animal with a secure d supply to support itself and its family: small a territory or too many greedy passers results in too little food and poor ess in rearing young. However, unlike ls, mammals do not all have the same ling habits. Many eat grass and many

others are omnivorous and have little trouble finding sufficient food, so they do not need such strict feeding territories.

Shrews are among those mammals that do conform to a territorial feeding pattern. Each shrew has a patch of about 500sq m (600sq yd) which it keeps to itself. Young animals begin by ousting their elders and then secure the area as their own. But as in all territorial systems, territory as exclusive space can only remain so long as the animal can defend it.

Moles behave similarly. Each one has a burrow system about 40m (130ft) long from which intruding moles are vigorously expelled. A female mole will tolerate a single visiting male during the brief – 10 day – mating season, even driving out her own young once weaned.

During the rutting season, and only then, red deer stags also defend a patch of ground,

Above: Foxes demarcate territory by leaving piles of droppings tainted with scent.

Left: Every shrew has its own territory to protect vital food resources.

Radio tracking
Many problems associated with trapping and observing mammals can now be overcome by radio tracking. An animal is caught, fitted with a radio transmitter, then let go and followed from a distance. Using this technique it is possible to determine exactly where an animal goes and what size and shape its home range is; even the time it spends asleep or feeding. Radios are now made small enough to fit on to mice and bats (offering a chance to study home range in bats for the first time), and there is no disruption to normal activity. Researchers are now getting accurate information on the home ranges of such species as the fox, badger and deer. They are also finding out what effect seasons and habitat have on home range and territory.

usually the same one year after year. However, this is only a small area, perhaps 250sq m (300sq yd), and is not related to the stag's food requirements since he hardly eats anything until the rut is over. In this case, the defended 'territory' is really only a secure place within which his harem of hinds is kept.

Scent-marking In preference to actual fighting, however, most mammals, other than the extremely belligerent moles and shrews, signal territorial ownership by using scent markers. This is equivalent to the territorial songs of birds: a public declaration of ownership is made and visitors are thereby warned to stay away.

Many mammals have complex scent secreting glands. These may be sited round the anus, where they add scent to droppings (for example the fox and the badger), or on some other part of the body, such as under the chin (rabbit) or tail (wood mouse). Scent glands are used to lay smell messages for the next animal that passes by. Dogs mark lamp-posts, for instance, and otters lay scent with their droppings (spraints) on prominent riverside stones and logs. Many other species (for example, the rabbit, pine marten, and perhaps bats) smear greasy scent on objects within their home range, or leave scent-tainted urine. The scent indicates the area individual mammals regard as their own 'patch' and other mammals of the same species tend to stay away.

Above: Molehills are the outward signs of a mole's territory – a system of tunnels from which all other moles are excluded.

Below: Red deer stag roaring in the rut. This has the same function as birdsong: it declares the stag's ownership of his patch and warns others.

Spaced out in time Scent-marking a te tory, like posting notices, saves the effor constantly having to chase out intruders, it is then easier for trespassers to sneak ignoring the implied threat posed by s marks. As a result, for most mammals (un many birds), space is not owned and u exclusively by one animal. Territorial a may overlap considerably, but the ow avoid contact with each other as muc possible by moving about. Thus, they arate themselves in time rather than by sp In fact, a great many species, including sr mammals like mice and voles, may 'mar fairly large territory, but only physic defend the small area they are actu standing in.

Home ranging If territories overlap s stantially, as they do in many species, t these areas are clearly not being rigoro defended for exclusive use by one individ They should perhaps not be called 'territ at all, but 'home range': the area used in course of normal day-to-day activity.

Home ranges differ considerably betw species. Obviously, a big animal is likel travel further than a small one, but in there are also significant differences betw species of similar size. For example, a b vole may travel in a straight-line distance say, 50m (55yd) in 24 hours, whereas w mice frequently travel two or three time far. However, neither animal would fol exactly the same track night after night, would it really travel in a straight line.

In order to make useful comparison home ranges between species, it is necess to measure their normally used area, just single journeys. This is done by mark animals and noting where they are s sequently seen or recaptured as often possible. For species like the mountain h which lives out in the open and is easily se this is fairly easy. Observations show hares have a home range varying from 1

rly 30 hectares (25-75 acres). For smaller
nals, however, things are not so easy, and
necessary to resort to trapping to discover
r movements.

rapping results The trapping of small
nmals has revealed considerable differ-
es in the home ranges of different species.
example, wood mice appear to be very
bile creatures, ranging over areas of
0sq m (2400sq yd) or more, usually in
ier open habitats such as deciduous wood-
1. Short-tailed voles, on the other hand,
in dense grass where it is difficult to travel
in the cramped runway systems. This
cies seems content with a home range of
than 1000sq m (1195sq yd), and in-
dual animals may travel no more than
1 (33yd) in any direction from their nest.
hese studies often reveal that males have
ger home ranges than females, especially
the breeding season. For example, the
k vole male covers about 2000sq m
0sq yd), compared with 1400sq m (1675
yd) for the female. Presumably this is
ause they wander more widely in search
mate. Similarly, it is normal to find that
ne range sizes vary within a species
ording to habitat.

No-go' areas A mammal does not neces-
ly use the whole of its home range. In
ny cases there may be included within it
te large areas where the animal never goes
all, a pond, road or building, for example.
en these 'no-go' areas help to define the
ne range boundary. For example, most
all mammals rarely cross wide rivers, and
n quite large species are reluctant to cross
l-carriageway roads. Normal activity (and
ce home range) thus tends to be confined
ne side or another of the obstacle.

above and below ground A home range size
asured in square metres is often misleading
ause it does not take into account the
ee-dimensional activity of the animals.
is is especially obvious in the case of
low-necked mice. On the ground, their
ne range is perhaps 2500sq m (2990sq yd),
they are often found up to 10m (11yd)
ove the ground among tree branches. Other
all mammals climb about much more than
usually supposed, thereby gaining access to
ra food. Squirrels, for example, effectively
rease their apparent range size by being
ive both on the ground and in the trees
ove. Similarly, many species may perform
ch of their activity undetected in under-
und burrows.

Such factors clearly make it impossible to
asure home range (or territory) accurately.
ung animals dispersing may travel much
ther than is 'normal', and the measure-
nts made by researchers are greatly in-
enced by the fact that the very act of trap-
g the animals disrupts normal activity.
ly recently has the technique of radio
cking started to resolve some of these
iculties.

Mammals such as the otter
(right) lay scent with their
droppings, or spraints
(below). The scent carries
information about sex,
breeding condition, social
status and so on, all coded
into complex chemical
molecules that are
deciphered and interpreted
by the sensitive noses of
other animals. In this way a
male mammal may 'stake
out' his claim to an area.
Mammals can cross scent-
marked territorial
boundaries, but they then
know they are on forbidden
ground and may be chased
out. Scent marks may
persist for weeks, so it is not
necessary for a territory
holder to patrol his borders
all the time in order that
potential visitors can see
him. The scent marks carry
his message.

Mammal trapping
It is rather difficult to study
small mammals by direct
observation since they are
usually nocturnal and live
either underground or in
thick vegetation. In such
cases (in fact in the majority
of British mammals) it is
necessary to use traps, such
as the Longworth trap shown
here, to find out where
marked mammals go. Live-
catch traps are used so
that the mammals can be
released and captured
somewhere else on their
home range. By doing this
repeatedly, and noting
all the places where
particular individuals are
caught, researchers can get
an idea of the general area
over which the mammals
wander.

A HOME FOR ALL SEASONS

The homes of mammals are as diverse as the animals themselves–each has a nest, burrow, hole or scrape which meets its own particular seasonal needs.

Mammal evolution has resulted in a great diversity of size and shape, from the tiny pigmy shrew, the smallest British mammal, to the blue whale, the largest that has ever lived. Although most mammals live on the ground, one species or another has managed to invade almost every other available ecological niche: the squirrels spend most of their life in the treetops, the bats have taken to the air, the whales and seals live in the sea and the mole has adopted an almost totally underground existence.

This great variety of habitat is reflected in the homes that mammals construct. Some dig deep underground burrows, while others merely make use of existing holes. Yet others construct nests above the ground in trees or bushes. A few hardy mammals merely inhabit temporary homes–a hollow in the ground, perhaps, or a hole in a rock.

Why build a home? There are many reasons why mammals construct homes. They may be designed to give protection from the weather, or provide protection from predators. Some mammal homes fulfill both these functions.

Like birds, mammals are warm blooded animals; they maintain their bodies at a constant temperature which is independent of their surroundings. Regulating their body temperature is very energy consuming, requiring the intake of great quantities of food. In winter, when food is often scarce, some British mammals are unable to cope with the cold conditions, or the lack of food, and so withdraw into a state of inactivity and torpor known as hibernation. In bats, dormice and hedgehogs, the body temperature falls until it is only a little above the temperature of the surroundings. Many small mammals, such as dormice and hedgehogs, build special winter nests into which they retire to hibernate. In their torpid state they are very vulnerable to predators, and the nests provide hiding places and some protection as well as acting as insulation and thus minimising heat loss.

Other mammals retire to shelter during cold weather and become drowsy.

Whether or not mammals build nests is related to whether the young are helpless at birth or are able to run about almost immediately. Even so, some deer, which have the most precocious young, usually give birth in a dense thicket which affords protection

Above: The otter has no permanent home except for the holt in which the cubs are born and reared.

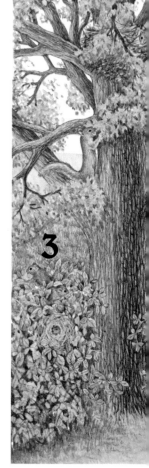

3

Left: Hedgehogs build several different kinds of nests. In winter they retire to their hibernation nest. During the rest of the year they use nests for daytime resting –an individual hedgehog may have several such sites within its home range. However, if the weather is warm they may lie up during the day in undergrowth. The breeding nest, which is larger than the other nests, is built by the female just before she is due to give birth.

a few days. The offspring of carnivores such as the fox, on the other hand, which are helpless at birth, are born in a well protected lair. Mammals such as squirrels and hedgehogs, which also give birth to helpless young, bear them in specially constructed nests.

A life underground Of all the British mammals the mole is the most highly adapted to a life underground: it has shovel-like front feet, a cylindrical body, a questing, sensitive nose, a soft coat in which the hairs can lie backwards or forwards, rudimentary eyes hidden under fur, and no outer ears. The mole digs with a breast stroke action using the strong claws of its large outward-turned front feet.

Within each mole's territory there is a labyrinth of hunting tunnels, punctuated at intervals by vertical shafts leading to molehills. The molehills serve several purposes: they allow the mole to dispose of the soil it excavated and give access to the surface, whenever necessary and they ventilate the subterranean passages. At intervals the hunting passages widen into chambers about 20cm (8in) in diameter. Some of these are lined with grass and dry leaves and are used for sleeping in and resting. Other chambers are used as food stores – here paralysed but live earthworms surplus to immediate requirements are stored. In spring the female builds a large breeding chamber deep inside the tunnel system and lines it with soft material.

Underground retreats Although no other British mammal spends as much of its life under the ground as a mole, many excavate underground burrows in which they rest, hibernate and rear their young, venturing above ground in search of food.

Rabbits are gregarious animals with great burrowing skills and their warrens can become quite extensive. A pregnant doe often digs a small separate burrow called a stop, which she lines with hay, or fur taken from her own coat. The young are born blind and sparsely furred, unlike the offspring of hares which are born above ground and fully furred.

The badger's sett is the largest and most elaborate underground mammalian home, an average sett being 10-30m (30-100ft) in diameter and 1.5m (5½ft) deep. A complicated system of communicating passages and nesting chambers is excavated at several levels, and there are usually several exits. The badger is an enthusiastic digger and over the years a sett may become extremely extensive and may be occupied by several generations at one time. Badgers are very houseproud, and on fine, dry nights they forage for bedding material such as moss, dry leaves and ferns with which to line the many sleeping quarters and the separate nursery. The bedding is frequently brought out into the open for a few hours for an airing, and when the young are being reared soiled bedding is constantly being replaced.

Where to look for homes

1 The fox's earth is easily recognised by the pungent, musty smell which emanates from it. It may excavate the earth itself, or take over another creature's den.
2 The mole's tunnel system is its hunting ground, food store, resting area and breeding place.
3 The dormouse builds different kinds of nests. This one in the hedgerow is the breeding nest where the female will rear her young.
4 The hare's form is a shallow hole concealed in vegetation. The leverets are born fully furred, with their eyes open, and are soon active; they do not require the protection of a nest.
5 The squirrel's drey is used for resting in during the night and the middle of the day. The breeding drey is larger and stouter.
6 Bats do not construct homes but they adopt particular sites as daytime roosts, hibernating sites and as communal breeding roosts.

Foxes are opportunists and often take o■
part of a disused rabbit warren or a badg■
sett for a den although they can excav■
their own if necessary. Badgers do not se■
to relish the fox's musty smell, and they bl■
up passages between the two parts of ■
burrow to isolate themselves from th■
smelly neighbours. Not only does the fc■
earth smell, it is also very untidy, the entra■
being littered with food remains.

Homes in hollows Several mammals–sto■
weasels, pine martens and wild cats, ■
example–neither build elaborate nests ■
dig tunnels, but seek shelter in any availa■
holes, nooks and crannies in the trees ε■
rocks that they can find. The hare's fo■
for example, is a shallow hollow scra■
away in the earth, with a clump of grass■
stone at one side for protection. It is a v■
temporary home and no special arran■
ments are made even in the breeding sea■
for, unlike young rabbits, the young ha■
are born open-eyed, furred and quite act■
and are soon able to leave their birthpl■
and fend for themselves.

Similarly deer rest on any suitable patch■
sheltered ground, leaving behind them t■
tale patches of vegetation flattened by th■
heavy bodies.

Dextrous builders Mammals are not v■
skilful at handling nesting material. O■
the smaller rodents come anywhere n■
matching the artistry in nest building of■
bird world. The dormouse and harv■
mouse, for example are able to use th■
nimble forefeet and long, powerful incis■
with great success. Their carefully construc■
summer breeding nests are usually concea■
in sheltered, inaccessible places above grou■
level. The smaller daytime resting nests ε■
made higher up in the shrub layer, about ■
(3ft) above the ground. Often several ■
built close together during the summer.■
winter the dormouse makes a nest at grou■
level beneath a pile of dead leaves or in ■
shelter of tree roots. There it hibernates ■
up to six months.

Above: The mammal that lives at the highest level is the squirrel. It constructs its bulky, untidy drey between 10 and 15m (33-50ft) up a tree. The drey is usually built close to the tree trunk and is supported by side branches. It is spherical, 20-50cm (8-20in) in diameter, made of loosely plaited twigs, and is well-roofed with a small entrance hole to one side. It is lined with grass, leaves and shredded bark. The drey can take 2-5 days to build.

Opposite: Wildcats do not build nests or tunnels, but make their dens in the natural chambers and fissures of rocky cairns.

Left: The harvest mouse builds its breeding nest 30-40cm (12-16in) above ground, among tall grasses, reeds or corn. It is a firm, dense ball 8-10cm (3-4in) in diameter with a round entrance hole to one side. It takes about 5-10 hours to complete.

Right: The rabbit is a gregarious mammal and lives in colonies called warrens, where the burrows of neighbouring animals often interconnect. There are numerous entrance holes at ground level with well-worn paths leading to them and often several concealed emergency bolt-holes. The nest chamber in which the rabbits rest during the day is about 40-50cm (16-20in) below the surface.

SCENT MESSAGES

For many mammals, the ability to perceive scent is one of the most important faculties they possess. Smells can warn of danger, signpost food, mark territory and indicate readiness to mate.

Most wild animals rely on the sense of smell to an enormous degree. Most mammals can detect scents that are diffused through the air in very small concentrations. Man's sense of smell is discriminating rather than acute – he can distinguish between closely related smells but they must be present in large concentrations.

Evolution Mammals' reliance on their sense of smell dates back 150 million years when they first emerged on the evolutionary tree. The first mammals were nocturnal and a highly developed ability to smell was more useful in the dark than sight. And hearing was of little use since these early mammals were very small – no bigger than a weasel – and lived close to

the ground where sounds do not carry well.

Some misconceptions Many of our assumptions about mammals' ability to smell are incorrect. For instance, the length of the nose is not necessarily an indication of the sensitivity or power of the particular animal's sense of smell. The shape of the nose is actually related to the shape of the jaw, which is in turn related to the type of food the animal eats.

Another misconception is that the nose is concerned exclusively with smell – only about 10% of the nose's function is to smell, its main function being to filter and regulate the temperature of the air entering the lungs.

Rabbits and rodents twitch their noses, not to sweep in as many smells as possible, but to select the important smells and prevent the scent discriminating organs from being overwhelmed.

A communication system There are two elements to any communication system: the transmission of messages and the ability to receive and interpret them. In mammals the nose is the organ which receives the messages which are then sent to the brain for sorting and interpretation. The appropriate action is then selected – run, kill, mate. The ways in which these scent messages are broadcast are as varied as the reasons for sending them.

Territory demarcation Many mammals are territorial and, rather than perpetually patrolling the boundaries of their territory or

Above: A badger marks its territory by depositing a globule of jelly-like secretion, produced by its anal glands, on top of its faeces. It then lowers its hindquarters and drags itself forward for a few centimetres in order to spread the odour.

Opposite: This rabbit is displaying special scent-marking behaviour called 'chinning'. The animal moves its head close to the object to be marked – it may be a gatepost, stone, twig or even a stem of grass. It then lifts its chin and rubs it over the object, covering it with a scented secretion from a gland beneath its chin. The whole process lasts three to fifteen seconds.

gaging in combat with every passing animal
their own species, they advertise the extent
their claim by leaving scent signals that will
recognised by others of their kind.
rritorial scent marks do not function like
eep out' signs; that is, they do not prevent
e border from being crossed, but they do
event unauthorised settlement. They also
ost the self confidence of the resident
ammal and greatly increase his chances of
nning a fight should an interloper ignore
e signs and try to settle.

Many mammals use their urine or faeces
delimit their territory. A fox leaves his
rid smelling droppings in an exposed site,
top of a tree stump perhaps, or on a
ssock of grass. Other animals, such as
dgers and rabbits, have glands that produce
ecial secretions with which they advertise
eir claim to an area. If you have ever taken
dog for a walk in a city street you will
ve noticed how some lamp posts are in-
stigated casually while at others the dog
owls, scratches the ground and finally
inates, lifting his leg to ensure that the
essage is left as high up the post as possible
here it will be most obvious to any other
ssing dog. Other mammals such as rabbits
much the same thing, rubbing their
cretions on twigs, posts and clumps of grass.

Sex scents The sense of smell is very
portant in the reproductive life of most
ammals. Unlike human females, other

Above: This Chinese water
deer established a scent
bond between herself and
her newborn fawn when she
licked away the foetal
membrane. She doesn't stay
with the fawn but hides it
away in undergrowth,
visiting it to suckle it from
time to time and locating it
by smell.

female mammals are on heat–sexually receptive and fertile–for only a very short time.
It is important for the continuity of the
species that the male should impregnate the
female during this critical period, so the scent
messages he receives are very strong signals.
A bitch on heat attracts eager males from
miles around.

The red deer stag sniffs the urine of the
hinds in his harem to detect which are at the
peak of receptivity–a hind is in season for
only a day. Many other mammals indulge in
this urine sniffing activity which is often
accompanied by a wrinkling of the nose
called 'flehmen'. It seems to be associated
with the entry of urine odours into the 'organ
of Jacobson'–a small, bone-encased structure
which lies just above the palate and is
probably more sensitive to sex odours than
the rest of the nose.

The primer sex odours work in a slower
more subtle way: they prepare the animal's
hormone system for later activity. Sheep
breeders know that they can bring ewes to
sexual maturity early if they run them with
a ram, and that means they can improve their
lamb production. It has been established by
experiment that it is, indeed, the smell of the
ram that is responsible for this acceleration
in the onset of oestrus. Similar observations
have been made in the laboratory for goats,
coypu and mice, so it seems likely that the
effect may be fairly common in the wild.

Mother and young bonding Unlike humans,
most mammal mothers recognise their offspring by smell rather than sight. It is
obviously important that the mother and
young learn to recognise each other as soon
as possible for, in the wild, the youngster is
very vulnerable, especially during the first
few hours of its life.

After giving birth most mammals lick the
caul or foetal membrane from their young
and in so doing establish an odour bond
between them. Deprived of these first few
minutes of vital contact, most mammals will
reject their young, sometimes by butting
them away. The afterbirth–foetal membrane

A stranger in disguise

Sheep today are bred to produce twins, but sometimes a ewe will reject the second lamb or has insufficient milk to suckle both lambs. A ewe which has lost one of her own lambs is sometimes persuaded to foster an orphan lamb. The shepherd ties the skin of her dead lamb over the lamb to be adopted and the ewe, recognising the scent of her own offspring, accepts the new lamb as her own. Commercially available aerosols are sometimes used to confuse the ewe's sense of smell. By spraying both the lamb and the ewe's nose the shepherd can disguise the stranger in the fold.

and placenta – is usually eaten to save waste of highly nutritious material and to destroy scent evidence which might lead a predator to the helpless, newborn offspring.

Young rats, mice and other rodents exhibit a marked tendency to wander from the nest as they grow older, so the mother produces a special maternal odour which helps counteract this 'wanderlust' until they are big enough to fend for themselves. The odour is produced by bacteria in the mother's gut.

A nose for food It is sometimes assumed that carnivores, being hunters, will have a better sense of smell than herbivores, but this is not always the case. It is just as important to a deer that it selects the most nutritious and succulent leaf as to a polecat that it should recognise a prey species. However, while herbivores are born with an innate knowledge of which plants smell right, the young of all carnivores have to be taught to locate prey, to hunt and to recognise the odour of prey species. If polecats do not come across a particular species in the first four months of life they will not recognise it

Above: Squirrels bury nuts in times of plenty. If they can find the hoard later they recognise it as their own by the smell of their saliva.

Below: Young polecats must be taught to recognise the scent of their prey.

as prey in later life.

Many carnivorous mammals hunt at lea partly by sight, but smell is obviously al important. For instance, the tracks of stoat hunting a rabbit are often just dow wind of the potential prey.

Scent is particularly important to tho hunters that live in woods, forests or den vegetation where their field of vision limited. However, one disadvantage of rel ing on smell is that it is useless if the wind blowing in the wrong direction. A huntin man knows that he can get quite close a mammal without being detected if he downwind – that is, if the wind is carryin his scent away from the mammal.

The ownership of food may be indicated scent marking – foxes often urinate on buried carcase, which they intend to return later, to warn off other foxes.

Mimicking Just as harmless species insects seek protection from predators assuming the warning colours of more harn ful species, so the young of many mamma are protected from attack by their elders assuming the smell of their mothers. You yellow necked mice have a tail gland whi produces a special odour that mimics that their mother. Then suddenly, at the onset sexual maturity, the males produce a distin tive male odour and are promptly expell from the nest by their father who n recognises them as a threat.

WHAT'S THE POINT OF AGGRESSION?

Aggressive behaviour in mammals often looks much more dangerous than it actually is. Not to be confused with predatory behaviour, the object of which is to get food, aggression is for protection of territory, food and homes, and to find a mate.

red fox vixen, plagued her over-exuberant cub, ns on him and displays gressively, her tail raised she utters screams and owls. The cub crouches in omission.

Aggression is a word that is loosely used to describe hostile or destructive behaviour in man, but when used scientifically to denote a certain type of behaviour in animals it has a precise meaning. People who keep pets or watch animals in the wild will easily recognise threats, quarrels and fights between the same species as aggression.

Aggression is not the same thing as predatory behaviour, as can be demonstrated by comparing a hunting tom cat with the same animal when it is threatening another male. In the first case it makes no sound as it approaches its prey with its body close to the ground. In the second, it stands with stiff legs and tail and utters a series of penetrating screams and howls. The results, too, are different: the successful conclusion to a hunt is that prey is caught, killed and eaten; aggressive encounters rarely end in death.

When aggression occurs All mammals show aggression at some stage during their lives, and it is an important aspect of their survival strategy. It takes place in defence of food, water, resting and nesting sites, and mates. Animals in competition for these resources are often members of the same species, so it is between them that aggression is most likely to occur.

It is to the advantage of animals that they settle their dispute as quickly as possible, thus saving their limited energy for other essential activities. Aggression must also be limited to

1

2

3

Above: The photograph at the top shows a wild cat in an aggressive posture. Before this stage is reached it stares hard **(1)**, then it flattens its ears **(2)**, then finally opens its mouth to show its teeth **(3)** and lets out an explosive spitting sound, accompanied by a howl (as in the illustrations above). The sound provides information about its size—the larger the animal, the bigger its resonating chambers and the longer its vocal cords, giving a deeper roar; and the frequency gives an indication of the wild cat's fitness and strength.

Right: European otters engaged in mock fighting. Animals often pretend to be bigger, stronger or more willing than they actually are. But aggression can easily escalate, so bluff is an uncertain game.

enable those that live together to do so in some harmony, particularly during the mating season and in those species that form social groups, such as badgers.

In many cases a preliminary level of threat is reached before the animals ever meet. This is known as territorial marking, which allows mammals to protect the resources within one area, and reduces the risk of fighting; it is tantamount to a sign saying, 'keep out'.

Limiting aggression One way the risk of actual fighting is reduced when mammals are in dispute over territory is by the use of signals in place of physical combat. They are graded in intensity, so there is a series of stages from mild threat to all-out fighting with opportunities at each level for either animal to break away.

When, for example, brown rats from different groups meet, they first pause; their backs arch, their hair stands on end; they gnash their teeth and approach each other, presenting the side of their bodies. Next they rear on their hind legs and, with noses almost touching, they begin to box. If one falls back, the other

lies on top, and they remain motionle except for the gnashing of teeth. Only aft these stages does the biting and wrestli begin. Often this last stage is never reach because one rat gives up and is allowed leave. If there is fighting, it seldom lasts f much more than a minute.

Mammals have many ways of demonstra ing their weapons, size, strength and willin ness to fight. The fox, for example, m display its teeth and snarl, curling its lips expose the full length of the canines. As snaps its jaws, and gnashes and chatters teeth, it provides ample evidence of ability to bite if it is further provoked.

Many animals draw attention to their si and enhance it, by standing upright, erecti tracts of hair on their backs, and presentin side view. Hoofed animals paw the groun showing a willingness to advance. Othe like squirrels, chase each other. Sound vital in animals with poor eyesight, such shrews which scream at each other when th first meet. Weasels hiss, while badgers a cats spit. All these types of behaviour enab the animals to assess each other.

Fighting, like the various stages of thre tends to be limited. Initial stages often invol boxing on the hind legs. Biting and wrestli are more serious and dangerous, because using teeth to bite the vulnerable parts of t other animal's body, the neck and sen organs of both animals are at risk.

Agonistic behaviour Because opposing a mals must have regard for their own safe pure aggression is rarely seen, and eleme of attacking and defensive behaviour are oft mixed. This is described as agonistic beha iour. It is best observed in the animal's fac expressions and postures. Head bobbir which is quite widespread, represents n only a forward attacking movement but a

ht: During the rut, red
r become extremely
ressive, vying with each
er for mates. Their
aviour is often said to
ritualised, because they
ear to struggle according
a set of agreed rules. In
st cases the competition
trial of strength which
olves pushing and pulling.
vices such as the tines
their antlers help to
vent them from slipping
ways.
never passionate his
ual frenzy, there is little
t in a strong animal
ning the battle and
ng the prize: the
ninant males need to
ch out for subordinate
es who are quite likely
neak off with the hinds
le the harem masters are
fighting.

ve: A female grey seal
highly agitated state,
he barks to defend her
. Young grey seals stay
e to their mothers for
first two weeks of
and any intrusion
provoke this
ressive display from the
her.

a backward retreating movement. Agonistic behaviour also accounts for the arched back shown by animals such as cats when they are facing vastly superior opponents. It appears that the hind legs are advancing, while the more vulnerable front part of the body is in retreat, so that the body bends in the middle and seems larger.

The extent of aggression depends on the animal's needs. Pregnant and suckling females are particularly aggressive, and normally subordinate animals, such as female weasels, may become dominant at this time. Attendant males are also aggressive in defence of their young. Hunger and thirst produce aggression that may quickly escalate to fighting. This observation also explains why animals nearly always successfully defend their own territories against even stronger competitors. The owner has more to lose because he is familiar with the sources of food, water and bolt holes, and therefore he tries harder.

Peace in the feud Animals often establish a hierarchy so that one dominant animal has priority in choice of items such as food, resting places, water and mates, while the rest must wait their turn. Thus the strongest are most likely to mate and reproduce, and so the fittest survive.

Social hierarchy within a pack or group is established by threats and fights, and eventually the rest of the group show that they accept the winner's superiority by behaviour known as submission or appeasement. This often involves postures that are the opposite of aggression. Many mammals, such as dogs and foxes as well, crouch close to the ground, their tails between their legs; some roll on their backs, a posture that is often emphasised by the lighter colour of the animal's underside. Deer, such as the fallow and red deer, lie down with their necks outstretched. Other gestures include the grooming of the dominant animal, or adopting postures normally associated with receptive females or juveniles and infants. Appeasement gestures are also used between solitary animals when they meet each other.

It is tempting to judge an animal's behaviour from a human standpoint. A mother, of whatever species, protecting her young is viewed with admiration; an adolescent finding his position, with tolerance; and a dominant male, fighting off rivals, chivying females or scaring away juveniles, with condemnation. Such judgements made about animals that lack our powers of reason are meaningless. Aggressive behaviour is just a way used by animals to gain or keep what they need to survive or reproduce. It is both instinctive and learned from experience within the social group and from encounters outside. It is essential for an animal's survival.

HERDING HABITS OF NATIVE PONIES

Although British native ponies show the same type of herd structure and behaviour as other horses and ponies living in wild or semi-wild conditions, there are variations, particularly the strongly defined hierarchy among the mares of a herd.

Left: Welsh ponies in the Brecon Beacons National Park. In the British Isles horses no longer live in herds –except for some breeds of native ponies. Some Shetlands, a few Highlands, some Fells and a significant number of New Forest ponies still live in at least a semi-wild state in their natural surroundings, and among these it is still possible to observe herd structure and behaviour. Of the Dartmoor ponies (below) there are now few pure-breds left in their native habitat, though in the past there were large herds which would have conformed with the herd structure of other British native ponies.

During televised show jumping commentators sometimes say 'that fence is causing problems–because the horse is jumping away from the collecting ring', or 'the horse is napping (trying to return) to the collecting ring'. In terms of show jumping this is disobedience, but in terms of equine behaviour the horse's actions are easily understood. Equines in the wild are herd animals, and even horses bred away from their natural surroundings for generations still retain the instinct to return to or remain with others of their kind. For show jumpers, this means returning to where their fellows are waiting in the collecting ring.

British ponies Some British native ponies live in a semi-wild state and differ in at least one aspect from those equines living under wholly natural conditions: there are far fewer males due to management policies by the owners. In the New Forest, for instance, something under 200 males (a high proportion of which are turned out on the Forest only for the breeding season) run with anything up to 2500 or 3000 mares. This compares with a

herd of truly feral horses in the United States which consisted of 270 animals with an almost equal division of the sexes. Under British conditions, the majority of males are removed at an early stage. This clearly influences herd structure, but, except during the breeding season, it appears to make little difference to herd behaviour.

In the British Isles, herds of 50 or more ponies occupy home ranges containing winter and summer food, water and shelter. At first sight it appears that the entire herd moves freely over that area, especially in daylight hours, but closer examination shows that individual herds are divided into smaller groups, each with its own smaller range that nearly always overlaps with those of neighbouring small groups.

The smaller groups usually consist of a mature mare (sometimes two, occasionally more), with a varying number of offspring. Most colts are removed from the New Forest during their first, or at least their second year, but the remaining fillies stay with their mother until their fourth or fifth year; then they usually leave the group, either to remain alone until they start another group with their own offspring, or to join another single mare. Sometimes they join another unrelated group.

Mare groups Among truly feral horses each mare group is headed by a stallion (usually a mature animal), and the surplus (younger) males form bachelor groups. However, in this country the comparatively small number of stallions that live all year with the herd, and those that are turned out for the breeding season only, tend to spend more time with one mare family group. This suggests that if more natural conditions were possible, native ponies, too, would fall in line with most other horses and maintain groups of mares with a single stallion.

Among the mares of the herd there is a more or less clearly defined 'pecking order' which is directly related to size and is evident in all situations. Mature stallions, when present, are usually dominant over the mares, but it is not unusual for a high-ranking mare to threaten a stallion if he approaches her foal too closely, or in winter when there is competition for hay that is put out by the ponies' owners.

Hierarchy Dominance is established by a range of threatening behaviour patterns. The mildest consists of a simple laying back of ears, but may be followed by biting or, more seriously, by kicking with one or both hind legs. Actual fights, involving bouts of kicking, occasionally occur.

Threats are more often provoked by the trespass of one pony within another's 'individual distance'—an area of variable size which each pony regards as its own territory at a given time. Although ponies do guard their individual distances, as a herd they do not show the rigid territorial behaviour seen in, for example, some bird species. Each family group has its own range, but there is

rarely an aggressive reaction if a strange animal strays within that area. The only consistent exception to this occurs during the breeding season when stallions chase off rivals from adjoining herds.

The whole herd shows distinct patterns of movement within the total home range. Depending on the weather there is a regular pattern of movement between morning, afternoon and night feeding areas, and there are also seasonal movements. For instance, ponies move to one part of the range searching for acorns in late autumn—an area they may rarely frequent at other times of the year.

Movement through the home ranges is not necessarily initiated by a dominant

Shading

During summer ponies often move as a herd to 'shade' during the heat of the day. This is a phenomenon observed in New Forest ponies but n other breeds. Shading is when the ponies congregate in a tight group on a particular area of ground, often out in th open, where they seek relief not from the sun bu from biting flies. The 'shades' are apparently areas where there is sufficient air movement t discourage the presence insects.

Left: Mutual grooming among Welsh pony foals. They nibble each other's neck, mane and withers–th parts the animals cannot reach themselves. This is most common in spring, m summer and winter and is believed to strengthen the bonds between the family near neighbouring groups. Surprisingly it is unusual fc the dominant animal to initiate the activity, but it is almost always the dominan one that terminates it.

ve: Dawn breaks over the sh Mountains and a up of native ponies.

ow: A dominant New est mare and her offspring s year's foal and a two-old. She will eventually off and the others will ow. Rolling (bottom left) sually initiated by one nber of the herd and the ers often follow suit. This aviour is believed to ve the itch of parasites.

animal, but the leadership is frequently taken over by a dominant mare, and the others follow in something approaching the established pecking order. Once again, because of interference by man, it is not easy to determine the role of stallions in normal herd or group movement. Observations show that they usually follow the herd, particularly when the ponies are moving away from possible danger, and this has been interpreted as the stallion putting himself between his mares and any source of danger.

During the breeding season, there is a certain amount of 'harem formation' by pony stallions. Each stallion begins the active herding and driving of one or a number of groups of mares. His attitude at this time is typical–ears laid flat against the head which is held low as it shakes and sways in an almost snake like manner. If more than one stallion is turned out in the same area, each herds his own group of mares, and chases and rounds up any that stray. Fights between neighbouring stallions are relatively common, but rarely result in serious injury. The fights differ from those between mares in that the stallions attack with their front feet, rearing up and striking out viciously at the adversary, as well as kicking with their hind feet and biting.

Communication There is a variety of social interactions between members of equine herds, and the ponies are no exceptions. The sounds or 'vocalisations' emitted by horses and ponies may be divided into four different types–the snort, squeal, nicker (or whicker) and the whinny. The first two are normally sounds of aggression, but the latter two may be regarded more as communication between the members of the group or herd. The nicker or whicker is a low-pitched call used between mares and their foals and vice versa, and sometimes as an alarm call. The whinny is a much louder, more definite high-pitched call, and is used almost exclusively when a pony is separated either by sight or distance from the herd. Another more direct form of social contact is mutual grooming, particularly in March and April, June to August and again in the winter.

THE NOCTURNAL LIFE OF THE HEDGEHOG

There is still a great deal to be learned about the night-time activities of hedgehogs, welcome and familiar visitors in many parts of the country. They may travel up to a mile in a night's wanderings, often stopping to take bread and milk and numerous garden invertebrate pests. But is this the exception or the rule?

Hedgehogs are typically nocturnal animals. Those seen wandering about in the daytime are behaving abnormally, either because of sickness or because they are young animals seeking extra food before hibernation. But why should hedgehogs be nocturnal? Their spiny coat is such an effective protection that they have few predators to fear. They do not really need the cover of darkness (unlike mice, for example). The answer probably lies in the nature of the hedgehog's main food items. These include worms, slugs and beetles, which are themselves nocturnal–partly to try to avoid predators, and partly because nights are cool and damp, these conditions being necessary for their own feeding and survival.

It is easy for us to forget that a nocturnal way of life is perfectly normal for most mammals. It is humans who are among the exceptions and it is diurnal behaviour that needs explanation, not nocturnality. In fact, the very first mammals to evolve probably needed to be active under the protective cloak of darkness and the hedgehog, as one of our most primitive and ancient mammals, has sinply kept up the habit, having had no good reason to change.

Life in the dark The hedgehog is well adapted to life in darkness. Its principal sense is smell. It can probably recognise other hedgehogs individually by smell rather than sight, and most of its food is found by sniffing about and poking its nose into every likely spot. Its hearing is acute too: its ears are so close to the ground that worms and other prey, silent though they may seem to us, may

Right: Hedgehogs are usua thought of as being rather slow animals, trundling ab like clockwork toys. So it comes as a surprise to lear that they travel over many acres each week as a matt of normal activity. On som nights male hedgehogs ma cover two miles in the cou of their wanderings. In fac hedgehogs are surprisingly athletic. They can run faste than a human can walk an they can dig, swim and ev climb fences and walls.

Below: Tens of thousands hedgehogs are probably killed on our roads every year, particularly in April a May, the breeding season. Two thirds of these spring-time casualties are males. male and female young of the year are killed on the roads in roughly equal proportions, but by autum three females are being rur over for every one male. Despite the numerous deaths, many more survive

...ily give away their presence as they squeeze ...ween grass roots and disturb crumbly soil. ...t such tiny sounds may alert a hunting ...dgehog. Certainly foraging hedgehogs of-... stop still, perhaps to listen carefully, ...ore resuming their sniffing and close ...pection of likely hiding places in which they ...ght find food.

...Hedgehogs also use their eyes, but probably ...se are most helpful for detecting distant ...jects silhouetted against the sky. They are ...rt to movements, but ignore a stationary ...rson, even when very close. Like most ...cturnal animals, hedgehogs are probably ...able to tell one colour from another. Blind ...dgehogs are also occasionally found, con-...ning that eyesight is not essential and that ...ell and hearing are the more important ...ses for hedgehogs.

...Each hedgehog travels about a mile in a ...ght's wanderings; sometimes revisiting the ...ne areas as on the previous night, and ...metimes going somewhere new. Males seem ...be much more active than females. In the ...urse of a few weeks their regularly used ...me range may be 30ha (75 acres) or more in ...ent. By contrast, females usually operate ...thin an area only one third that size. These ...ures apply to hedgehogs living in open ...assy habitats; those that live in dense ...odland or town gardens may move about ...her less.

Sharing territory Hedgehogs do not appear

Above right: A hedgehog dropping is likely to contain the remains of beetles, caterpillars and earthworms in large quantities, as well as earwigs, slugs, small mammals and millipedes.

Below: Gardens offer the hedgehog a very varied menu of invertebrates. Many of the prey items that it finds and eats among flowerpots and rockeries are destructive garden pests, so the hedgehog is the gardener's friend.

to be territorial–one reason why several may be seen at the same time in a single small garden. They wander widely and freely without bothering to defend territory and keep out other hedgehogs. There is probably no need: food is usually fairly plentiful and easy to get, especially as hedgehogs are not fussy about what they eat and will consume almost anything edible. Why waste energy trying to keep other hedgehogs away, especially as, in the dark, it is more difficult to know where intruders might be? The exception to this peaceful behaviour comes when hedgehogs actually meet and confront each other. A brief scuffle may then ensue, with one animal driving away the other. Such contests are often observed when hedgehogs come to bowls of bread and milk, but they probably have more to do with establishing social dominance than with trying to defend a territory for the exclusive use of a single hedgehog.

Even though they do not defend a private patch of ground, many hedgehogs (especially females) remain in the same general area for long periods and even from one year to the next. Despite this, it is not easy to say how many hedgehogs live in a particular place. There are always some coming or going and it is difficult to keep track of them all. People who think they have two or three regular hedgehog visitors to their garden have marked the animals and found to their

Left: The hedgehog's most obvious characteristic is its spiny coat, which leads people to assume that it is closely related to other conspicuously spiny animals such as porcupines. In fact porcupines are rodents (like squirrels and rats). Australian spiny anteaters and Madagascan tenrecs also have spines, but they are not related to hedgehogs either. By chance during their evolution they have come to resemble each other.

Right: Breeding females often have a large nest made of leaves, grass, paper and other debris, in a secure place such as under a garden shed or deep in a bramble thicket. Male hedgehogs play no part in raising the family, and live alone, as do non-breeding females. These solitary animals often do not bother to build a proper daytime nest, especially in warm weather. They simply retire to a dry spot under some grass or leaves, shuffle round a few times and go to sleep.

astonishment that five or more may come in one evening and over a dozen in a month. This might suggest that hedgehogs live at a high population density, maybe one per 10-20 square yards.

However, it would be quite wrong to suppose that 12 hedgehogs all live permanently in a small garden. In fact they come in from a wide area and they are also likely to spend much time in neighbouring gardens

Below: A radio-tagged hedgehog taking bread and milk and (right) a young hedgehog. Pregnant and nursing females in a cold spell, and young animals seeking extra food in a cold autumn, can all benefit from this food. In dry summers it may save many from dying of thirst, too.

too. In suitable habitats there may be an average hedgehog density of one per hectare (2-3 acres), but in poorer habitats there will be many fewer. The truth is that we just do not know; there is no scientifically accurate way of carrying out a hedgehog census and measuring population density. For this reason, we cannot say whether hedgehogs are increasing in numbers or in decline, nor can we accurately compare population densities in one habitat with those in another.

At the end of a night's wanderings, a hedgehog retires to a nest to spend the day asleep. Curiously, it does not necessarily choose a quite place to spend the day, and may use a daytime retreat right beside a busy road

summer. In winter, the pattern is quite different; hibernating hedgehogs usually stay put for longer periods and do not move about nearly so much. They also build larger, more weatherproof nests in winter than in summer.

Bread and milk Many people put out bread and milk for hedgehogs and it might be expected that this would disrupt the normal patterns of hedgehog activity. If food is always abundantly available in a garden, why should a hedgehog go anywhere else? Could it be that bowls of bread and milk act like hedgehog-magnets and cause the animals to wander about less widely and maybe nest closer to the garden, or perhaps within it? People who regularly put out food for hedgehogs may be causing the hedgehog population to be clumped round their garden and not evenly spread out as would be the case under natural circumstances.

It is certainly true that hedgehogs like bread and milk. It is also true that they will travel long distances (a quarter of a mile for example) to include a visit to a garden bowl in the course of their wanderings. However, they do not become addicted to artificial food, nor heavily dependent on it. Hedgehogs certainly make use of food put out for them and they also pick up scraps from around bird tables and perhaps raid plates of cat and dog food; but this is all in addition to their normal feeding activity. Such items are a supplement to their natural diet, not a replacement. So when householders go away and the regular hedgehogs do not get fed, starvation and misery do not follow; the hedgehogs simply feed on something else. Their 'go anywhere, eat anything' casual life-style means that they are very flexible animals.

The exception to this comes in periods of drought or cold weather when natural food is hard to get. At such times, plates of table scraps, bread and milk put out in gardens may save many hedgehogs from starvation. Even where extra food is regularly provided, the hedgehogs do not cluster round it; instead they live as near as possible. Many choose a daytime shelter 200 yards or more away, even though many equally suitable resting sites are available nearer to the food.

:n when traffic noise is only a short distance ay. Often the hedgehog will sleep in the ne place for several days in succession, then somewhere else, perhaps going back again the original place. Meanwhile, in its sence, the site may have been briefly cupied by another hedgehog, although ult hedgehogs do not normally share a nest the same time. A single hedgehog may use a zen or more nests in a few weeks during the

Below: It is a pleasure to watch hedgehogs this close to the house, but remember they can drown in a pond or swimming pool. A piece of wood acting as a raft, or chicken wire at the side of the water will help them back to land. A pile of leaves helps with hibernation (right).

BIRD TERRITORIES

Several kinds of territory and territorial behaviour can be observed in the birds of Britain and Ireland.

A territory is a defended area. Experiments have shown that there is constant pressure on bird territories: when researchers captured and removed the territory holders, new occupants of the same species quickly replaced them, often in hours rather than days.

Social behaviour in birds contrasts with territoriality, for sociality involves flocking, colonial breeding or the common ownership or use of a particular area. However, sociality and territoriality can be combined in the same species in various ways. For example, in the crow, pairs of breeding birds occupy territories, while non-breeding crows live in a flock nearby, often in an area that is unsuitable for breeding due to a shortage of nest sites. Should a crow territory fall vacant, it is quickly taken by another member of the flock.

Territorial song With such pressure on territory holders, it is essential that they devote as much time as possible to securing their hold on their own plots. However, in many situations it is not possible for a territory holder to see all of his boundary from one vantage point, and he cannot therefore be on hand to see and drive away any marauder. Furthermore, it would take up far too much of his time and energy if he attempted to patrol the boundary with the constancy needed to keep out intruders. In fact, such constant vigilance is rendered unnecessary by a form of communication that works over long distances—song.

Song has several functions, of which mate attraction is perhaps the most obvious. But in an experiment where male great tits were

Above: A scene on the Grassholm gannetry, Wales. These are non-breeding birds that do not hold territories, but occupy a small area on the edge of the colony known as a 'club'. They include adults who have failed to secure a territory as well as immature birds such as the mottled sub-adult at the centre.

Below: The nesting colony, Grassholm. The nest sites are densely packed and vigorously defended, making a regular pattern.

oved, their territories were kept free of
uders for some time by playing tape
ordings of great tit song over loudspeakers.
n other birds, the posture of the territory
ner may be sufficient to signal to a potential
ler that an area is already occupied. For
mple, starlings adopt a characteristic
ture while singing, with the wings held
htly away from the body, the feathers of
crown and throat puffed out and the tail
cted downwards, giving a 'hunch-backed'
earance. Starlings often adopt this posture
le not singing, but while perched on an
osed song post within easy view of any
l looking for a territory.

t first sight, it appears strange that a bird
king for a place to settle should be deterred
a bird that is simply singing or displaying.
en this system fails, however, and the
uder does try to stake a claim, the home-
ner almost always wins the ensuing con-
s, whether these consist of threatening
lays or physical combat.

t is not entirely clear why a male is usually
orious on his own territory. It may be
ause of his superior knowledge of the
ain. Whatever the advantage, the presence
bird advertising that he is the landowner is
n sufficient indication to an intruder that
ie does attempt to settle, he will use up
uable time and energy in a conflict that he is
ikely to win.

Kinds of territory The kind of territory with

Above: Starlings going to
roost at sunset. The birds live
in flocks all year round,
sometimes joining together in
vast communities. The area
over which the flock ranges
in search of food is known as
the home range. Since the
birds nest in holes, which are
naturally some distance
apart, their breeding colonies
have to be spread out over a
large area. For this reason,
starling colonies are not as
obvious to view as those of
rooks or seabirds.

Left: Part of a rookery, in tall
trees by a motorway.

Below: The territorial song of
the robin can be heard clearly
all round its territory. This
spares it a lot of the work of
patrolling its boundary.

which most people are familiar is that of the
garden blackbird. In this type, a breeding pair
defends a plot of land of around one fifth of a
hectare ($\frac{1}{2}$ acre) against other blackbirds.
Within this territory, the pair feed and build
their nest.

Breeding pairs of robins also vigorously
defend a territory in the breeding season but,
unlike blackbirds, robins become aggressively
territorial again in the autumn. Now, however, males and females defend separate
territories in which each individual feeds, and
these autumn territories are smaller than
those held by pairs in the spring.

Starlings and rooks, on the other hand, are
far more social than robins and blackbirds.
They stay in flocks during the breeding
season, just as they flock at other times of
year. It is readily apparent, from looking at a
rookery, that rooks are social while nesting.
The same applies to starlings, although their
requirement for holes as nest sites leads to a
somewhat greater dispersal of nests and their
coloniality is less readily visible. Sociality
has its limits, however, and around the nest

both species drive off intruders. In these species, the territory is therefore restricted to a small area around the nest. The birds are content to share their feeding grounds, and do not even defend them against birds of their own species from neighbouring colonies.

The area over which the breeding rooks and starlings travel in search of food is thus not a defended territory, and is known as a home range. A tiny nesting territory and an even larger home range, sometimes extending 100km (60 miles) from the nest, is typical of many seabirds, such as the gannet, kittiwake and guillemot. In the case of the guillemot, the defended area is limited to a small length of cliff ledge around the egg or chick, so that each narrow ledge looks from a distance like a line of black and white birds.

Territories with no nests In the breeding territories mentioned so far, the nest site has been a vital component. While this is the case for most British birds, there are exceptions. When shelduck return to their breeding grounds from the moulting areas to which

Above: This scene on a great tit territory illustrates two display postures at the same time. The male (on top of the stump) is displaying to his own mate, but in many species a similar posture is used in defence of a territory. Vanquished males adopt postures rather like the submission posture of his mate, with bowed head and trailing wings.

Below: Robins defend territories in winter as well as spring, as the two photographs clearly show. On the left, a territory holder confronts a stuffed robin that has been placed on his 'patch'. On the right, he triumphs over the intruder, of whom little can be seen but the upturned wooden base.

they migrate in autumn, they spend much the winter in flocks. In late winter, howev they form pairs. These pairs are territorial a defend feeding sites on the muddy banks estuaries.

The ownership of a territory is, as in ot species, essential for breeding: but sheld do not breed on their territory. They br under cover of thick vegetation, or use rab burrows in dunes and sea walls, some dista from the feeding territory. During incubati the feeding territory remains the centre activity for the non-incubating male, and mate leaves the nest about four times each to feed on the territory.

In the case of ruff and black grouse, a sm and vigorously defended territory is u neither for nesting nor for feeding, but o for display. Such display territories, or le are used by those males that have been abl obtain one in complex ritualised displ which become more and more intense w females are around. The females are attrac to the display territories by the activity of males, and visit the territories to mate. T lekking area is generally on an open piece ground, and while 20 or more males h territories there, the females are attracted some males more than others. As a res most copulations are achieved by relativ few of the males. Presumably this polygam mating system selects the 'best quality' ma to father the next generation.

Pied wagtails in winter Like the robin autumn, some pied wagtails occupy dividual territories in winter. These are sim feeding territories, and the occupation of of these depends both on the individua status and on how much food is availab Where food is predictably plentiful, hi ranking individual birds hold territories. juvenile pied wagtail may be allowed to fe within the territory, and when it does it he in territorial defence. Where food supplies a more transient or scarce, pied wagtails feed flocks. Should the 'dependable' food sup fail, as when a river bank freezes, then territory-holders vacate their plots, and j the flocks. The pied wagtail thus alterna between the two forms of territoriality.

ypes of territory

ls are either solitary or communal nesters.
eding territories vary from relatively large (eg
:kbird) to very small (eg gannet). Similarly birds
d either alone or in flocks. Some solitary feeders
shelduck) defend feeding territories, while

flocking birds use undefended areas. Pied wagtails are unusual because in winter they feed either in defended territories or in flocks, depending on conditions. The most unusual type is the lek territory (eg ruff): this is used for neither nesting nor feeding, but purely for display and mating.

- • nest site
- defended breeding territory
- defended feeding territory
- defended display territory
- home range (non-defended area used for feeding)

Blackbird

Robin

Starling

Rook

Shelduck

Gannet

Ruff

river

Pied wagtail in winter

LAPWINGS: TUMBLING FLIERS

The lapwing is one of the easier birds to spot in our countryside, with its distinctive crest and dark green plumage with white wing patches. It can be seen at all times of year, breeding on hillsides, marshes and farmland, or wintering near ploughed fields.

Peewit, green plover and lapwing are three of a multitude of colloquial names this particular bird, an indication of h diverse and confusing local names can Nevertheless, each name has a meaning: 'p wit' clearly comes from the plaintive rasp cry so familiar over meadows and marsl 'Green plover', too, is a more appropri name than would, at first, seem. Take a cl look at this apparently black-and-white b on a sunny day: the 'black' back is really d bottle-green, shot with iridescent pur Often you see lapwings in the air, when th floppy, clumsy looking wingbeats give a cl indication of how this, their most wid accepted name, was derived.

Lapwings are medium-sized waders, ab as large as a pigeon but with the horizon body posture and long legs of a wader. Besi their pied plumage, they have other use identification features, such as the short be and the slender, upturned crest, which rather longer in the male than in the fem lapwing. It is well worth seeking a closer lc (using a car as a hide is an excellent idea) appreciate the beauty of the crest and sheen of the back feathers.

When they hatch, the young chicks superbly camouflaged: the basic coloration the down is a sandy fawn, with copious bla or dark brown markings. There is a co spicuous white patch on the back of the he easily seen when the chick is upright and rv ning about, and doubtless an aid to its pare in keeping track of its whereabouts. When chick squats, this prominent mark vanish As they grow, the chicks begin to resem their parents, but with much reduced cre and with fawn fringes to the greenish-bla back feathers, giving them a markedly sc appearance.

Many habitats Lapwings are classed amc the wading birds, but unlike the majority these their prime habitat is not the sho Their short, typically plover-like beaks ideal for catching small ground insects a other invertebrates. They often feed well aw from the water, and in Africa many of th close relatives are birds of arid grassland. In winter, most lapwings are found

Above: A male lapwing incubating the eggs. Even a small tuft of rushes is sufficient cover for the lapwing's nest.

Left: The lapwing's nest is relatively elaborate for a wader, but the eggs are typical: irregularly blotched, and laid with their pointed ends inwards.

Right: When the parent bird gives an alarm call, the chicks squat down to hide in the grass.

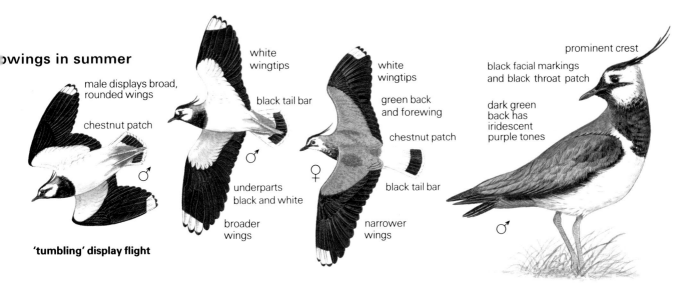

wings in summer

male displays broad, rounded wings

chestnut patch

♂

'tumbling' display flight

white wingtips

black tail bar

♂

underparts black and white

broader wings

white wingtips

green back and forewing

chestnut patch

♀

black tail bar

narrower wings

prominent crest

black facial markings and black throat patch

dark green back has iridescent purple tones

♂

ap grassland or ploughed fields, with tively few on the moors. They occasion- visit the shore, but usually only when w or hard frost has made feeding difficult nd. On farmland, it is amazing to see how ck of such conspicuously black and white ls can apparently vanish into the ground n they land. Their food at this time in-les a great many worms and insect larvae ven out of the soil by the shallow flooding ociated with winter rainfall. Often, lap-gs congregate in flocks, sometimes hun-ds of birds strong, but towards the end of ter these flocks begin to fragment as mig-ts return to their breeding areas overseas as local birds begin to take up their itories.

apwings breed in a considerable range of itats, but these do have a common feature: territories always have patches of short etation or bare ground nearby, suitable for ling. In some areas, most breeding birds found on waste or marginal land, such as surrounding gravel pits, chalk quarries, se tips or sewage farms. Elsewhere, they farmland birds, breeding on permanent ture or on freshly ploughed land sown with ter or spring corn. In upland areas, lap-gs tend to congregate in the more sheltered ations, rather than on the moors. They ally set up their territories in the valleys, ere any arable farming also tends to be centrated, so improving the range of feed-habitats available.

Defending the home Territories are easily ognised as the air overhead in spring is full tumbling, calling birds performing their obatic displays. Besides the calls, the wing-ts themselves are audible: the rounded, gered' wings of the lapwing produce a que 'whooshing' noise. Interestingly, male female can be told apart at this time by the lth of the wings: with the major role to y in display, it is natural that the male's g is noticeably broader and thus noisier. ng noise is not just used for display, but as a terror weapon to repel invaders of pair's territory.

Ground-nesting birds are vulnerable to cks from predators—magpies, crows and

Above: The breeding plumage of the lapwing. The pied plumage proves, on closer inspection, to be a combination of black on the outer part of the wings, white mainly on the undersides and bottle-green with iridescent purple tones on the back. The winter plumage is similar to the summer plumage, but looks mottled, for many of the feathers have buff edges.

Lapwing (*Vanellus vanellus*). Wader adapted to inland habitats including farmland and upland meadows. Resident, with additional wintering population from Europe. Length 30cm (12in).

Below: A small flock of lapwings over a ploughed field in winter.

foxes—and any marauders, even humans, are instantly attacked by both birds as they cross the territorial boundary. The swooping, screeching lapwings, with these thumping wingbeats, are usually enough to put off any intending predators and thus increase the chances of the eggs being unharmed and the young surviving. It need not be the threat of losing in combat that deters the predator, for if there are other good hunting grounds nearby that are free from the distracting noise and behaviour of lapwings, the predator simply takes the easier option and hunts else-where. It is the aggressive appearance of the lapwing, rather than its fighting capability, that keeps danger away.

Often quite innocent parties become in-volved, and the sight of a pair of partridges straying accidentally into a lapwing territory while feeding, and then attempting to with-draw and maintain some dignity under such an onslaught, can be extremely amusing to watch.

The breeding season The lapwing's breeding

behaviour is, in many ways, typical of all the wading birds. The nest, at first, is a mere scrape in the ground. The male makes several of these, using his feet to do a little excavating and then his breast to round off the hollow. The female chooses one of these nests, which both birds then line with fine, dry grasses. Almost always it contains four eggs, though on rare occasions clutches of three or five are found. The eggs are stone-coloured, with copious black blotches giving excellent camouflage, and are arranged points facing inward in a neat square.

The sharply pointed shape of the eggs is characteristic of most waders, and has a logical explanation. Young lapwings hatch down-covered and with their eyes open, and as soon as they are dry they scamper around, feeding themselves under the watchful eyes of their parents. To do this, they must have well-developed and relatively long legs, and it is these that are housed, compactly folded, in the pointed part of the egg.

Both sexes share the work of incubation, which lasts about a month. Although the sitting bird may seem conspicuous in the middle of a field, it is likely to leave the nest and go into hiding if danger appears: once the bird has gone, the eggs are so well camouflaged that they are difficult to find. During the five weeks that it takes the chicks to fledge, each parent may take responsibility for part of the brood. Alternatively, the female may shepherd them about while the male stands guard.

A nomadic bird The movements of the lapwing lack the routine patterns that are characteristic of migration, and might, therefore, better be called nomadism. After the breeding season, the birds disperse widely. A lapwing may not necessarily breed in the same area in successive years, nor does it always migrate to the same wintering areas. Young birds bred

Above: A flock of several hundred lapwings lifting off from a winter field. Lapwings on the wing usually form ragged and shapeless flocks. Towards the end of winter these flocks begin to fragment: some birds are migrants from further north, and these return early in the year. Non-migrants depart to take up their breeding territories for the new season.

Below: A male lapwing broods the chicks: his dark throat is clearly visible.

in Britain or Ireland are as likely to be fou[nd] nesting the following spring in central Euro[pe] as in the country of their origin.

This nomadism may be a factor that [has] prevented the species from subdividing i[nto] distinct regional groups (subspecies). T[his] effect is seen in several widespread b[ird] species: one example is the yellow wagt[ail] subspecies of which occur in different parts [of] Europe and Asia. The lapwing's distributi[on] also extends into Asia, but it is thought t[hat] the bird's nomadism helps to mix the st[ock] together, thus preventing a separation i[nto] distinct groups.

In winter, lapwings in Britain and west[ern] Europe react very quickly to changes in [the] weather. Any really cold spell is usua[lly] heralded by flocks of lapwings, flicker[ing] black and white across a stormy sky, head[ing] westwards in the hope of finding warm[er] weather. If the cold is short-lived, a ret[urn] movement may be seen as soon as the th[aw] sets in.

Lapwings are our most widespread spec[ies] of wader, and are among the most numer[ous] members of this group, in both summer a[nd] winter. Winter numbers depend greatly [on] their nomadic wanderings, and on the w[ea]ther, but are always greater than those in [the] breeding season. Various estimates have p[ut] the breeding population in the region [of] 200,000 pairs, a figure that drops shar[ply] after a very cold winter.

In the north of Britain, breeding numb[ers] are on the increase, while in the south (pro[b]ably as a result of land drainage and oth[er] changes in cereal production), some are[as] show signs of a decrease. Thus there a[re] indications of a geographical shift in the p[op]ulation, though the total numbers are [not] changing.

WADING BIRDS: WORLD TRAVELLERS

ll waders breed in the Northern Hemisphere, and all
e migratory, many crossing the equator for winter.
The British Isles are sufficiently far north to be the
breeding grounds of some waders, yet southerly
enough to serve as wintering grounds for others.

waders form a major part of one of the
st diverse of bird orders–the Charadrii-
nes or shore birds–which also includes
s, skuas, terns and auks. About 60 species
waders have occurred at one time or
ther in Britain and Ireland, half of them
g sufficiently common for the average

Above: In the last 60 years
the curlew has extended its
breeding range to lowland
fields. In July curlews desert
their breeding grounds in
field, marsh or moorland, and
make their way to the coast.

birdwatcher to have every expectation of
seeing them–winter or summer–without too
much difficulty.

The main characteristics Waders are distributed among several different families within
the shore bird order, but they have a number
of general characteristics. All have long legs
and long-toed feet relative to their size, and
many have long slim wings, well adapted to
fast and long-range flight. This is just as well,
as perhaps more than any other group of
species the waders exploit their powers of
migration to the full. Of those occurring in
western Europe, many winter as far south as
the extreme tip of South Africa, and many
(including most of these southern winterers)
breed well north into the Arctic Circle.

Another widespread characteristic is that
most waders in winter have extremely drab
plumages. These are well suited to offer
camouflage against the background of sheltered sandy or muddy coasts and estuaries,
where the majority spend the winter.
Exceptions to this generalisation include the

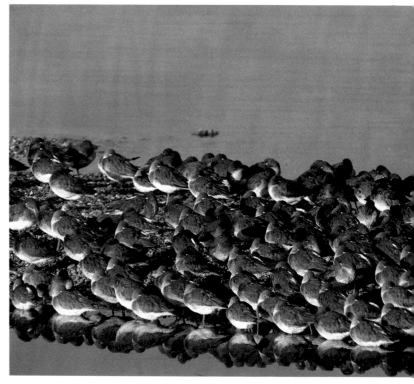

Above: A flock of redshanks roosting on a lagoon. Waders are not gregarious in the breeding season, but in winter they gather together like this. Few of our redshanks winter overseas, and those that do so travel no further than France.

Above left: In winter, most lapwings are found on wet grassland or ploughed fields. If snow or hard frost make feeding difficult, they then retreat to the coast.

Below: This young dotterel was photographed on an airfield in Cornwall. It was September, and the juvenile bird was on its first migration to wintering grounds in southern Europe—probably Spain or Portugal.

phalaropes, which winter out to sea; the rocky coast specialists like turnstone and purple sandpiper; and those that winter on damp meadows, often inland, like the lapwing and golden plover. The woodcock, as its name suggests, tends to frequent damp woodlands often far inland.

The main genera Many of the waders fall conveniently into broad sub-groups. Taking those with the longest bill first, the genera *Numenia* and *Limosa* contain the curlews and godwits, and *Scolopax* and *Gallinago* contain the woodcock and various snipes. Shorter-beaked are the shanks, mostly in the genus *Tringa*, while most of the sandpipers fall into *Calidris*. Those with the shortest beaks of all,

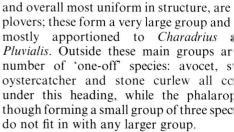

and overall most uniform in structure, are plovers; these form a very large group and mostly apportioned to *Charadrius* a *Pluvialis*. Outside these main groups ar number of 'one-off' species: avocet, s' oystercatcher and stone curlew all co under this heading, while the phalaro though forming a small group of three spec do not fit in with any larger group.

Adaptations in winter Perhaps the wir months are the best in which to survey range of feeding habits of the waders, anc see how each has a beak structurally adap to its needs. Snipes and godwits have lo straight beaks, relatively robust and v suited to probing deep into the mud for wor and shellfish, but the curlew, with an e longer beak, can reach deep-burrowing fo supplies. Many others have fine, mediu length beaks, perhaps best called 'gene purpose'–suitable for entering shallow b rows and for picking small animals fr seaweed or the water surface; the redshank good example. The avocet, with its unus upturned, almost needle-fine beak, special in scything through water and fine mud food.

On the mud, shorter-beaked waders like dunlin and knot probe for shellfish and wor near the surface, while higher up on the bea where the terrain is drier, ringed plov scamper about seeking the small, n burrowing animals which form their diet. C short-beaked, highly adapted bird is turnstone, its beak flattened to a mini-sho with which it overturns stones and frond: seaweed in its search for small invertebra Larger in scale is the oystercatcher, its b stout enough to dislodge a limpet from rocks but slender and sharp enough to s through the adductor muscles that h

ether the shells of bivalves such as cockles
l mussels.

Summer plumage In summer a few waders
ain drab plumage: the curlew for example,
l the woodcock. In the latter case, the
nouflage that the plumage provides retains
value in summer as well as in winter, as the
odcock is exceptional among waders in
ting among the bracken and fallen leaves
the woodland floor. Most of the others
w richly patterned and richly coloured
nmer plumage, in golds, blacks, browns
l a wide range of russets. Some–grey and
den plovers for example–have bold black-
l-white belly patterns. Here a compromise
been struck: the mottled rich russets offer

Above: Hundreds of golden
plovers taking off in a mass
from a sheltered bay on the
south coast of Ireland. This is
a northerly species of wader,
and although Britain and
Ireland together hold some
400,000 golden plovers in
winter, our southern coasts
are about as far south as they
are found.

Below: The knot is seen in
Britain and Ireland only in
winter; by April it is on its
breeding grounds in the
tundras of the high Arctic.

astonishingly good camouflage against the
tundra mosses and flowering plants, while
the black breast pattern with its vivid white
borders gives a brilliant impression in the
territorial and pairing displays of the grey and
golden plovers. Other waders lack any dramatic aspect of plumage for use in display,
and these exploit some other attention-
catching behaviour instead. The drab curlew
uses its bubbling song flight as a conspicuous
gesture.

Summer habitats During the breeding
season, the majority of waders desert the
shore line. In Britain, most depart for
breeding grounds far to the north. Others, like
the common sandpiper, arrive and establish
breeding territories on fast-flowing rocky
streams. The curlew, dunlin and golden plover
move up into the hills, preferring high-altitude
moorland on which to nest: the extreme
example is the dotterel, nesting only on high,
windswept mountain tops in the Scottish
Highlands.

The lapwing, redshank and oystercatcher
remain along lowland coasts and estuaries to
breed, while on inland marshes other redshanks and snipe nest, with the occasional
curlew, beside low-altitude marshes and bogs.
The lapwing and oystercatcher breed on
grazing marshes (as do the ruff and black-
tailed godwit, both very rare as breeding birds
in Britain), while some lapwings also often
nest successfully in arable fields. In some, now

scattered, areas of high chalky farmland or arid heath, a few stone curlews come to breed each summer, their weird cries penetrating the darkness as effectively as owl hoots.

Wintering strategies For some of the waders that breed in the far north–dunlin, purple sandpiper and knot for example–the estuaries of Britain and Ireland may be as far south as they need to venture during the winter. For the rest of the northern breeders, the British Isles with their mild oceanic climate offer suitable wintering habitats for some birds, while others of the same species seek the safer refuge of the Mediterranean or North Africa. Examples of this type of behaviour are ringed plovers, many lapwings and oystercatchers, redshanks and greenshanks.

Yet other northern breeding waders perform really prodigious long-range migrations, though again, a few may remain to over-winter in the milder temperate areas: these include the curlew sandpiper (which rarely overwinters in Britain) and the sanderling (which often does). Long-range migrant waders head either for West Africa or, just as often, the extremes of South Africa.

Europe's stock of waders Of the approximately 60 species of waders in the world, half are common over much of Europe. The remainder are rarities, some native to Europe and some (vagrants) arriving accidently from other continents. Native rare species number about ten, and include such birds as the terek

Above: Black-tailed godwits on the Dee estuary in North Wales. Almost all of the black-tails wintering in Britain and Ireland belong to the Icelandic breeding population of the species. Conversely, almost all of our breeding population belongs to the Continental race.

Below: The little stint is seen only on passage: it breeds within the Arctic Circle, and winters in Mediterranean or tropical countries.

sandpiper from the Soviet Union and broad-billed sandpiper from Scandinavia a the Soviet Union. The vagrants compr about one third of the total list, amounting some 20 species. Perhaps surprisingly, o three of these species originate from eastern side of Europe, in Asia; at least 17 (number increases almost annually) are No American species.

Most of these American wanderers occu late autumn. Like all waders, they powerful fliers, and it seems that mc migrating south on the other side of Atlantic, are caught up in the fast-mov winds of depressions crossing the Atlar from west to east.

COMMON NAME	HABITAT		FOOD	
	WINTER	BREEDING SEASON	WINTER	BREEDING SEASON
DOTTEREL	—	mountain plateaux	—	insects, spiders
LITTLE RINGED PLOVER	—	gravel pits, river shingle	—	insects, spiders
RINGED PLOVER	coastal fields, mudflats	shingle and sandy shores	worms etc near surface	terrestrial and coastal invertebrates
GOLDEN PLOVER	farmland	upland moors	beetles, earthworms, plants	as winter
GREY PLOVER	estuaries, mudflats	—	worms etc near surface	—
LAPWING	farmland, coasts	moors, farmland	insects, worms etc on surface; plants	as winter
TURNSTONE	rocky shores	—	insects, crustaceans, molluscs	—
PURPLE SANDPIPER	rocky shores	—	insects, crustaceans, molluscs	—
KNOT	estuaries, mudflats	—	marine molluscs	—
SANDERLING	sandy shores	—	insects, crustaceans, molluscs in sand	—
LITTLE STINT	lakes, coasts on passage	—	insects, worms etc on surface; plants	—
DUNLIN	estuaries, mudflats	upland moors	insects, crustaceans, molluscs, worms	as winter
RED-NECKED PHALAROPE	—	tussocky marshes	—	insects etc
GREY PHALAROPE	sea, lakes on passage	as winter	insects, crustaceans, molluscs, worms	as winter
COMMON SANDPIPER	—	river and lake shores	—	insects, spiders etc
GREEN SANDPIPER	wetlands on passage	as winter	insects, spiders, molluscs, fishes	—
WOOD SANDPIPER	wetlands on passage	as winter	insects, molluscs, worms	as winter
OYSTERCATCHER	sea and lake shores	as winter	molluscs, earthworms	as winter
CURLEW SANDPIPER	wetlands on passage	as winter	insects, crustaceans, molluscs, worms	as winter
RUFF	creeks and inland waters	damp grassland	insects, plants, seeds	as winter
STONE CURLEW	—	dry heaths	—	invertebrates on soil surface
SNIPE	inland marshes	marshes and moors	insects, crustaceans etc, frogs, plants	as winter
JACK SNIPE	inland marshes	—	insects, molluscs, worms, seeds	—
WOODCOCK	woodland	as winter	worms, insects, plants	as winter
GREENSHANK	mudflats, wetlands	upland moors	insects, crustaceans, worms etc, fishes	as winter
REDSHANK	estuaries, mudflats	damp grassland	insects, crustaceans, molluscs, worms	as winter
SPOTTED REDSHANK	mudflats, wetlands on passage	—	insects, crustaceans, molluscs, worms	—
AVOCET	mudflats, wetlands	brackish lagoons, marshes	sifts insects, crustaceans from water	as winter
BLACK-TAILED GODWIT	estuaries, mudflats	damp grassland	insects, worms, molluscs, seeds	insects, worms, molluscs
BAR-TAILED GODWIT	estuaries, mudflats	—	worms, crustaceans, molluscs	—
WHIMBREL	estuaries, mudflats	upland moors	molluscs, crustaceans	molluscs, worms, seeds, leaves
CURLEW	estuaries, mudflats	marshes, moors	worms, crustaceans, molluscs	insects etc, small vertebrates, seeds

RINGED PLOVER

KNOT

COMMON SANDPIPER

SNIPE

CURLEW

RIVERS AND LAKES: FISH HABITATS

Freshwater fish species have very distinct preferences for particular habitats, thus partitioning the living space and minimising competition.

If one stands at the mouth of a large river where it joins the sea, the mass of turbid, brackish water looks totally different from the tiny tumbling brook at its origin in the distant hills. The physical conditions are different, too: the estuary water is brackish, relatively warm and well oxygenated at its surface, though less so on the river bed. The bed is mostly muddy, and the currents are moderate.

The headwater stream, in contrast, contains clean, more or less pure fresh water which is cold and well oxygenated throughout. The bed is rocky and the flow fast–and always downstream, in contrast to the estuary, where tides wash the water to and fro. In between these extremes almost all the physical features

change, and it is not surprising that there are no fish which can be said to belong to both. A few species, however, spend some of their lives in both environments.

Brackish water At the estuary the fish fauna is affected by the presence of salt water from the sea. The fishes are those which, by their physiology, are capable of living in brackish water. Some of them are sea fishes, such as sprat, herring, whiting, sole and dab. Most of these are young fishes, for the wide, shallow estuary is an important nursery for such species, with its sheltered waters and abundance of small food organisms.

More typical of the mouth of the river are such fishes as the flounder and the smelt (*Osmerus eperlanus*). The flounder breeds in the sea, but the young fish quickly find their way into river mouths. While no larger than the size of a postage stamp, they migrate up the river. Too small to swim against the downstream flow, they ingeniously use the tidal currents, swimming in mid-water or at the surface while the tide is running upstream, and then seeking shelter on the bottom when the tide ebbs and the flow is downstream.

The smelt, on the other hand, migrates upstream early in the year to spawn in spring, shedding its eggs over the exposed gravel bed of the river.

The estuary is the temporary habitat of the salmon and the sea trout, while on passage as young smolts downstream to the sea, or as

Above: Cadman's Pool in the New Forest, Hampshire, is a lowland lake with a good supply of nutrients for algae and larger aquatic vegetation such as reeds. Although the water is still, the lake is a habitat for a range of fishes broadly similar to that of the lower freshwater reaches of a river fishes of the carp family (cyprinids) predominate. Bream, roach, tench, crucian carp and rudd all occur. The submerged vegetation offers sanctuary to smaller fishes, especially the three-spined stickleback, and to the young of the cyprinids. It also offers hiding places for the pike, both for the baby feeding mostly on insect larvae and for the well-grown jack lurking under cover before charging at a passing roach or perch. The quiet water beside landing stages or bridges also provides hiding places for large, fish-eating trout, and for big perch.

ılts making their way upstream to
wn – mostly in the early winter. The
:hwater eel is also an inhabitant of the
iary. Many eels actually live there, al-
ugh most pass through in January to April
:lvers, having migrated from the sea, while
ge eels come downstream later in the year
route for their spawning grounds in mid-
antic.

₋owest freshwater reaches Further up-
·am, the river's character changes. The
's influence is no longer felt and the water
ws downstream all the time. The slope of
river bed is very gentle, indeed it is usually
, and the current is slow (except when the
:r is in spate after heavy rain). The water is
mparatively warm, sometimes in summer
ıigh as 20°C (68°F), and oxygen levels are
derate at the surface and in mid-water,
ugh may be low on the bottom. The water
loudy with detritus. This region of the river
typical of the lowland area, with tree-
:d banks and the rich grazing land of the
odplain meadows. Most of the landscape is
iields interspersed with copses and bounded
hedgerows, but many towns and human
ibitations also exist in these regions.

n a typical river of this kind in England, the
ıes mostly belong to the carp family: bream
I roach are particularly common. Bream
:d to keep near the river bed, for their
otrusible mouths are well adapted to
ding on the bottom, sucking worms, insect
vae and even molluscs out of the bottom
ıd. Roach, being very adaptable, also feed
ır the bottom and in mid-water, as well as
ır bankside vegetation, which may be dense
olaces.

Near the surface of the river the bleak is
nmon, feeding as much on insects which
 into the river from overhanging trees or
m the air, as on crustaceans in the water. In
:kwaters where the flow is even slower and
ter plants grow densely, tench, carp and
Id live in conditions where temperatures
y be higher and oxygen levels lower than in
main river.

Man-made waters Lowland rivers of this
:d have always been important for
vigation, and particularly during the 18th
I 19th centuries most of the larger rivers of
gland, and some Scottish rivers, were
red together by canals to allow barge
ffic. This greatly increased the area of living
ice for fishes. So, too, did the construction
 reservoirs to store drinking water in
vland areas, the extraction of gravel in river
od plains leaving gravel pits, and the build-
 of ornamental lakes.

All over the lowlands, more habitats
·ame available, and most of these were
·ticularly suited to the fishes of lowland
ers. Carp, which were introduced in med-
al times for monastic fish ponds, are
·ticularly successful in the warm, still
ers created by man, as are tench, crucian
p, roach, bream, perch and pike. As a

Mountain tarn
A shallow tarn in the
mountains of northern
Scotland (right). Ben Loyal
and Ben Hope are on the
skyline. Like the peaty soils
of the surrounding
countryside, the water that
drains into this tarn is acidic
and poor in nutrients. The
fish fauna is similar to that of
the uppermost headwaters of
a river: probably only trout
and salmon. The habitat is
relatively safe from predatory
birds and fish (other than the
trout).

Upper reaches
The rushing stream at
Langstroth in Cumbria (right)
is a typical example of the
upper reaches of a river: it is
narrow and has a steep bed,
giving a rapid current.
Minnow, bullhead, trout and
grayling occur in upland
rivers at this altitude, each
species requiring its own
type of habitat. In such
tumbling waters as these, the
fish take refuge from the
fierce current in the lee of
rocks or under stones.

Lowland reaches
The river Ivel (right) near
Sandy in Bedfordshire has a
relatively fast flow for a
lowland river. It drains rich
agricultural land and is well
supplied with nutrients: the
resulting prolific growth of
aquatic weeds, and plentiful
vegetation on the banks,
create good conditions for
fishes of the carp family:
chub, bream and roach, with
bleak near the surface. In
slow backwaters, carp and
rudd are found.

Brackish waters
An estuary in the south of
Ireland, seen at low tide
(right). The bed is composed
of mud and the current is
moderate. Young flounders
are typical of this kind of
environment, as are adult
smelt. Salmon, sea trout and
freshwater eels occur here at
various stages of their life-
cycles. There are also visiting
thin-lipped grey mullet, and
the young of many sea fish
species: sprats, herring,
whiting, sole and dab.

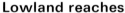

result, the total area of water available to these fishes has been greatly increased and their distributional range has also grown.

The perch is often common in such habitats, usually keeping close to submerged plants, but sometimes can be seen in large scattered schools searching for food along the concrete aprons of reservoirs. As a fish-eating predator, at least when fully grown, it is never so common as the prey species, such as roach.

The closest native relative of the perch, the ruffe, is a bottom-feeder and lives in rather clouded water, but as it has a series of open sensory pores along the underside of its head, it scarcely needs good vision to find the larvae of the chironomid midges on which it feeds. These live buried in the mud and must be detected by non-visual means. The ruffe has found that canals and man-made lakes are particularly good places to live.

Middle reaches Further upstream in a typical river, physical conditions change. The slope of the river bed increases and as a result the river flow is faster. The water is turbid after rain, but runs clear in dry weather; it is moderately warm, often up to 60°F (15° C) in summer, and oxygen levels are high, but may be a little lower near the bottom. The river bed is gravelly, with sandy mud at bends and mud in the backwaters, and submerged vegetation is fairly rich but grows mainly outside the areas of strong flow.

This region is again dominated by carp family fishes, the most common being dace, chub and barbel, while the roach is still common, and in the deeper pools gudgeon live on the river bed. Perch and pike are still common in this kind of river, but usually avoid the strong current by lying close to weed beds and in the deeper meanders. In shallow water under stones the stone loach is common, as are occasional minnows, which also live in weeds in shallow water where sticklebacks abound.

Millpools and weirpools In many places, rivers like this are maintained at a fairly

Above left: A fully grown flounder. Young flounders migrate up the rivers to freshwater reaches, then return to the sea to breed.

Above: The perch feeds mostly by sighting its prey from afar and then stealthi[ly] moving close; it lives for preference in clear water n[ear] the surface.

Above right: A jack or you[ng] pike. These hunt among th[e] submerged vegetation, wh[ile] larger pike may simply fin[d] quiet water near the mainstream of the river an[d] lie in the shadow of a tree [or] moored boat. Here they w[ait] for prey.

Far right: Barbel spawning [in] a gravelly stream. The dark[er] fish is the female.

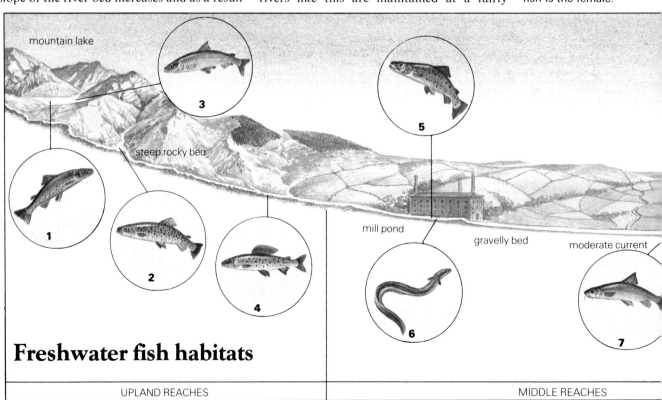

mountain lake

steep rocky bed

mill pond

gravelly bed

moderate current

Freshwater fish habitats

UPLAND REACHES

MIDDLE REACHES

118

constant depth and rate of flow by the building of weirs. The resulting weirpools have become a special habitat in which large chub, trout, roach and pike live. The weirpools are plentifully oxygenated by the turbulence of the falling water. A similar habitat for these fishes is the millpool, where the river has been dammed, producing a pool with less turbulence but plenty of deep water. These pools are classic sites for migrating salmon to gather their way upstream, sometimes perhaps just resting in the deeper quiet waters, at others waiting for rain to increase the flow of the river so that the journey can commence.

Upper reaches Further upstream the river becomes narrower, the slope of the bed steeper and, as a result, the flow faster, with clear cool water which is well oxygenated. This is the region where the grayling, minnow, dace and trout are most common, all of which find such conditions to their liking. Here, too, many salmon spawn, cutting their nests in the gravel beds of the fast flowing river. Only the strongest and most athletic of large fishes can cope with the current and most of the small species, and young fish of all kinds, hide among rocks or shelter in the backwaters or tributaries, while bullheads hide under stones.

Mountain lakes The physical conditions of the upper reaches of rivers, with their low temperatures and high oxygen levels, are similar to the conditions in many mountain lakes–particularly those known as 'acid' lakes, which are characterised by a relative scarcity of plant and animal life. Not surprisingly, native fishes in the lakes tend to be the same as those of the upper rivers: trout are the most widespread, but minnows and bullheads are also common. These lakes also contain populations of charr and whitefish which have a limited distribution in Britain. However, man has busily introduced fish to such areas and many upland lakes now contain pike, perch, roach, rudd and other species that are not native to them.

1 Charr: mountain lakes
2 Trout: mountain streams; rivers; lakes.
3 Whitefish: as charr.
4 Grayling: upland reaches.
5 Salmon: all reaches.
6 Freshwater eel: all reaches; lowland lakes.
7 Barbel: middle and upland reaches.
8 Chub: middle reaches.
9 Carp: lakes, man-made waters, lowland rivers.
10 Tench: man-made waters, backwaters.
11 Bream: lowland waters.
12 Pike: lowland and middle reaches; lakes.
13 Zander: lowland rivers and lakes; man-made waters.
14 Perch: lowland and middle reaches; lakes; canals.
15 Flounder: estuaries.
16 Grey mullet: as bass.
17 Bass: sea, estuaries.

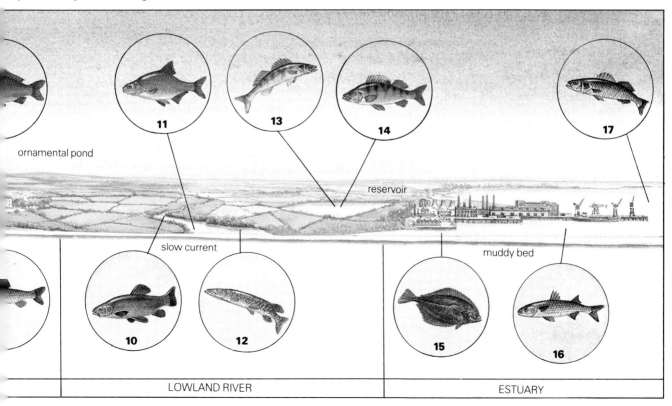

ornamental pond

slow current

reservoir

muddy bed

LOWLAND RIVER

ESTUARY

DEFENCE TACTICS IN FISHES

Defence, that is the avoidance of predators and care of the young, is an important aspect of a fish's life if it is to survive long enough to breed.

The essential element in the success of any animal is its ability to survive long enough to breed and produce a new generation. In fishes, as with many other animals, the defence tactics adopted for survival are numerous and elaborate and occupy virtually the whole of their existence, often dictating their body form, colouring, perception of surroundings and their behaviour. The finding and catching of prey, avoidance of predators, keeping competitors away, surviving in the habitat and eventually finding a mate and breeding are all activities for which defence can be necessary. Some fishes take this a step further by actively protecting their eggs and young.

Defensive colouring Coloration plays an important role in helping a fish to avoid being seen – an advantage both in that it protects the fish from predators and also in that, in some cases, it permits the fish to approach its prey unseen.

In general, concealing coloration is exploited most by fishes leading a sedentary life

Above: Fishes such as dace are ideally coloured for protection in the water. From above their dark backs merge with the overall colour of the water, so helping them to escape the notice of such predators as birds, while from below their silvery bellies and sides are lost against the reflections from the surface of the water.

Below: The vertically striped body of the perch is superbly well camouflaged for hiding motionless among reeds. As well as allowing the perch to hide from potential predators, the stripes also enable it to remain unnoticed as it hunts for food.

on the sea bed – most flatfishes, angler fishe and, in rivers, such fishes as the bullhead an the eel. Many fishes which live on the shor between high and low tides are adept a changing their colours to match the back ground, examples being the shanny, the long spined sea-scorpion and young corkwin wrasse. They can change their backgroun colour to dull red if they are living among re algae, greeny brown when close to clumps c brown seaweed or rocks, and bright gree when living in pale sea lettuce.

Even fishes which appear to be brilliant coloured when they are out of water may k well-concealed by their colouring when i water. Many fishes living in open water hav dark greeny brown or blue backs shading t silver on the sides and belly. Examples a dace and bleak in fresh water, herrin, mackerel and blue shark in the sea. Co spicuous as they may look on land, the colouring offers protection or concealment the water. Where the light comes from abo the dark back merges with the overall colou of the water, while from below the silve belly and sides are lost against the reflectio from the sea's surface. This type of conceali coloration is known as counter-shadi and can be seen in many aquatic and lan dwelling animals.

Schooling Many of the fishes which ha counter-shading live in schools, the dac bleak, herring and mackerel being obvio examples. But school forming is not confine only to such fishes since it offers gre defensive advantages.

Schooling fishes secure protection by bei part of a crowd. A predator viewing approaching school is confused by the mass individuals which, while keeping close t gether, do not keep in the same positi relative to one another as they swim. Singli out a suitable victim, the predator is thwart when the intended victim's place is taken another fish, and that by a third, producing relay effect.

School formation imposes certain restrair on the fishes involved. They must all be ca able of swimming equally well and, as swi ming ability is strongly correlated with si

pressure made by their neighbours.

A moving mass of fishes makes a soft rustling sound in the water and it is likely that the blind fish hears this and adjusts its swimming accordingly. Its lateral line system also detects pressure changes in the water.

'Panic' protection An additional defence system, little understood, is the production of an alarm substance by certain fishes. First discovered when an experimental study showed that an injured minnow gave off a substance which resulted in the appearance of panic in the remainder of the school, it was later identified as coming from certain cells in the minnow's skin. Water in which pieces of skin from a freshly killed minnow had been soaked produced the same panic reaction in minnows, but not in other fish species.

Later studies have shown that alarm substances are present in the skin of many members of the carp family (and it can be assumed that all carp are so equipped), and some members of the perch family. Each apparently produces a reaction in its own species.

The advantage of such a defence system is that while one individual is sacrificed, the remainder of the community is alerted to danger. Its development in the carp family is particularly advantageous as carp are mainly schooling fishes, living in fresh water in which, because of sediment and plant plankton, visibility is often poor.

Spines A further defensive measure that helps fishes to survive is the development of spines in the fins and on the body. These are most remarkable in some late larval stages and serve to make the tiny fish too big for many potential predators to engulf it. Sticklebacks have long stiff spines on their backs and bellies, which can be 'locked' upright to make an inconveniently spiky mouthful.

...is why all members of a school are the ...e size–little fishes form their own size ...ools. Likewise, disabled fishes tend to ...at a disadvantage–individuals blinded by ...ident or parasitic infestation of the eyes ... to pick up the movements of a school as ...ckly as normal fishes, and as a result tend ...lag behind, possibly falling victim to a ...dator.

...mall and solitary Paradoxically, it seems ...t, while schooling offers protection to ...all fishes, so does a solitary existence. But ...itary fishes are forced to adopt a low pro- ... and to remain hidden–this is why it is a ...m of protection adopted by small fishes. ...fresh water the stone loach and the bull- ...d live under stones or in dense weed beds ...l emerge at night or in twilight to feed. ...th are rarely longer than 9cm (3½in). In ... sea, numbers of gobies, clingfishes and ...nnies adopt similar habits. Not surpris- ...ly, these fishes are also all notable for their ...ncealing coloration.

...mall size can be a positive advantage, for ... species as well as for the individual. One ... the most successful families of fishes in ...ms of numbers of species worldwide is that ... the gobies–there are 18 species in British ...s alone. They are small fishes, few ever ...wing longer than 20cm (8in). One advan- ...e in being small is that they can exploit ...ni-habitats–crevices in rocks, coral or ...nges–and thus be safe from many preda- ...s. Another is that sexual maturity is ...ched at an early age, many gobies breeding ... year after they themselves hatch.

...ight and sound All these behavioural ...ans fishes have of preserving themselves ...m being eaten rely on highly sensitive ...sory capabilities. Fishes swimming in ...ools keep together by employing both ...ht and sound. The school retains its ...iesion by visual contact, the individuals ...eping their place relative to one another by ... awareness of the eyes of the other fishes– ...e eyes being the most obvious visual refer- ...ce point. But blinded fishes can usually ...n a school with only a slight disadvantage ...d must therefore get their clues as to speed ...d direction from changes in the water

Above: So important is the protection given by schooling that the young of many fish species form schools even though they will be solitary fishes when full-grown. The 10-spined stickleback, shown here, is a classic example for in late summer the young of that year band together in the shallows in large loose schools, yet by the next spring they will be spread out through their habitat, the males (at least) each possessing a territory.

Below: A mass of minnows at the edge of a lake. The minnow was the first fish in which a special 'alarm substance' was discovered. This substance, given off by an injured minnow, results in the appearance of panic in the other fishes and alerts them to danger.

SEA-URCHIN DEFENCE SYSTEMS

To help them survive the hazards of sea-bed life, sea-urchins have evolved a remarkable array of tiny pincer-like defence organs.

Right: Protruding beyond the mass of spines of this edible sea-urchin (*Echinus esculentus*) you can see the thin, prehensile tube-feet. These are not defensive organs: their main function is to feel round for hard surfaces, grip them and pull the animal along.

Below: A closer view of a living sea-urchin. Hidden among the bases of the spines, still too small to be clearly seen, are the various kinds of pedicellariae.

Adult sea-urchins are cumbersome bottom dwellers that move slowly over the sea-bed in search of food and shelter. Although life on the sea-bed is not fraught with the hazards of temperature and salinity changes found on the shore, the sea-bed habitat does present other problems. Sea-urchins are at risk from other echinoderms–mainly starfishes–which feed upon them. For example, the edible sea-urchin is liable to be attacked by the common starfish, while the green sea-urchin is often a victim of the spiny starfish.

Predation is not the only problem. The vast majority of bottom-dwelling marine animals reproduce themselves by means of myriads of planktonic larvae, and many of these need a hard surface on to which they can settle and attach themselves at metamorphosis. Echinoderms, such as the sea-urchins, are potential landing sites for these tiny intruders, and need to protect themselves from the encrustation that their growth would cause. A third hazard is that sea-bed animals are at times showered with particles of silt. Heavy silting on a sea-urchin would impede its water intake, which is vital to its existence, as well as its food intake. Sea-urchins live successfully under these conditions, and this prompts the question how they cope with these hazards on the sea-bed.

The sea-urchin's twofold armoury As a first line of defence, sea-urchins are covered with long, sharp spines, which deter large opportunist predators such as fishes that lack the specialised techniques required for eating a sea-urchin. Starfishes, however, are able to insert the tips of their arms in between the spines. This would enable them to feed easily on their victims if it were not for a second line of defensive organs, the pedicellariae.

Pedicellariae of sea-urchins are minute, pincer-like organs, usually with three jaws that open and close. These are borne on flexible stalks that pivot on a minute boss on the main skeleton (test) of the sea-urchin. With the help of a good hand lens, you can just discern them between the bases of the spines of a live specimen. The smallest are less than a millimetre in length, while the largest are under three millimetres. There are four

...tinct types of these intricate defence ...ans.

...he cleaners The tridentate pedicellariae ... the tallest kind, and have long, finger-like ...s. Their principal function is to remove ...all items such as silt particles and the ...ling larvae of other marine animals. The ... blades are touch-sensitive, particularly ...ards their tips and on the inner faces, so ...t any tactile stimulus causes them to snap ...t and seize the intruding object. Minute ...ve tracts run from the tips of the blades to ... muscle blocks at the base of the jaws, and ...en the stimulus occurs two groups of ...scles close the jaws; one group snaps the ...s together, and the other holds them shut ...er they have closed.

...After the intruding object has been re-...ved a third set of muscles opens the jaw ...in. The point about which the jaws hinge is ...ed the fulcrum; this intricate structure ...sists of a set of cog-teeth on each jaw. Each ... interlocks perfectly with its partners and ...ws precisely equivalent movements to be ...nsmitted from one jaw to the next so that ...re is perfect opening and closing.

...he trappers The second type, the ophio-...halous pedicellariae, are similar to the ...dentates but their jaw blades are shorter ...d rounder, and carry gripping teeth which ...sh together like the teeth of a man trap. ...eir function is indeed to trap intruding ...mals, mainly small crustaceans such as ...pepods and small shrimps.

...he bases of these jaws have an additional ...cture called a handle, over which a minute ...ment in the stalk passes. If these ophio-...halous jaws seize the leg of an intruding ...mal and this then tries to escape, the ...sion in the stem and in the ligament is ...reased. This increase in ligament strain is ...nsmitted by the handles to the jaw blades,

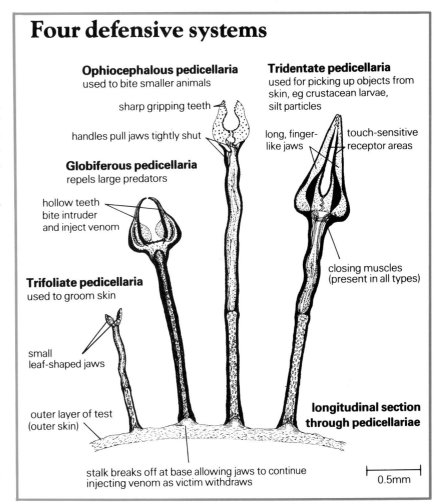

Four defensive systems

Ophiocephalous pedicellaria
used to bite smaller animals

sharp gripping teeth

handles pull jaws tightly shut

Tridentate pedicellaria
used for picking up objects from skin, eg crustacean larvae, silt particles

long, finger-like jaws

touch-sensitive receptor areas

Globiferous pedicellaria
repels large predators

hollow teeth bite intruder and inject venom

closing muscles (present in all types)

Trifoliate pedicellaria
used to groom skin

small leaf-shaped jaws

outer layer of test (outer skin)

longitudinal section through pedicellariae

stalk breaks off at base allowing jaws to continue injecting venom as victim withdraws

0.5mm

Below: Two green sea-urchins (*Psammechinus miliaris*) gripping the side of a rock. A few strands of seaweed are entangled among their spines, but otherwise they are clearly free from any encrusting organisms.

forcing them to close more tightly.

The poisoners The globiferous pedicellariae are a defence against larger predators, mainly starfishes. They are the only ones which can readily be pulled free from the urchin's test. They also differ from the others in that their jaws carry venom sacs. This venom can be injected into the tissue of a predator.

Special chemical receptors on the insides of the jaws are sensitive to certain chemicals in the skin of natural enemies such as starfishes, whose appearance triggers off the venom response in these pedicellariae. Once they have closed upon an object such as the tube-foot of a starfish, they do not open again, and as the starfish withdraws they break free from the test and continue injecting their venom as the intruder makes off.

The groomers Trifoliate pedicellariae, un-like the other three kinds, are spontaneous in action and do not require a stimulus to set the jaws in action. These are the smallest and most numerous pedicellariae on the urchin's test. By their constant action, these minute organs groom the urchin's skin, keeping it free from silt and bacteria.

A remarkable feature of some of these pedicellariae is that their inner faces are inhabited by communities of minute proto-zoan animals known as thigmotrichs. It is possible that these act as 'biological dustbins', eating up the bacteria that are collected by the jaw blades.

WANDERING MARINE TURTLES

Marine turtles occur as rare vagrants on our coasts: barely a handful arrive each year, straying far from their habitats in warmer seas.

Marine or sea turtles belong, with the tortoises and terrapins, to a group of reptiles known as chelonians. Tortoises (confusingly called turtles in America) are land-dwelling chelonians, while terrapins are semi-aquatic freshwater animals and marine turtles spend almost their entire life at sea.

Marine turtles are well adapted to their habitat. They are superb swimmers, the graceful movements of their flippers enabling them to move through the water swiftly, in marked contrast to the slow walk of tortoises.

Female turtles go ashore to lay their eggs, but this does not occur in temperate countries such as Britain and Ireland. Marine turtles have an annual cycle of activity, some migrating vast distances to reach favourite nesting beaches; there they crawl up the beach, dig

nests in the sand and lay their eggs.

There are seven species of marine turtles worldwide, and five of these are sometimes seen swimming close offshore or stranded on British beaches. For the turtle concerned, this is in all cases a misfortune, for the animal is a vagrant, diverted from its usual course in warmer waters by storms or unusually strong sea currents. The vagrant is unlikely to find its way back to its normal habitat, and will probably die because it is not suited to our cold temperate conditions. Sometimes the carcase of a marine turtle is washed up on the strandline.

The leatherback turtle The leatherback, the larger of two species from the Mediterranean

Above: The green turtle, o of the tropical turtles that are seen on rare occasions on British and Irish coasts. It is normally found in Latin American, African and Asian waters.

Right: The vividly coloured head of the green turtle. The chequered pattern ma serve as camouflage, blending with the backgrou of sea grasses among whi the turtle often feeds.

Below: The hawksbill is also a tropical species.

subtropical waters, is found relatively
en in British waters. It has been seen as far
th as Shetland and the Norwegian sea, but
ally it appears around the south and west
sts of England and Ireland. The leather-
k's shell can be up to 1.9m (6ft) in length,
l is not likely to be confused with that of
other species of turtle, for it is made up
small bony plates covered with a leathery
n–instead of the smooth, hard plates
aracteristic of other marine turtles. In
lition, there are several prominent ridges
ning the full length of the carapace. In
eral, the leatherback is dark brown or
ck, with small spots of white or yellow
ticularly noticeable on the young animals.

The loggerhead turtle This is the smaller of
two species usually sighted, having a
apace up to about 1m (3ft) in length. The
apace is horny and consists of several
ularly arranged plates. The loggerhead
ds to be reddish-brown or olive on the
apace, and somewhat yellowish under-
th. Algae, barnacles and other small
rine creatures often grow on its shell, and
results in considerable variation in
our.

Rarer visitors Three tropical species of
rine turtle are found around our coasts,
t sightings have been very few indeed. The
allest is the Kemp's Ridley turtle, which

has a shell no longer than 65cm (a little over
2ft); the plates are blackish and grey or olive
coloured. The hawksbill turtle, about 90cm
(3ft) in length, is largely brown with darker
markings. The shiny substance of its carapace
was used for making ornaments, combs and
spectacle frames. Today, trade in turtle
products is banned in many countries, including Britain and Ireland. The name of the
species refers to the prominent hooked beak
on the snout. The third tropical species is the
green turtle, which is usually brown or olive,
with darker markings. Green turtles grow to
about 1.4m (4½ft) in length.

Infrequent records At best, only a handful
of turtles arrive in our coastal waters each
year. Of these the leatherback is the most
frequent. Even so, only about two turtles on
average are seen each year. Although there
are a number of records of hawksbills, only
one (in 1953) was identified with certainty.

Right: The hawksbill has a
shiny carapace which is
largely brown with darker
markings. It is one of the
larger tropical turtles to
be found in British waters,
growing to a size of 90cm
(3ft).
Note: These illustrations
are not to scale. When fully
grown, the loggerhead is
a few inches longer than
the hawksbill, but the
leatherback grows to twice
the hawksbill's length.

Above: A hawksbill surfaces
for air. The 'bill' is
a modification used for
hooking crabs and other
small animals out of crevices
in coral and rocks. The bill is
particularly useful during
the early years of the
turtle's life, for at this
time the species is wholly
carnivorous. On reaching
maturity, it becomes
omnivorous, eating grasses
and seaweeds as well as
small marine animals.

lustrous shell

hooked bill

Hawksbill turtle

horny plates

Loggerhead turtle

Above: The loggerhead has
a horny, reddish-brown
carapace; sometimes it is
olive-coloured. The
underside is yellowish.

prominent ridges

eatherback turtle

ove and right: The
therback has a distinct
pearance because of its
thery skin and its
minent dorsal ridges.

leathery skin

side view

INSECT SONGSTERS AND MUSICIANS

The chirping of the grasshopper and the buzzing of the bee are both familiar insect sounds we expect to hear in the countryside. However, would you feel the same about a moth which squeaked like a mouse, or a creaking beetle? These are just two of the unexpected sounds made by insects.

Below: If you were to handle a death's-head hawk-moth it would emit an audible squeak. It also makes this noise when it is flying about, though why it does so, no one yet knows. You have to be very lucky to find this moth, however, for it is one of our rarest hawk-moths. The most likely place to see (and hear) one is around a bee hive–these moths have a fondness for honey.

Like the songs of birds, insect sounds are of associated with the establishment of t ritories by males competing for a mate and business of recognition and courtship betwe sexes. Since these insects are communicat with each other, they must also be able 'hear' the sounds produced by other dividuals. Therefore most are to some ext sensitive to sounds; caterpillars make flin ing movements in response to a loud nc because their bodies are covered with min hairs which respond to the air movemen created by sound waves. True, speciali hearing organs, however, are mainly confir to insects that call to members of their o species.

The sounds produced by insects arise fr many different mechanisms, which can placed in one of five broad categories: rubb one part of the body over another; tapp some part of the body against wood; vibrat special membranes; vibrating wings dur flight; and, finally, expelling air through mouth or spiracles.

Scrapers and grinders The hard ou covering of insects consists of a substa called sclerotin, and is particularly suited producing sound-making, or stridulato organs. The most familiar stridulatory org are those of the grasshopper, which prod sound in the same way as you do when y stroke your finger nail along the teeth o comb. In the grasshopper, a row of min evenly spaced pegs on the inner side of thigh-joint of the large hindlegs is rubb across prominent veins of the forewing. T causes the wing to vibrate and so produce 'song' of the grasshopper. Each species has own distinctive song which some naturali can use to identify the singer.

Crickets and bush-crickets stridulate quite a different way. At rest their forewi overlap to form a cover over the abdomen rib on the upper wing, bearing fine teeth rubbed over a ridge near the hind margin the lower wing. This causes the wings vibrate and produce the distinctive chirp the cricket.

Screeching and creaking One would expect underwater insects to be vocal yet species of water boatman, *Micronecta pow* is known as the water singer for the ext inarily loud noise it produces. It does this ·troking a spiny area of its front legs over a ·e on the side of its face. As the song is fined to males it is fairly certain that it is ·ociated with courtship. This tiny, 2mm ·g, bug also has small hearing organs on its ·omen.

·Iany of the beetles of the family ·ambycidae, known as longhorns after ·ir long antennae, can produce a creaking ·nd by rubbing their thorax against their ·d wing-cases. This sound is produced when ·beetles are handled and appears to serve ·purpose other than that of alarming or ·erring predators. In the larger species, such ·he musk beetle (*Aromia moschata*), poplar ·ghorn (*Saperda carcharias*) and ·*panthea villosoviridescens*, the noise is ·te loud.

·he screech or squeak beetle is another ·er insect that can produce sounds. This ·wn and black beetle, about 1cm ($\frac{1}{2}$in) long, ·s at the bottom of ponds and water-filled ·hes. If dredged up in a pond net it soon ·ounces its presence by loudly squeaking—a ·nd is produced by the beetle rubbing the ·of its abdomen against a row of projections ·the inside of each wingcase. The sound may ·a form of communication: if a screech ·tle in an aquarium is approached by ·ther while eating a scrap of food, it ·eaks in protest. Water is able to carry ·nd waves and the tiny pressure waves ·ated by the squeak would easily be detected ·the multitude of sensory organs over the ·face of the beetle.

·**Vood tapper** An unusual method of sound ·duction is found in the death-watch beetle. ·s is the famous pest that lives and breeds in ·timber of old houses. Its common name ·ives from the regular ticking sound heard ·he dead of night as the adult beetle taps its

Above: The only British representative of the tropical group of songsters, the cicadas, is *Cicadetta montana*, which is found in the New Forest. This insect has a quiet, high pitched song.

Below right: The carnivorous screech beetle is named because of the loud screech it makes when dredged from a pond.

Below: In the rafters of old houses death-watch beetles communicate to each other by tapping their heads against the walls of their tunnels.

head against the wooden walls of its burrow. This sound is heard mainly in spring when mating takes place and probably serves to bring together beetles in the maze of burrows which they inhabit.

Singing cicadas One of the most characteristic sounds of the tropics is the rhythmic pulsating 'chirr' of cicadas. In Britain we have one species, *Cicadetta montana*, which is rare and confined to the New Forest. Unlike its tropical relatives, the New Forest cicada has a very quiet and high pitched song which is inaudible to many people. Its song is restricted

Ears for defence

Some insects have specialised hearing organs–ears–but cannot produce sounds of their own. For example, many moths in the families Noctuidae and Geometridae have ears in the form of sheets of cuticle, called tympana, on each side of their abdomen. These have been shown to be sensitive only to ultrasonic sounds in the same range as those used by the 'sonar' of their enemies, bats, for whom night-flying moths are an important source of food. The moth's ears give it advance warning of an approaching bat and the moth takes evasive action, sometimes by folding its wings and falling to the ground.

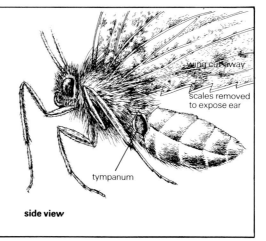

side view

Right: Longhorn beetles a▮ distinctive group because their long antennae. If handled, many, including ▮ adult *Agapantha villosoviridescens*, can ma▮ a loud creaking sound by rubbing the edges of their wing-cases against their thorax.

Below: Bees, such as this worker of *Bombus pratoru▮* buzz loudly as their wings beat up and down, but the▮ can also hum when restin▮ or, as here, feeding.

to males and produced by a pair of ridged drums called tymbals, one on each side of the abdomen. The tymbal consists of a thin membrane of cuticle which can be distorted by the pull of a special type of muscle attached to its inner surface. As the muscle, called the fibrillar muscle, contracts, the tymbal is drawn inwards; when the muscle relaxes, the elasticity of the cuticle snaps the tymbal back into shape. The fibrillar muscle is capable of contracting and relaxing more than 500 times a second. The sound of the cicada is amplified by hollow spaces in its thorax and abdomen, which act as resonators. If you try to find a cicada by its singing you are likely to be disappointed, for as soon as soon as the male

cicada senses your approach he will stop his song and remain safely in his leafy hideaway. The song of the cicada is thought to be a means of bringing together the sexes as both the singing males and the silent females have 'ears' near the base of their abdomen.

Buzzing wings Some insect sounds are produced as a by-product of some other activity. By far the most common such sound is the humming and buzzing of flies and bees. A very familiar insect with a high pitched hum is the mosquito, which beats its wings around 500 times per second. Male mosquitoes possess elaborately branched antennae with a sensory organ at the base of each. These organs are particularly sensitive to the pitch of the note

given out by a female of the male's own species when in flight. This helps him to pick her out from females of other mosquito species, and also from other males of his own species– male mosquitoes produce a slightly higher frequency hum than females.

The familiar buzzing of bees is only partly produced by wings, the basic tone of the wing beats being modified by the rapid vibration of the cuticle of the bee's thorax and possibly also by the exhalation of air through its breathing holes, or spiracles. Bees also make a high-pitched sound while not flying which can be attributed to the last two mechanisms. Queen honey bees can produce a shrill piping sound by passing air through

Far left: One of the British moths that can hear the sound of an approaching ▮ is the swallowtailed moth. Without such an advance warning this pale-coloure▮ moth would be easy prey ▮ bat, despite the latter's po▮ vision.

Below: Grasshoppers use their songs to attract mate▮ and warn off competitors. This male rufous grasshop▮ can be seen actively singir▮ by 'fiddling' with his back legs.

their spiracles. The queen uses this sound as a way of communicating with her colony.

Squeaking moths Mammals and birds make sounds by expelling air from the lungs and passing this over elastic membranes or cords. Voices of this kind are rare among insects, but they are found in a few species. One such British example is the death's-head hawk-moth, which can squeak both when handled and when in flight. This remarkable noise is produced by the expulsion of air through a restricted opening where the proboscis enters the moth's mouth cavity, or pharynx. The moth can make this sound even before it has emerged from its pupa, and the sound mimics the piping of the queen honey bee.

How insects produce sounds

The common feature that enables different insects to produce sounds is their hard resilient cuticle. This is an ideal material from which to make the files, spines or flexible plates necessary for sound production. Shown here are some typical sound-producing insects and the different ways in which they make their noises. The number of clicks or taps made in a second is represented diagrammatically as frequency plots.

Stridulation

Stridulating grasshoppers (right) produce their sounds by rapidly scraping a fine row of tiny teeth on the inside of their hindleg across a stout vein on their wing edge. This produces a sound made up of repeating clicks, as shown in the frequency plot for this common field grasshopper.

Common field grasshopper
(Chorthippus brunneus)

hindleg moves rapidly

pegs on inner edge

stout wing vein

SONG PATTERN

Wing beating

Many insects produce a humming or buzzing sound as they fly. In the bumble bee (right) this sound is partly caused by the rapid beating of its wings, but it is augmented by the movement of the cuticle on its thorax. This occurs when the muscles inside the thorax distort the cuticle as they contract, and then allow it to click back as they relax.

wings beat up and down

Bumble bee

CONTINUOUS HUM

Tapping

Death-watch beetle
(Xestobium rufovillosum)

head movement

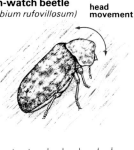

TAPPING SOUND

The sound produced by the death-watch beetle (left) has been described as a scaled-down pneumatic drill. This strange sound is produced by the adult beetle banging its head on the wooden beams and furniture in which it breeds, and can be heard to consist of distinct taps, produced about seven or eight times a second. It is thought to be the beetle's mating call, serving to draw together males and females.

Air vibration

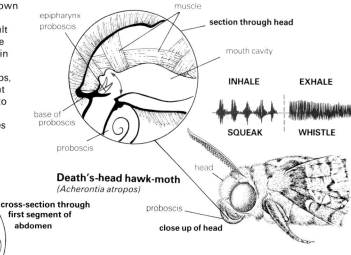

epipharynx
proboscis

muscle

section through head

mouth cavity

INHALE   EXHALE

SQUEAK   WHISTLE

base of proboscis

proboscis

Death's-head hawk-moth
(Acherontia atropos)

head

proboscis

close up of head

Vibrating membrane

The sound-producing mechanism of the cicada (right) is best seen as a section through the base of the abdomen. This shows how the tymbals vibrate in and out so quickly that they appear not to move at all. Each 'click' of the elastic tymbal (represented as a dash on this frequency plot) blends in with the next.

SONG PATTERN

rod connecting muscle to tymbal

tymbals

cross-section through first segment of abdomen

air spaces

fibrillar muscles

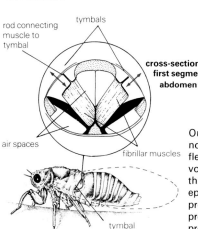

tymbal

New Forest cicada
(Cicadetta montana)

One of the most extraordinary sounds made by an insect is the noise produced by exhaling or inhaling air and passing this over a flexible flap. This is similar in many respects to the way our own voice is produced. The death's-head hawk-moth can suck air through its proboscis and cause a flap of cuticle, called the epipharynx, to vibrate rather like the reed in a clarinet. This produces a squeak when air is pulsed over the epipharynx or can produce a shrill whistle if air is rapidly forced out through the proboscis.

fly off in search of new food supplies. Thi
the time when we are most aware of t
insects normally overlooked.

Breakaway bees In the honey bee the ﬁ
swarm of the year follows the production
new queens in the hive. Before these ha
from their pupae, the old queen flies av
with a swarm, leaving her home and hal
more of its population of workers to
maintained by whichever of her daught
manages to establish herself over the oth
The old queen gathers her swarm of work
around her on some support such as a bran
Scouts then fly out from the swarm in sea
of a hollow tree or some other suitable sit
establish a new colony.

From the point of view of the beekeep
once the swarm has gathered on a branch
can shake it off and collect it in a suita
receptacle. The swarm can then be put int
hive where the bees settle down and forr
new colony. The earlier in the season thi
done the better, for a hive established ea
has a longer time to produce honey. 'A swa
in May is worth a load of hay' is an
country saying that reflects the value of
colonies founded early in the year.

Among social bees and wasps, swarmin
associated only with those species wh
colonies survive through the winter. In
British Isles only honey bees fall into ﬁ
category; bumble bees and wasps do ﬁ
swarm as their new colonies are founded
spring by hibernated queens.

The purpose of spring swarms is rep
duction of the colony. Swarms of honey b
that appear a little later serve a differ
function. These are called mating swarms ;
result from workers following virgin que
out on their mating flight. The misled work
may seek new homes or return to their origi

THE MYSTERY OF INSECT SWARMS

Swarming behaviour is seen in many kinds of insects
in the British Isles. It can be destructive, as in
the local plagues of crop-eating thrips, or
terrifying, as in the swarms of honey bees—which
are harmless as long as they are handled correctly.

A great many different insects swarm, and
they do so for a wide variety of reasons. Some,
such as honey bees and ants, swarm to help
found new colonies; others, such as ladybirds
or aphids, gather together as a means of
gaining mutual protection. Huge swarms of
flies, thrips or beetles can appear occasionally
when their numbers increase rapidly and they

Above: A swarm of bees,
with up to 30,000 workers
and a single queen,
clustering round a branch.

Right: Many gardeners have
suffered from swarms of bean
aphids on their crops.

ony.

Winged ants The nests or colonies of ants
also reproduced by a sort of swarming, but
has a very different pattern from that of
ey bees. One of our most abundant ants is
black garden ant which is seen swarming
ry summer. In this species the emergence of
ged adults is simultaneous over a wide
a of the country. The emerging winged
les and females, or queens, are tended by
frantic workers before flying upwards in
early evening. They usually make for a
spicuous object in the landscape and
her in large numbers around it. If high
ve the ground the swarm may look like
ke, and there are records of the fire engine

Myriads of bugs
Every few years abundant
food and suitable weather
conditions enable some
insects to undergo a
population explosion. In
the summer of 1983
sallows became infested
with tree hopper nymphs.
These feed on sap, and in
normal circumstances hide
within white frothy
'cuckoo-spit'. However,
when numbers are high
the froth turns to water
and drips from the trees.

Left: At the start of winter 7-
spot ladybirds hibernate in
swarms under logs or in
vegetation. There they
produce an evil-smelling
chemical to deter birds and
other predators from
attacking them in this
vulnerable state.

Below: A memorable sight in
late summer hedgerows and
woods is the mating swarms
of sepsid flies. These small
black flies gather on leaves or
dead stems and engage in
characteristic wing waving.

ng called out in response to an alarm call
sed by thousands of flying ants swirling
und a church steeple.

or ants the swarming is really a 'marriage'
ht in which males and females, often from
erent colonies, meet and mate in mid-air.
queens then descend to the ground and
berately break off their wings. Some may
er existing nests, but most of them seek out
vices in which to shelter and lay eggs for the
ndation of new colonies. Needless to say
y a minute proportion of the swarming
ens achieve success; birds and other
dators take a heavy toll of the ants both in
air and on the ground.

ood for fish On warm, still days in summer,
lt mayflies emerge at the water surface.
er having lived for two or three years in the
ter as aquatic larvae, they fly briefly as dull
oured immature adults before finally
dding their skin to reveal the true adult.
males then perform a mating dance over
water, the occurrence of which is an
ouraging sight to trout fishermen as the
are stimulated to feed by the emerging
rms of mayflies. The movement of numer-
males in the swarm attracts females,
mating takes place in the air. The adult
of mayflies is very brief, lasting from one to
r days.

Mating midges Similar behaviour occurs
ely among the true flies or Diptera. On
m evenings small swarms of non-biting

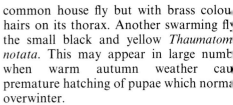

common house fly but with brass colou... hairs on its thorax. Another swarming fl... the small black and yellow *Thaumatom...* *notata*. This may appear in large numb... when warm autumn weather cau... premature hatching of pupae which norm... overwinter.

Some kinds of flies, especially those of genus *Coelopa*, breed in stranded seaweed... the shore. These sometimes upset holi... makers by appearing in huge numbers ab... the sand, all moving in one direction. They... attracted to various aromatic substances s... as sun-tan oil and perfume and may b... nuisance, albeit a harmless one, in sea-fr... chemist shops.

Flies and man Some swarms of flies o... their existence to human activities. The filt... of large sewage works attract many inse... normally found in mud and sludge. Am... these are the tiny moth flies (*Psychoda* spec... and non-biting midges. The inevitable rubb... dumps which are formed near towns and ci... can be ideal breeding grounds for a whole h... of flies, some of which may carry disease.

midges (*Chironomus* species) can often be seen rising and falling in the air with a characteristic motion, yet remaining above the same place despite the light breeze and eddies of air that are always blowing. They keep in position by visual reference to some conspicuous object such as a tree or post. The coherence of the swarm and its up and down motion form a rallying point for males to gather and also signals to females, which fly into the swarm to be mated.

Similar swarms can sometimes be seen on sunny days in winter. These also consist of flies, but belong to the genus *Trichocera* which are relatives of the craneflies. They are appropriately known as winter gnats, and swarms of males gather and dance up and down to attract yet more males and females.

Thrips and flies On hot summer days the tiny black insects called thrips or thunder flies may appear in vast numbers without exhibiting any particular swarming pattern or behaviour. Each one is only about 2mm long yet collectively they can be a great nuisance if they appear in large numbers and swarm over your skin. They are particularly common around cereal fields where the adults and larvae feed upon the crop. In such country areas they appear in huge numbers on hot summer days and crawl into every conceivable crevice.

Some kinds of flies hibernate in large numbers together, and may cause alarm by congregating in upper rooms or attics of houses. There is a tendency for the same places to be used year after year, possibly because outdoor air currents carry the flies there, or because the sites have some quality suitable for hibernation. The cluster fly, *Pollenia rudis*, is one of the most frequent invaders, and is a little larger than the

Above: Many insects swarm to bring together the sexes for mating. An example is the longhorn moth, *Adela reaumurella*, which collect on bushes in spring.

Right: Greenfly gain some protection by swarming on plants. There they secrete a sweet substance to attract ants, the presence of which deters the greenfly's predators, birds.

Below: Winged males and queens of the black garden ant swarm in summer.

DEFENCE TACTICS AMONG INSECTS

Because of their small size, no insects can put up a fight against an attacking bird. Instead, they have developed ingenious protection devices. The pug moth, for instance, is disguised as bird droppings, while the bombardier beetle emits a cannon-like explosion.

ove: The lappet moth, ich rests on leaf litter ring the daytime, escapes attention of predators by sely resembling its ckground of dead leaves. sides its autumnal reddish- wn colouring, it adopts a culiar resting posture in ich it pushes forward its dwings beyond the front rgin of its forewings, so t its normal moth shape ompletely disguised.

right: The beautiful rveille-du-jour moth ts on tree trunks d stone walls during the , relying on its emblance to lichen for cealment.

Insects have numerous enemies, ranging from birds and mammals to other insects. However, since it is extremely difficult to examine the ways in which one insect defends itself against another, most study on insect defence has, so far, been concerned with how insects protect themselves against birds.

Hide-and-seek An insect's first line of defence is, quite simply, to hide. A large number of species do this by restricting their movements to the hours of darkness, when most birds cannot detect them; during the daytime they remain concealed, burrowing or creeping under debris and into crevices.

In order to see a number of flightless insects which move only at night and are seldom seen during the day, you may have to trap them. One easy way of doing this is to sink a jam jar into the soil in a broad-leaved wood or garden so that its rim is level with the ground surface. Leave this over night, and

you should find it contains a number of flightless insects, particularly ground beetles – well-known nocturnal wanderers.

Flying insects are much easier to spot at night. Many night-flying moths hide during the day in long grass or under low-lying bushes, some of the more lightly built species (for instance, the geometrid moths) hiding in the foliage of trees and bushes. Butterflies that overwinter in the adult winged stage of their lives, such as the comma and the tortoiseshell, also hide among vegetation or in hollow trees and outhouses.

Cunning camouflage Although most of the insects already mentioned rely mainly on being under cover, and therefore out of sight,

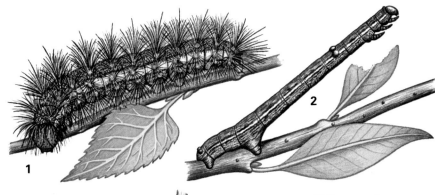

y do exhibit some elementary stages of
nouflage.

Insects living among the foliage of trees
d bushes inhabit a world of green leaves
eaded with brown twigs. A sample of these
ects, shaken from a leafy branch on to a
ite sheet, will consist almost entirely of
en or brown bugs and caterpillars—for
tance, shield bugs, weevils and green oak
der caterpillars. Likewise a sample of in-
tebrates collected from the leaf litter will
predominantly black or brown. The reason
this is obvious—an insect which is effect-
ly camouflaged in its environment has by
the best chances of survival.

The next stage in the elaboration of cam-
flage is the disruptive pattern. In military
erations large, characteristically shaped
jects, such as tanks and 'pill-boxes', are
inted with large-scale irregular patterns of
rk and light green, which break up and con-
l their outlines. This principle is of more
portance in concealing large animals, but it
es occur in insects, and is usually combined
th a resemblance to their specific back-
ound.

The oak beauty moth provides a good
ample of this, since its wings closely simu-
e the bark of oak trees (where it commonly
sts) and it has a mottled band running right
ross its forewings which breaks up its tell-
e arrow-head shape.

Another concealment principle seen in
me of the larger caterpillars (the hawk-
oth caterpillars, for instance) is that of
untershading. Light, under natural con-
ions, comes mainly from above, and a
unded body tends to betray its shape when
ongly lit above and shaded below. If, how-
er, it is coloured dark above and pale
low this effect is counteracted.

The caterpillar of the eyed hawk-moth is an
teresting example of this countershading,
ing dark green underneath and light green
top. Since its normal resting position is
side-down, this 'reversed countershading'
ectively conceals it.

Although butterflies and moths present a
eater variety of camouflages than any other
sects, they by no means have a monopoly.
me members of the Orthoptera are also
otected by camouflage; bush crickets are
een or brown according to whether they
e mainly among foliage or on the ground,
ile grasshoppers frequently have a pattern
longitudinal brown and green streaks, well
ited for concealment among grass stems.

Resting position Butterflies and moths add
their diversity of colour, pattern and shape,
variety of resting postures which makes them
e foremost exponents of camouflage among
animals. When the comma butterfly is
sting, particularly during its winter hiber-
tion, it closes its wings in such a way that it
sembles a withered leaf.

The lappet moth is adapted for conceal-
ent among dead leaves not only by its

Caterpillar defence

1 The buff ermine caterpillar
defends itself with a thick
coat of poisonous hairs.
2 The caterpillar of the
willow beauty moth is an
example of a stick
caterpillar—it resembles
a twig.
3 Reverse countershading
is adopted by the eyed
hawk-moth caterpillar to
help disguise its shape—
it feeds upside down.
4 The bold black and white
markings of the magpie moth
caterpillar warn predators
of its unpleasant taste.

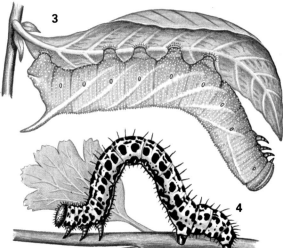

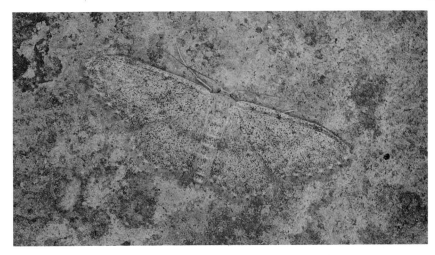

Above: In areas where
exposed rock and stone
walls are prominent
features, some moths—such
as this dusty wave—are
patterned to blend with the
background. The oak beauty
moth (opposite page) is
almost indistinguishable
from tree bark.

Right: The flamboyantly
coloured cinnabar moth may
be attractive to our eyes,
but for birds the bright
red and black colouring
warns of the moth's
distasteful properties.
These are acquired during
the moth's larval stage,
when the caterpillar feeds
on ragwort—a plant
containing toxic substances.

Left: Some harmless insects, such as the spectacular wasp-beetle (*Clytus arietis*), gain protection by resembling other species which have their own means of defen This concept is known as mimicry—the genuinely harmful species (the was) is called the model, while the harmless deceiver is known as the mimic. The wasp-beetle, like all other wasp mimics, is active during the day, moving jerkily among flowers and foliage, such as the guelder rose shown here. Other wasp mimics in Britain include the hoverfl and clearwing moths.

reddish-brown colouring but also by its peculiar resting posture, in which it completely disguises its moth shape by bringing its hindwings forward so that they project beyond its forewings.

One of the most impressive kinds of camouflage is adopted by the so-called stick caterpillars of some geometrid moths. Their bodies are coloured and patterned to resemble the twigs of the trees and bushes on which they feed, often even having humps on their backs to represent buds. When they are not walking or feeding, these caterpillars adopt a rigid pose, clasping a twig with their two pairs of abdominal feet so that they resemble growing twigs. The resemblance is so exact that it

Below: When resting, the buff-tip moth is extremely difficult to spot as it closely resembles a short piece of freshly broken twig. The thorax (in front) and the wing-tips (behind) are yellowish in colour, giving them the appearance of exposed wood, while the wings, which are rolled around the body to form a cylinder, are the greyish colour of tree bark. If you are searching for buff-tip moths, they occur in almost any habitat where trees are abundant.

deceives our eyes—and presumably those predators—almost totally.

Warning colours A number of brightly c oured insects, which make no attempt to h or camouflage themselves, would appear to sitting targets for hungry birds, yet someh they manage to escape predation. To many of these insects appear beautiful, the message their coloration conveys predators is one of warning, for nearly all them are distasteful or poisonous, and the fore inedible.

In dry open spaces, such as chalk downla and sand dunes, where there is little cover concealment, brightly coloured burnet mo are often abundant, flying about and rest on flowers in the sunshine. Despite their c spicuousness, nearly all birds ignore them a young or inexperienced bird dares peck a burnet, it immediately drops it and th exhibits signs of distress, salivating, a wiping its beak. It will never touch anotl burnet moth.

The body fluids of burnets are not only pleasant in taste; they are also poison since they contain hydrocyanic acid a various histamine substances. This has curious consequence—burnets are not affec by the insect collector's old-fashioned cyan killing bottle since they are necessar immune to the cyanide in their own bodies.

The magpie moth, a white species w black and yellow markings, is another co mon insect which displays warning col ation. Once a well-known entomologist v bold enough to taste specimens of this mc during its larval, pupal, and adult stages. N surprisingly he found they all had a parti larly bitter flavour.

Some species of caterpillar protect the selves with a coat of hairs, which may be tremely thick, as in the tiger and ermi moths, and poisonous as well. The hairs the caterpillar of the brown-tail moth, instance, are capable of causing a severe a

itating rash on human skin.

Butterflies and moths are not the only in-
·ts which adopt these fearsome tactics. The
gs of the suborder Heteroptera (which in-
des shieldbugs) taste and smell extremely
pleasant—a fact you soon discover on
ndling them. Some, such as the well-known
dybirds (which secrete a vile-smelling liquid)
d the rare black and red *Lygaeus equestris*,
ve warning colours, but many species are
en and brown, appearing to use camouflage
a first line of defence, and inedibility as
econd.

Wasp warnings Wasps display a striking
rning coloration in the form of yellow and
ck stripes which inform potential pred-
rs of their capacity to sting. A rather un-
pected feature of this is that, as well as
ing armed with a dangerous sting, they
te extremely unpleasant.

The distinctive colouring of wasps has
me to be recognised by birds as a danger
nal and wasps are therefore left well alone.
is has led to the development of an extra-
dinary phenomenon in the insect world.
large variety of completely harmless insects
ve evolved markings and colours similar to
ose displayed by wasps. They gain a distinct
otective advantage from this resemblance,
ich is known as insect mimicry.

In Britain the only obvious examples of
micry are those insects (hover-flies, clear-
ng moths and the attractive wasp-beetle)
at mimic wasps and hornets. In the tropics,
wever, complex associations also exist
tween distasteful and palatable butterflies,
d between many other insects.

Curious colouring A minor curiosity of
aptive colouring is seen in some small
oths and caterpillars, which rest on leaves
d are coloured black and white so as to
semble bird droppings. Whether they are
ding, or are imitating something unpleas-
t, or using cryptic camouflage or mimicry,
is a most effective way to discourage
ngry birds.

Above: Ladybirds exude an
evil-smelling fluid which
they advertise with their
bright colours. They
hibernate in swarms,
maintaining a protective
deterrent odour.

Below: The lime-speck pug
moth is most effective in
discouraging the attentions
of birds—it resembles
their droppings.

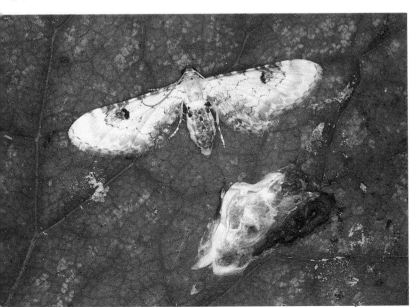

The bombardier's cannon

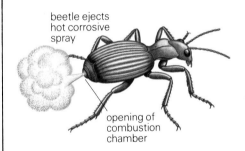

beetle ejects
hot corrosive
spray

opening of
combustion
chamber

The bombardier beetle has the most
remarkable defence mechanism, consisting
of a series of minor explosions emitted
from the beetle's rear. Chemical
substances called hydroquinones and
hydrogen peroxide are secreted into a
'reservoir' near the beetle's rear end,
which opens into a 'combustion chamber'.
When alarmed, the beetle passes the
mixture into the combustion chamber,
together with catalytic enzymes which
cause the two substances to combine in a
violent chemical reaction. This produces
water, oxygen and highly caustic quinones,
and at the same time enough heat to
vaporise some of the liquid, so that
the charge is blasted out as a boiling hot
corrosive spray. Ten to twenty discharges
may be produced, deterring even
the most persistent predators.

reflecting the immense adaptability showr
the spiders themselves in their wide rang(
habitats from sand dunes to lakes, and fr
coal mines to mountain tops.

Evolution of webs Since spider webs have
fossil record, their development thro
evolution can only be inferred. Early primi
spiders were probably nocturnal hun
preying upon insects which were, at that t
(400-350 million years ago), wingless. R
mentary webs, which trapped grou
dwelling prey, were probably initially forn
by accumulations of draglines (safety lir
which the spiders trailed behind themselve
they moved around. From this beginning r
breeds of spiders evolved which, behaving
trappers, joined the hunters in the cc
petition for insect prey.

It has been speculated that this predat
pressure spurred the evolution of inse
towards flight as a means of esca
Unfortunately for the insects, spid
responded by evolving the ability to constr
the more advanced orb web which, pla
above the ground, catches flying insects.

Simple webs A primitive type of web
constructed by the spider *Segesr*
senoculata, a member of the fan
Dysderidae; it has a cylindrical body witl
conspicuous adder-like pattern on
abdomen. Widespread and particula
common in dry stone walls, its tubular w
comprises a concealed retreat with seve
straight 'fishing lines' radiating from the h
where the spider lurks. These silk lir
communicate vibrations from potential pr
and indicate the direction of the chase. If c

SPIDER WEBS

Spider webs vary considerably in design, so it is easy to distinguish the webs of different species.

Where would spiders be without their ability
to spin silk? Not one species has abandoned
silk production and, indeed, the great
majority of spiders have many uses for it.
These include the building of egg sacs and
nursery tents, the emission of gossamer
threads for 'ballooning', and the laying of
safety lines, but by far the most obvious and
significant use is in the construction of webs.
The form and strategy of webs vary markedly,

Above: A Christmas tree
entangled in hammock
webs–a form of sheet web.
These, constructed by
linyphiid spiders, are found
throughout the country
among the branches of trees
and bushes and in long
grass. They are abundant,
especially in autumn,
although many are so fine
that they are difficult to see
unless covered in dew.

Right: The orb web is
considered to be the most
highly evolved of all webs,
since it is the most effective
trap, despite using only a
little silk and taking less time
to make.

the silk threads is gently vibrated by [tap]ping a tuning fork near the web, you may [suc]ceed in luring the spider into the open.

Found in similar situations, but also [co]mmon on trees and around houses, are the [me]shed webs of *Amaurobius fenestralis* and *[Am]aurobius similis*. These thick-set spiders of [th]e family Amaurobiidae have a dark mark at [th]e front of the abdomen and a shiny, black [he]ad which contrasts with the rest of the [cep]halothorax (hard outer case).

These meshed webs are much untidier than [th]ose of *Segestria senoculata*, but as well as [co]nveying vibrations they also effectively [ent]angle the prey's legs. If you examine a [me]shed web under a lens, you can see that the [net]work of main threads is surrounded by [tan]gled support threads (calamistrated silk). [Th]is woolly and rather bluish web lacks the [glu]ey droplets, which stick to prey, found on [ma]ny webs and consequently weathers well, [las]ting a long time before renewal is necessary.

Scaffolding webs Irregular three-dimen-[si]onal webs are characteristic of the families [P]olcidae and Theridiidae whose structures, [ter]med scaffolding webs, are often built in [th]e corners of neglected rooms.

The long-bodied cellar spider *Pholcus [ph]alangoides* is a pale, delicate and rather [ne]rvous spider, restricted to the southern half [of] the country. It hangs upside down in its [lo]ose web, and when alarmed shakes so [ra]pidly that both the spider and the web blur. [W]hen prey touches any of the threads [att]ached to the walls or ceiling the spider, [in]stead of rushing towards the victim, keeps at [a] distance and, with the aid of its long legs, [dr]aws threads from the spinnerets and flings [th]em over the victim. Only when the prey is [se]curely trussed in silk is the first tentative bite [de]livered.

The scaffolding web of *Steatoda bipunctata* [fa]mily Theridiidae), found in most garden [sh]eds, is studded with gluey droplets. Tight, [cr]iss-crossing threads stretch above and below [a] central tangle, under which hangs the

Spiders and silk

A spider secretes silk with the spinnerets at the end of its abdomen, and the silk immediately hardens on contact with air. Since silk is the strongest natural fibre known, spiders have numerous uses for it. Apart from building webs, they use silk for constructing retreats, egg sacs, nurseries for spiderlings, laying safety lines and wrapping up prey or–in the case of some species–even their prospective partners.

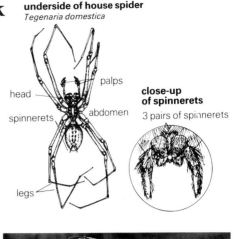

underside of house spider
Tegenaria domestica

head
palps
spinnerets
abdomen
legs

close-up of spinnerets
3 pairs of spinnerets

Araneus quadratus, a colourful orb web spider found on heaths and moorland, uses its silk to build a formidable egg sac (right).

Below: The hammock web of a linyphiid spider. Unlike some of the other sheet web spiders, the spiders of the family Linyphiidae, hang upside down beneath their webs. When an insect is trapped by the silken threads (seen at the top of the gorse) the spider shakes the web, causing the victim to fall into the sheet section, where it then bites the prey. Other sheet webs may be dome-shaped, such as those made by *Linyphia marginata* and *Linyphia triangularis*.

rotund, shiny brown spider. Insects which walk into a thread adhere to the sticky droplets and are lifted into the web as the thread contracts. Struggling only causes further entanglement in the neighbouring threads, and as the spider throws more gummy silk over the unhappy victim it finally delivers a *coup de grâce* by injecting a potent venom into the prey's nearest leg. Beetles, which might break free by sheer strength, are quickly defeated by *Steatoda bipunctata*.

Some theridiid spiders, for instance *Achaearanea riparia*, build a retreat consisting of a long silk tube which hangs downwards in the middle of the web and is heavily cam-ouflaged with plant material.

Cobwebs and sheet webs The unwelcome cobwebs, which are the work of house spiders (mostly *Tegenaria* species), are sheet-like, usually with a retreat in some dark corner. The brown hairy spiders dart in and out of the retreat, running on the surface of the web with an upright stance. These cobwebs are most effective in catching crawling invertebrates, but as they lose their efficiency when covered in dust, new webs are built while the old ones just accumulate dust and dirt in the corners of abandoned rooms and houses.

The more attractive sheet webs are built by the silvery members of the family Linyphiidae (money-spiders). These rather delicate webs are either dome-shaped or they resemble hammocks, and include hundreds of prey-entangling trip threads.

A feat of engineering The orb web, a two-dimensional structure (unlike sheet webs, scaffolding webs and cobwebs), is considered to be the most highly evolved and effective

Ballooning

Most linyphiid spiders, and the spiderlings of some other families, migrate by means of airborne dispersal. They climb on to a high point—the top of a fence post or a plant—and squeeze silk out of their spinnerets; this is blown upwards by air currents and drawn out. The pull of the silk threads by the wind is strong enough to lift the spiders into the air and carry them away—a phenomenon known as 'ballooning'. The distances covered by the spiders can be vast: Darwin records that on the voyage of the *Beagle* large numbers of spiders landed on the ship while in the South Atlantic.

trap, requiring less silk than most other kinds of webs. However, orb webs weather badly, losing their stickiness and therefore requiring frequent renewal, although this is helped by the fact that many species are able to roll the web into a ball and eat it, thereby recycling the nutrients.

There are many species of orb web weavers (families Araneidae, Tetragnathidae and Uloboridae), but the garden spider (*Araneus diadematus*), recognised by the cross marking on its abdomen, is the best known. Other orb web spiders range from the large and colourful species *Araneus quadratus*, which can be red, brown or yellow, to the smaller, bright green *Araneus cucurbitinus*, which builds its orb web in the curl of a leaf.

An orb web contains between 1000 and 1500 connected points, mostly of radii and spiral threads. The number of radii is constant

for each species, hence the web of the gard spider has 25 to 30 radii, that of *Tetragna extensa* has about 18, and that of *Mang acalypha*, between 50 and 60.

Miscellaneous webs In the fam Uloboridae, which is more closely related the Amaurobiidae (meshed web builde than to the Araneidae and Tetragnathi (orb web weavers) the webs show so unusual features. That of the rare south species *Uloborus walckenaerius* is horizon and comprises 30 to 40 radii, but instead fixing sticky globules to the spiral (as is do by most orb web weavers), the spider sp threads of calamistrated silk. *Ulobo walckenaerius* lacks poison glands; thus wh the prey becomes entangled in the web it is bitten but simply immobilised by be wrapped in silk.

While the orb web of *Ulobo*

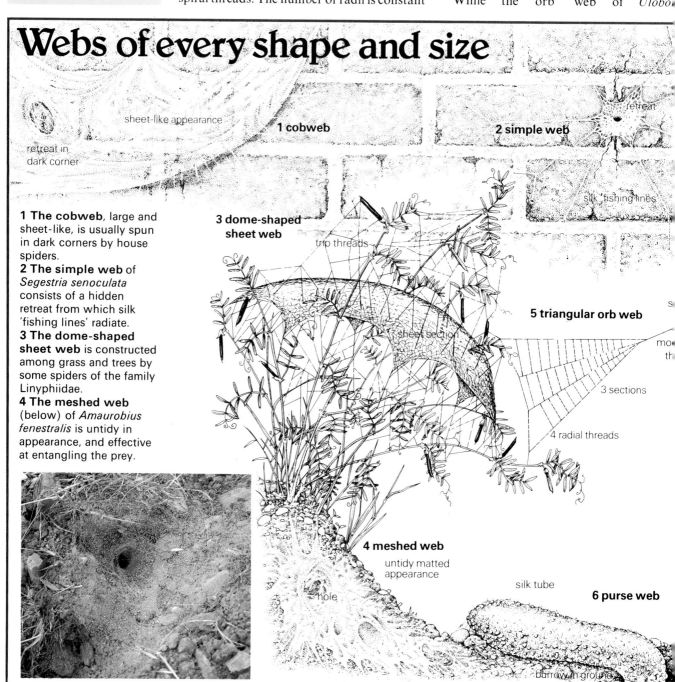

Webs of every shape and size

1 cobweb — sheet-like appearance — retreat in dark corner

2 simple web — retreat — silk 'fishing lines'

3 dome-shaped sheet web — trip threads — sheet section

5 triangular orb web — 3 sections — 4 radial threads

4 meshed web — untidy matted appearance — hole — silk tube

6 purse web — burrow in ground

1 The cobweb, large and sheet-like, is usually spun in dark corners by house spiders.
2 The simple web of *Segestria senoculata* consists of a hidden retreat from which silk 'fishing lines' radiate.
3 The dome-shaped sheet web is constructed among grass and trees by some spiders of the family Linyphiidae.
4 The meshed web (below) of *Amaurobius fenestralis* is untidy in appearance, and effective at entangling the prey.

ht: An orb web essentially
mprises three elements: a
mber of **radial threads**
5-30 on the web of
neus diadematus, shown
e) converging on a central
ot, the hub; **frame
reads** which delineate the
b and serve as insertion
es for the radials; and the
pping spiral which is the
ly sticky element.

ow right: The orb web
der *Araneus quadratus*
its on the side of the web,
h a couple of legs resting
the line, so it can feel the
rations made by any
atures landing on the
b.

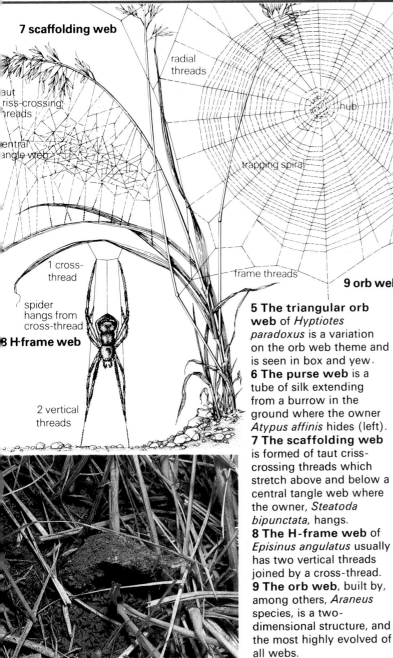

7 scaffolding web

radial threads

aut
riss-crossing
reads

entral
angle web

hub

trapping spiral

1 cross-thread

spider hangs from cross-thread

8 H-frame web

frame threads

9 orb web

2 vertical threads

5 The triangular orb web of *Hyptiotes paradoxus* is a variation on the orb web theme and is seen in box and yew.
6 The purse web is a tube of silk extending from a burrow in the ground where the owner *Atypus affinis* hides (left).
7 The scaffolding web is formed of taut crisscrossing threads which stretch above and below a central tangle web where the owner, *Steatoda bipunctata,* hangs.
8 The H-frame web of *Episinus angulatus* usually has two vertical threads joined by a cross-thread.
9 The orb web, built by, among others, *Araneus* species, is a two-dimensional structure, and the most highly evolved of all webs.

walckenaerius forms a complete circle, the web of the related triangle spider (*Hyptiotes paradoxus*) is triangular and much reduced. Four radial threads, enclosing three sectors, converge on one mooring thread at the apex. The body of *Hyptiotes paradoxus*, which is brown and rather lumpy, bridges a gap between the mooring thread and another strand attached to a twig. When an insect is caught, the spider pulls the web taut, and then lets it go slack again to entangle the prey further. A new web is built after each catch.

Interesting webs are built by *Episinus angulatus* and *Episinus truncatus* · (family Theridiidae). The type of web built by these spiders shows an extreme reduction from the usual theridiid scaffolding web, with just two vertical threads joined by a cross-thread (H frame), from which the spider hangs. Sticky droplets at the bottom of each thread adhere to insects when touched, and the spider lifts the insects clear. Ants, usually rejected by most spiders, appear to form the main prey.

Silken tube The purse web of *Atypus affinis* is in a class of its own. A tube of silk, like the finger of a glove, extends from a burrow in the ground, excavated by the spider in areas of light soil. This pale greenish species lives inside the tube and, with its huge fangs, bites through the web fabric to transfix any insect which alights on the surface. Slicing a hole sufficiently large to pull the prey through, the spider repairs the damage later.

Adaptation

Adaptation is the process by which animals adapt to their environment to allow them to succeed. This can include changes in behaviour within the lifetime of an individual – such as a fox learning to take food from a bird-table on a new housing estate, or it may include longer term alterations to a population that adapts genetically or numerically to a changing situation. An example is the peppered moth, which developed a dark variety that was harder for birds to see against the grimy backgrounds of industrial England in the 19th century.

The environment is changing constantly, even when it appears to be quite stable, and animals constantly have to adapt to these changes. The climate is never static, and a series of warmer or cooler than average years will soon give rise to changes in the fauna of an area. Similarly, agricultural management, building, changes in the populations of other animals, and many other factors all affect the lives of animals. Some species are highly adaptable, and are able to take advantage of changes – such as the house sparrow that follows man everywhere, or the collared dove that has found modern Britain so much to its liking. Others fail to adapt, and decline in numbers in the face of change, such as many of our bat species, which cannot survive in an intensely farmed landscape with fewer insects than formerly.

One interesting aspect of adaptation is the way in which introduced animals respond to their new environment. Many mammals, birds, amphibia, and even invertebrates have been introduced into Britain over the years. Some, such as the grey squirrel, have adapted, often in circumstances very different to their original home, and flourished, becoming a part of the British scene. Others, such as the marsh frog, have failed to adapt and have simply remained in small, static or declining populations. Either way, study of the process can usually tell us something about the animals and about our environment.

Left: The mountain hare changes the colour and thickness of its coat to suit the season. From October onwards white fur becomes visible around the feet, legs and flanks as the autumn coat grows. By mid-winter the hare is covered in a thick white coat, lasting until the end of February when the spring moult starts.

Left: Pygmy shrews are able to adapt themselves to many habitats – they can be found throughout the British Isles, wherever there is adequate ground cover. These tiny, aggressive creatures use their minute size to advantage by entering the holes and tunnels of prey, such as beetles.

MAMMALS OF THE BRITISH ISLES

There are about four thousand species of mammal known throughout the world, only forty-one of which are native land mammals in Britain. Many live in a wide range of habitats, others are more restricted, and a small number are expanding their range.

Many of our native land mammals are so adaptable that they can live in almost all the wide variety of habitats in the British Isles. Some other species have been forced by man's activities to adjust to new conditions; and a number of introduced species that were originally confined to a small area have now spread successfully to colonize widely differing parts of the countryside.

Widespread colonizers The smallest British mammal, the tiny, mouse-like pygmy shrew, and two of the largest, the fox and badger, are both examples of native species that are universally distributed, although not equally common. Hedgehogs, some bats and rodents are other examples.

Right: The harvest mouse lives mainly in long grass, corn or reed-beds above standing water. In such relatively precarious surroundings its balance is greatly aided by its tail, which can grip stems with the strength of an extra limb.

Below: The fox's varied diet of small animals, fruit and berries–supplemented in winter by scavenging–allows it to survive in a wide range of habitats.

The pygmy shrew has been recorded at the ⋅ of the tallest mountain, Ben Nevis, and is ⋅nd throughout the British Isles, wherever ⋅re is adequate ground cover. Like other ⋅ew species, it spends its life in bursts of ⋅ntic activity looking for invertebrate food, ⋅owed by short periods of rest. Its slightly ⋅ger relative, the common shrew, is also ⋅nd in most habitats.

⋅nother insectivore, the mole, although ⋅hly adapted to an underground life in its ⋅tem of burrows and tunnels, is nevertheless ⋅ more widespread than many people ⋅ise. Its presence in fields is obvious from ⋅ mole-hills it creates in its digging, but it ⋅ occurs less conspicuously in woodlands, ⋅vell as in gardens, under hedges, or on steep ⋅sides: anywhere, in fact, with soil that is ⋅ too stony, wet or acid, and where there are ⋅quate quantities of earthworms and in-⋅ts.

⋅ number of mammals whose main habitat ⋅deciduous woodland are widespread in ⋅er types of vegetation as well. The wood ⋅use, for example, despite its name, breeds ⋅ moorlands and sand dunes, and in ⋅gerows, gardens and crop fields – the ⋅ains of its food are often found in old ⋅d's nests in trees and shrubs, even in potting ⋅ds.

⋅Videspread hunters The commonest car-⋅ores in most habitats are the weasel, stoat, ⋅lger and fox. Stoats once relied mainly on ⋅bits for their food and so were especially ⋅nmon in grassland and crops, but since ⋅xomatosis reduced the rabbit population ⋅he 1950s the stoat has readjusted its diet, ⋅ing rabbits and hares, birds and small ⋅lents as well as fruit and invertebrates. The ⋅aller weasel lives in similar situations from ⋅land farming areas to mountains and

Above: The pipistrelle bat, the most widespread and common of the British bat species, is mainly active at dusk and dawn as it flies in search of insects.

Below left: The mountain hare is restricted to the uplands of mainland Britain.

Below: An unusual picture of a badger emerging from its sett during the day. Badgers have no predators and can live wherever they can dig their setts.

moorlands, although it takes smaller prey than the stoat, especially mice and voles.

The fox is probably the most famous large British mammal species because it is highly adaptable and versatile, and so occurs in nearly all parts of the country from the beach to high mountainsides. Once familiar to city dwellers mainly as a character in children's books, it is now a common urban inhabitant.

Although it is mainly nocturnal in the countryside, the fox is often seen trotting across fields at quite a speed: up to 10km (6 miles) an hour has been recorded. It is not unusual to see it sunning itself on an autumn day on top of a roof or up a tree. It is an opportunist feeder, caching away what it does

Above: The red squirrel is one of our few arboreal mammals and so is only found in areas of woodland, usually coniferous woodland, where it eats pine shoots and the seeds from pine cones.

Below: Some of the main habitats of the British Isles showing (top) the species that are resident and (bottom) some of those that are occasional residents or visitors.

not eat immediately.

More restricted habitats In terms of numbers the field vole is undoubtedly one of the most important mammals and its populations can reach plague proportions, especially after a mild winter. Its persistent gnawing of vegetation causes severe damage to young plantation trees. It is mainly restricted to damp moorland, grassland and plantations. Its relative, the bank vole, is abundant in the thick cover of deciduous woodlands and scrub; it is rare for it to venture far into fields.

Two other rodents, the red and grey squirrels, are arboreal woodland dwellers. Red squirrels are mainly confined to pine plantations, and grey squirrels to mature

hardwood or mixed woodlands and par Neither species hibernates in winter and relies on buried nuts, bark seeds and foli; for its basic diet. A dry winter can be a disas for squirrels since scent rather than mem« helps them to locate their buried nu particularly in hardwood habitats. A li lower down in the shrub layer of deciduc woodlands the common dormouse nests summer, although it spends winter hiberm ing at or below ground level.

Restricted distribution Although m mammals can swim, some are restricted wetland habitats; the water vole (famous Mr Ratty in *The Wind in the Willows*), coy; water shrew, otter and mink all suffer if th land is drained or parched.

One mammal, the mountain hare, is excl ively an upland dweller on the Brit mainland, mainly in the Highlands and Pennines. Here its coat turns white in wim to camouflage it against the snow, but Ireland, where there is no competition fr« the brown hare and much less snow, it ke« its brown coat all year and lives in lowla areas as well. The mountain hare has b« persecuted by man, because, given a chance will choose to eat the young shoots of heatl which gamekeepers intend for their grou Like other small mammals, the hare is fc for wildcats, foxes, eagles and other rapt« although its formidable powers of runn; away in a zig-zag fashion up slopes help it

Mammal habitats: from mountain to sea shore

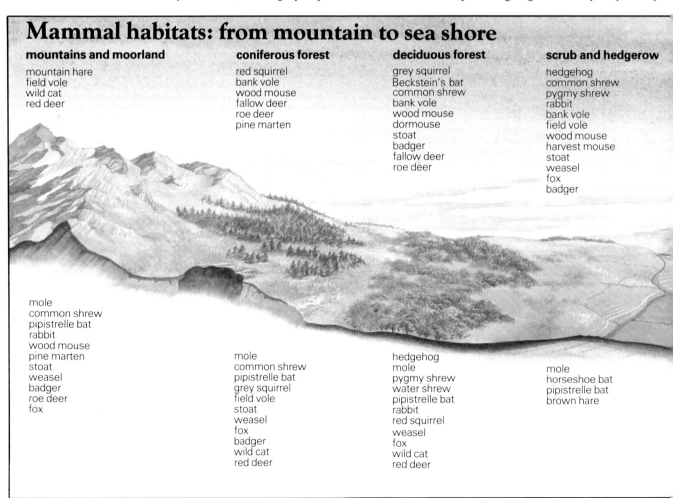

mountains and moorland	coniferous forest	deciduous forest	scrub and hedgerow
mountain hare	red squirrel	grey squirrel	hedgehog
field vole	bank vole	Beckstein's bat	common shrew
wild cat	wood mouse	common shrew	pygmy shrew
red deer	fallow deer	bank vole	rabbit
	roe deer	wood mouse	bank vole
	pine marten	dormouse	field vole
		stoat	wood mouse
		badger	harvest mouse
		fallow deer	stoat
		roe deer	weasel
			fox
			badger

mole		hedgehog	
common shrew		mole	
pipistrelle bat		pygmy shrew	
rabbit		water shrew	
wood mouse	mole	pipistrelle bat	
pine marten	common shrew	rabbit	mole
stoat	pipistrelle bat	red squirrel	horseshoe bat
weasel	grey squirrel	weasel	pipistrelle bat
badger	field vole	fox	brown hare
roe deer	stoat	wild cat	
fox	weasel	red deer	
	fox		
	badger		
	wild cat		
	red deer		

id predators.

Moved on by man The mountains and
orlands are today the home of several
mmals that were once lowland forest
ellers. As the forests were gradually cut
wn, some species–for example the native
and roe deer (roe deer is native in Scotland
northern England)–were forced to adapt
an open moorland life or become extinct.
day, particularly in summer, these deer live
ong the tall heather and coarse grasses of
Highlands, only moving to the lowlands as
ter approaches.

Whereas some species have been driven to
her ground through gradual loss of ha-
t, in other cases it is man who has been
ectly responsible for their restricted dis-
ution. The pine marten, polecat and
dcat, once all inhabitants of woodlands,
e been treated as vermin by man and so
e forced to retreat to the uplands. Today
pine marten is mainly confined to the
ghlands and rarely to Wales and the Lake
trict. The polecat has survived in some
and areas of Wales and is now spreading
o the Marches; and the wildcat, a predator
pinewoods and moors in the Cairngorms, is
w colonizing areas in southern Scotland.
The reindeer, present in Britain in the Ice
es, has been reintroduced in the Cairn-
ms, but it has not extended its range. The
ck rat is now relatively rare but the brown
is widespread in and around buildings.

Above: A water vole, the
largest of the British voles,
builds tunnels in the banks of
streams, rivers and canals.
This species is often seen
during the day as it searches
for suitable grasses and other
waterside plants to feed
upon.

Right: Often called the long-
tailed field mouse, the wood
mouse lives in fields, woods
and almost all areas with
sufficient low cover of
vegetation.

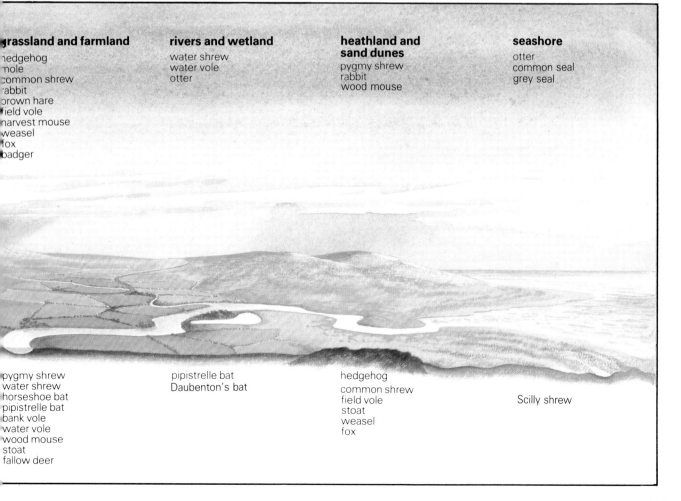

grassland and farmland
hedgehog
mole
common shrew
rabbit
brown hare
field vole
harvest mouse
weasel
fox
badger

rivers and wetland
water shrew
water vole
otter

**heathland and
sand dunes**
pygmy shrew
rabbit
wood mouse

seashore
otter
common seal
grey seal

pygmy shrew
water shrew
horseshoe bat
pipistrelle bat
bank vole
water vole
wood mouse
stoat
fallow deer

pipistrelle bat
Daubenton's bat

hedgehog
common shrew
field vole
stoat
weasel
fox

Scilly shrew

DIVERSITY OF SIZE IN MAMMALS

The largest wild land mammal in the British Isles, the red deer, is about fifty thousand times heavier than the smallest, the pygmy shrew. Between these two are a great variety of species of all shapes and sizes, each adapted to a particular way of life.

If you look at sizes within the anim[al] kingdom, it is clear that even the smalle[st] mammal in the British Isles–the pygmy shre[w] –is bigger than most insects.

Large and warm This relatively large size [of] mammals is possibly due to therm[o] regulation: the ability of warm-blood[ed] animals to maintain their constant temper[a] ture, regardless of their environment. A sm[all] animal has a large surface area in relation [to] the volume of its body, and a large animal [a] relatively small surface area in relation to [its] volume. It follows, therefore, that sm[all] animals warm up and cool down more rapid[ly] than large ones because heat can be gain[ed] and lost through their larger surface area;

y need more energy to maintain their body
mperatures.

This is reflected in their feeding strategies:
w much an animal eats, how frequently and
at type of food. The common shrew, which
ighs only 8g (¼oz), takes proportionately
ge amounts of high energy food such as
rms–3.5kg (8lb) annually, equivalent to
times its own weight. A weasel, which
ighs 100g (3½oz), needs 11kg (24lb) of
e, voles and other prey animals–only
out 100 times its own weight. A red deer
ighing 50kg takes 400-500kg (800-1100lb)
ood annually, just ten times its own weight.
th shrews and weasels use high-energy food
y efficiently and assimilate 80-90% for their

Left: A red deer stag with
hinds. The red deer is our
largest wild land mammal,
and a stag can easily weigh
up to 85kg (187lb) and
measure 122cm (48in) at the
shoulder. At the other
extreme is the tiny pygmy
shrew (above) which can
weigh as little as 3g (⅛oz)
and measure just 4cm (1½in),
with a tail of 3cm (1¼in). It
needs to eat twice its own
weight daily to survive; thus
its territory is defended
fiercely.

Below: Otters, our largest
freshwater mammal. The size
of prey captured is
determined by the size of
the predator–thus the
otter can only take fish of
up to a certain size.

metabolism–respiration, growth and reproduction, for example. The red deer, on the
other hand, has a low energy diet of herbage,
of which it assimilates only 40-60%.

These different strategies are paralleled by
different levels of activity. The pygmy shrew
remains active in its small territory throughout most of the 24 hours. If it is to survive it
must ensure that other individuals do not eat
its precious food resources, and so it defends
its territory fiercely, and even to the death if
necessary. The weasel is also active for a large
proportion of the 24 hours, often ranging over
considerable distances to find food. The
limitation on the quantity of food an individual herbivore, on the other hand, can
ingest may simply be the time it takes to digest
it. When the vegetation dies back during
winter and its nutrient value declines, large
herbivores such as red and roe deer may then
have to depend on the huge energy reserves
they have stored as body fat.

If mammals are large when compared with
most cold-blooded animals, most whales are

Above: The two sexes of a species are often of different sizes. In bats, such as this pipistrelle, the females are larger than the males. Sexual dimorphism also occurs among weasels (below) and stoats, with males 50% larger than the females. The wood mouse (left) is almost identical in size to the yellow-necked mouse but it tends to live in different habitats. In both species the sexes are similar in size.

certainly large when compared with la[r] mammals: for example, the smallest Brit[ish] porpoise is one metre long, about the size [of] our largest carnivore. The largest mamm[al] on earth are the great baleen whales—a b[lue] whale may reach a weight of 120 tonn[es] equivalent to the weight of 30 elephan[ts]. Locomotion is achieved by the verti[cal] movement of the tail which propels forwa[rd] the streamlined, torpedo-shaped body. T[he] baleen whales subsist on huge quantities [of] plankton (particularly the euphausiid, kr[ill] which occur in polar regions in summer. T[he] rest of the year is spent at lower latitud[es] where mating and breeding occur. Plan[k]tonic food in these areas is relatively sca[rce] and insufficient to meet the needs of a la[rge] whale, so it has to depend upon the resour[ce] it has acquired in the summer and stored a[s] thick layer of blubber. By the end of [the] winter, a whale will have lost much weig[ht] and it must return to high latitudes to fe[ed] again.

So that whales do not freeze to death th[ey] are covered in a thick layer of blubber: o[nce] again, the smaller the whale, the greater [the] proportion of blubber in relation to its si[ze]. Whales have other ways of coping with t[he] cold: they migrate to warmer waters to g[ive] birth and to build up insulating fat for t[he] following winter. Smaller mammals also st[ore] energy as fat. This, in addition to reduci[ng] heat loss during periods of inactivity, he[lps] them to survive winter.

Although the need to conserve heat affe[cts] mammal size and strategy, there are oth[er] constraints on the size of a terrestrial ma[m]mal. Above a certain weight it becom[es] difficult for an individual to move, ev[en] though it may be able to support itself. Tod[ay] the limit is reached by the elephant. Abo[ve] this weight an aquatic environment is need[ed] to help support the huge bulk.

Size and sex Although there is a great ran[ge] of size in mammals, even within a particu[lar] species the sexes may be of different size. T[he] tendency is for the males to be larger th[an] females: over 100 years ago Charles Darw[in] suggested that this may have evolved becau[se] the larger the male, the more successful it w[as] at competing for mates. The consequence [of] this would be that large males mate with [a] greater number of females, so passing on [to] their offspring the genes for large size a[nd] strength, and hence success in competing [for] food and mates.

This may explain situations where t[he] species are polygynous (the male mating w[ith] more than one female) as occurs for examp[le] among red deer where a dominant st[ag] controls a harem of hinds and defends the[m] from intruding males. Among mamma[ls] males are often able to 'gain' from seve[ral] such matings in this way because they are [not] investing so much in nourishment, care a[nd] protection of their offspring. Parental care [by] the male is usually absent in polygyno[us] ecies.

The females of many bat species are often ·ger than males, even when the latter are lygynous, mating with a number of females. ∶re it is probably the nature of the maternal ∶re which is a crucial factor: females often ∶rry their nursing young with them, making ∶ort flights with their babies clinging on to ∶ fur of their mother's belly. If females were ∶aller they might not have the same abilities ∶ transport their young in flight. Thus the ∶olutionary advantages of a particular body ∶e may vary between the sexes. In some cases ∶will be beneficial for the males to be larger, ∶ others it will be so for the female.

Size and food Whatever the causes of a ∶vergence in size between the sexes, the ∶nsequences are that they may exploit ∶fferent energy resources, feeding upon ∶fferent sized prey. A male sperm whale, ∶ich is twice the size of a female, dives to ∶eater depths and may take much larger deep ∶ter squid.

However, whereas we might also expect ∶les to be the same size or larger than ∶nales, there are a number of instances where ∶ converse is true. In baleen whales, for ∶ample, the female is usually the larger, and ∶ account for this we must look elsewhere for ∶ explanation.

It may be that some females become bigger ∶ be more effective mothers. A large mother ∶ay produce a larger baby with a greater ∶ance of survival; she must therefore pro-∶ce a larger quantity of milk to enable it to ∶ow more rapidly, and she may be better at ∶rrying or defending her young. It has been ∶ggested that a relatively large individual can ∶bsist longer than a smaller one because its ∶t stores will be larger, lasting longer. This ∶ay be the case for some baleen whales where ∶e females use reserves stored in summer for ∶ producing after their migration to warmer ∶ters. They may also provide relatively more ∶lk, which allows their single young to grow ∶ a rate which is the fastest in the animal ∶ngdom.

In stoats and weasels this sexual size ∶morphism has some particularly interesting ∶nsequences. A male weasel is about twice as ∶g as a female and within the size range of a ∶male stoat. Thus whereas the male stoat and ∶male weasel are of different size and take ∶fferent sized prey, the female stoat and male ∶asel overlap in the size of prey they capture ∶d hence come into potential competition. In ∶eas where they occur together, the weasel ∶nds to be twice as abundant and has small ∶me ranges. It shows no apparent difference ∶ the time of day or the nature of the habitat ∶ere it hunts. The stoat is a more general ∶∶der and can move from one prey to ∶ other, whereas the weasel tends to concen-∶te upon one or two species of small rodent, ∶rticularly voles. There is also some evidence ∶at stoats catch most voles outside their ∶ nways, unlike weasels which enter the holes

and can take prey from within.

As we have seen, the closer in size that two related species are, the greater the likelihood of competition between them for the same prey, and so the greater the need for habitat separation. Two such species are the wood mouse and yellow-necked mouse in southern England. In the British Isles, these are similar in size and form, and only the presence of a broad yellow collar and the pale underfur of the adult yellow-necked mouse dis-tinguishes it from its close relative. Where the two occur together, the yellow-necked mouse tends to live in woodland with thicker cover than the wood mouse, which is more often found in fields of crops and in scrub.

Above: A humpback whale surfacing briefly. Whales are the largest mammals on earth. They can support their great size because of the buoyancy provided by the water.

Below: Grey seals mating, showing the much larger size of the male. Seal pups put on weight fast– around 1.8kg (4lb) each day– and they are soon able to withstand their cold, wet environment. The adults are protected by a thick layer of fat.

CAMOUFLAGE AND WARNING COLORATION

An extraordinary array of devices for escaping detection has evolved in the animal kingdom. Predator and prey alike have developed ways of camouflaging themselves. Other creatures are brightly coloured to advertise the fact that they are inedible–a trick often mimicked by edible species!

Camouflage is a form of visual deception in which an animal attempts to merge into the background so that it may be overlooked by predators or its prey. Although many of the best-known examples of camouflage come from the tropics, we need not travel far in the British Isles to see a whole array of adaptations to inconspicuousness and disguise.

These adaptations are most useful against animals such as birds, lizards and fishes which are active by day and depend upon sight to detect prey or predators. They are of little use against animals that rely on other senses such as hearing, smell, taste and touch. Thus the warning colours of many moths are no protection against bats, which detect their prey by echo-location, and cryptic coloration is of little use against a mole or shrew, which detect their prey by smell or touch.

Blending into the background Cryptic col-

Above: Spot the ptarmigan her summer plumage as she nestles close to the moorla to incubate her eggs. This species is camouflaged to blend well with the heather background during summer yet by mid-winter its browr feathers will have been replaced completely by whi ones. The process takes a little time but this is ideal fc the ptarmigan: patches of snow and frost in early winter go well with the patchy brown and white feathers of those months. A the snow starts to melt in spring the ptarmigan loses all-white plumage and grov brown feathers again.
The mountain hare and the stoat also change their coa colour for winter in the Highlands.

oration may be found in virtually all animal groups. Among British mammals we see it in the roe deer fawn whose speckled coat merges into the background of sun-dappled leaves of the forest floor; we see it also in the coats of mountain hares and stoats which change from brown to white in winter to merge with the snow slopes of their mountain haunts. Ground-nesting birds such as the woodcock and hen pheasant are superbly camouflaged by their mottled brown and buff plumage, and many incubate their eggs right out in the open without being detected by potential predators. Often they will lay eggs blotched black or brown or grey– whatever merges best with the background. Anyone who has ever tried to find a ring plover's nest on a shingle bank will testify to the success of this strategy. The same applies to the young of many ground-nesting birds such as gulls, terns and waders.

Counter-shading Many animals use counter-shading effectively to help them merge into the background. Many seabirds, such as the razorbill and great black-backed gull, have dark upperparts to their wings and white underparts. The upperparts when seen from above by other predatory birds blend in with the dark waves beneath, while the pale underparts are inconspicuous to their fish prey against a background of grey and white clouds. In the same way, marine mammals such as the comon dolphin and fishes such as the herring have counter-shading of light and dark areas so that they are difficult to spot from above or below.

Counter-shading is not only achieved by the simple gradation of colour, as in the above examples, but also by the use of bold patterns of spots and stripes which blend when viewed from a distance, for example in the adder and a number of fish. Some species have reversed counter-shading–this is most effective in the eyed hawk-moth caterpillar as it hangs upside-down on its food plant. The caterpillars of the purple emperor rest in a perpendicular position with the head uppermost; the shading is darkest on the head and palest behind. The cuttlefish can alter its counter-shading by rapid colour change to suit the background on which it lies, or its orientation, with the part of the body that is uppermost being instantly shaded darker than the rest.

Changes in behaviour Concealment of shadow may also be achieved by structural or behavioural modification. Detection of animals by their shadow is most likely over open flat ground, and to avoid being caught this way animals often flatten themselves as much as possible upon the surface. The little tern chick crouches over pebbles on the beach, the shore crab flattens itself on the sand. Shadows may also be eliminated by orientating a particular way to the sun. Butterflies can reduce their shadow to a thin line by facing the sun and closing their wings above their backs. They may also tilt to one side or another, as

Above: A crab spider well camouflaged on cork bark and (left) another species of the same family on bird's-foot trefoil. Crab spiders are perfectly camouflaged; many can change colour to suit their surroundings.

Below: Like other flatfish species, the colour of the brill's top side is a speckled sandy or grey brown colour, exactly matching the gravel of the sea-bed. Flatfishes can also change their colours to a limited extent.

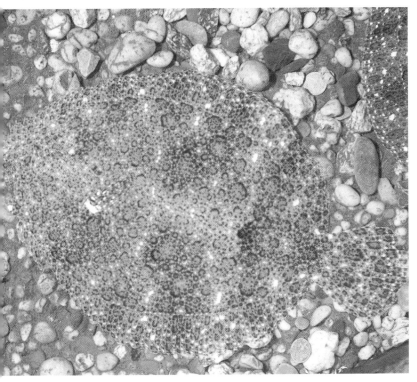

es the green hairstreak which lies almost flat against the leaf upon which it has settled.

Camouflage is obviously best achieved when an animal remains still, and a number of insect predators that sit and wait for their food to come to them are disguised to appear part of their natural background. Praying mantids are well-known tropical examples but in the British Isles, spiders and frogs are both examples of predatory animals that match their surroundings by their coloration.

Disruptive camouflage Some frogs have a pale dorso-lateral stripe which runs back from each eye. This, together with irregularly shaped dark patches on the back, helps to disrupt the frog's outline, particularly its bilateral symmetry. Some of these patches tend to match the immediate background, and this contributes to the disruptive effect by causing some, but not all, of the animal's outline to blend with its surroundings. The zigzag pattern over the back of the adder and bold markings on some other snakes serve a similar disruptive function, making smooth surfaces appear as a random collection of black or brown or grey leaf-like surfaces.

Disruptive coloration may also work by making various parts of the body of an animal appear joined together, so disrupting the characteristic shapes of different parts. For example, many cryptic moths that rest on tree trunks have a bold disruptive pattern which runs continuously across both pairs of wings and the body. This pattern must nevertheless blend with the surroundings to be effective. The classic and much quoted example of this is the peppered moth.

A similar example of the importance of predation in evolution for moulding the appearance of animals is to be found in the land snail *Cepaea* which is eaten by a number

Above: A roosting tawny owl, and (below) a woodcock guard their nests. They both blend into their leafy backgrounds with their mottled brown and buff plumage. This cryptic coloration makes them hard to see, even in daylight.

Opposite: The roe deer fawn's dappled coat helps it merge into the landscape.

Right: A brilliant deception: the head of a buff tip moth resting on a twig and mimicking it exactly.

of predatory birds, notably thrushes. This snail has many distinct forms (and so is referred to as polymorphic)—it may be yellow, pink or brown, banded or unbanded, and if it is banded the number of bands may vary. Although these different morphs are partly determined by environmental conditions (for example, brown forms overheat at high temperatures more readily than yellow forms) an important factor determining their distribution is the habitat in which they live and the degree of concealment the habitat offers from bird predators.

A bad taste in the mouth Many animals protect themselves by producing nauseous tastes or smells, or by inflicting painful or poisonous stings. Obviously it is important that a potential predator recognizes that the prey is noxious, preferably before it has taken a bite out of it, both for the sake of the predator as well as the prey. Such animals are usually brightly coloured with bold contrasting patterns of black, red, orange, yellow and white. Examples are bees, wasps, ladybirds and the striped caterpillars of the cinnabar moth. They may also make themselves more conspicuous by clustering together in large groups or by resting in exposed positions, or by emitting sound signals, such as a loud buzzing noise.

Animals with warning coloration (termed aposematic) are often difficult to kill, having tough skins or elastic tissues which simply

Above: The pupa of a purple emperor butterfly is almost indistinguishable from a leaf.

Right: The bright markings of the five-spotted burnet moths remind experienced predators that they exude poisons if they are attacked.

Below: A leaping dolphin shows its pale underside: counter-shading makes an animal less conspicuous from a distance by counteracting shadows caused by overhead light.

spring back into shape after the animal h been released. This is an important adap ation because, for warning coloration to successful, predators must learn by experien which animals are palatable and which be left. To do so they must suffer a fe unpleasant experiences and learn to associa them with the bright colours of the anim concerned.

Although warning coloration is perha most important among invertebrates, it is al found in other animal groups. Many fish have striking patterns, such as the puffe fish, which has black and white thro markings and white spots to discourage woul be predators. Puffer-fishes make litt attempt to conceal themselves and general manage to survive attacks from inexperience predators by inflating themselves with air water until they become difficult to swallow

Most aposematic animals are diurnal (acti during the daytime) and their distincti markings are readily seen in daylight, but son nocturnal mammals are noxious and posse conspicuous patterns, particularly over the fa

running along their backs. In Britain
mustelids such as the polecat and badger show
this patterning. In many cases these markings
probably also serve a social function.

It is important that an animal with warning
colours has toxic or nauseous properties
which are neither so strong as to be lethal nor
so weak as to be ineffectual. Their poison is
usually combined with an emetic causing the
predator to vomit. Animals with warning
colours must tend to be scarce in comparison
with cryptic species, otherwise predators
would quickly evolve adaptations to exploit
such conspicuous sources of food.
Occasionally a species has evolved ways to
capitalise on this: the European cuckoo takes

Above: A wildcat and her
kitten rest in a tree, their
striped coats helping them to
merge into the habitat.

Below left: A wasp beetle
feeding on spurge. A number
of defenceless animals use
warning coloration to mimic
distasteful or noxious species
–the hoverfly, wasp beetle
and hornet clearwing moth
are all mimics of wasps and
hornets. All are harmless but
gain protection by the
avoidance of predators which
have been stung by a
genuine wasp or hornet.
These are termed Batesian
mimics, after the English
naturalist H W Bates, and are
widespread among insects:
ants are mimicked by
spiders; ichneumon wasps by
bugs, cockroaches and
dipteran flies; bombardier
beetles by grasshoppers;
ladybirds by cockroaches.

Right: The adder has a
zigzag pattern over its
back, making its smooth
skin less visible against
leafy backgrounds. Snakes
often have bold markings to
disrupt their outline, so
that they blend in with
their surroundings.

hairy caterpillars that are noxious to other
species. Some defenceless animals daringly
make use of warning coloration to mimic
distasteful or noxious species. All are harmless, but will be avoided by predators which
have been stung by a genuine poisonous
species.

To avoid unnecessary losses, many animals,
especially insects, use the same combinations
of colours. The black and yellow bands of
wasps are recognised by predators as an inter-
national warning of a creature to be avoided.
This economy of colour pattern helps both
mimic and predator: the latter needs to learn
only a few patterns, while the former is less
likely to be eaten.

LIFE IN THE CONCRETE JUNGLE

Nature's resilience and ability to adapt are nowhere clearer illustrated than in the heart of our towns and cities, where many species have taken advantage of added warmth and food supplies to survive and thrive in the seemingly barren wastes of concrete.

It is only in recent years that students of pla and animal ecology have turned their atte tion seriously to a habitat that now occup an increasing amount of the landscape a accommodates over three-quarters of o population – the urban environment. T heart of the city, a maze of roads, pavemen walls and buildings, is of special interest sin its very artificiality would seem to offer one the last frontiers to living organisms. M of the soil lies compacted beneath an alm unbroken blanket of concrete and aspha fumes from cars and factories pollute the a blocking out sunlight and coating surfac with grime.

Some life forms, like most lichens a

conifers, simply cannot survive such conditions. Nevertheless the spread of urban man has been doggedly followed by a motley crew of opportunist plants and animals, all of which have found in the city some compensating feature. Unlike a recently bared patch of ground which is systematically colonised stage by stage by different plant species, development of this urban community contains a strong element of the novel and the unforeseen; conditions may alter with dramatic speed to extinguish some colonist or favour a newcomer.

Plants in strange places Annuals, with their speedy growth and prodigious powers of dispersal, are ideally suited to the fleeting opportunity such as is offered by a building site; typical examples are groundsel and Oxford ragwort. The ability to flourish in nooks and crannies favours ivy-leaved toad-flax; ferns and mosses can grow on walls, along with several escapes from garden rockeries. Few plants can withstand the bustle of feet on the pavement, but plantain's low profile allows it to survive in cracks between the slabs. Here, also, dandelion and dock extend long tap roots to counter the problem of a soil which is shielded from the rain by concrete. Trees, with deeper root systems, are better off but can suffer badly in drought years.

Because cities are human community centres, often on a cosmopolitan scale, their

plant communities can contain an exotic element. Some, like sorghum and millet, are aliens from tropical shipments, spilled in quiet corners of dockyards and railway sidings. From the cleaned-out bird cage may spring hemp, canary grasses and sunflowers. Apart from beans traced to the leftovers from a Chinese restaurant, the Far East has given city wasteland one of its most rampant shrubs–buddleia. Introduced from China in 1890, it quickly proved nutritious to insects, attracting up to 20 butterfly species to its flowers, aphids to its leaves and ladybirds to feed on the aphids.

Adapting to pollution The two-spot ladybird belongs to a select group of insects that exhibit 'industrial melanism'. In areas polluted with coal smoke, black (or melanic) forms with two or more red spots are more common than the well-known ladybird–red with black spots–that you find in clean air environments. The peppered and pale brindled beauty moths develop darker forms which camouflage them, when they settle on soot-coated tree trunks, against bird predators. Ladybirds do not need camouflage since predators find them distasteful and usually avoid them. The reason ladybirds have a melanic form is therefore probably because this form is less susceptible to some toxin in the smoke and has replaced the red form.

With smokeless zones and cleaner air, melanic forms have become rarer, while insect life has generally increased. It is the constant revelation of cities, therefore, that even the most disruptive conditions seem to favour at least one plant or animal and allow it to gain a foothold.

Bomb-site rubble The World War II blitz of London created in bomb-sites a completely new habitat almost overnight. At first glance these heaps of rubble and ruined walls were not too promising, but a few species were astonishingly quick to take advantage of the pockets of exposed soil. As if from nowhere, rosebay willowherb (also called fireweed) appeared to spread a carpet of shining mauve over the ashes, its foliage creating food for the caterpillars of the elephant hawk-moth, alien to most Londoners and large enough to intimidate many of them. The black redstart, until then a vagrant bird from Europe, discovered in the crumbling masonry an ideal hole-nesting habitat and started breeding.

As the bomb-sites were cleared and built upon, many associated species retreated; willowherb, however, remains common in these areas and the odd redstart still breeds at power stations and gasworks. The kestrel, which was numerous in cities after World War II, also used bomb sites to prey on rodents. But partly because the sites were cleared and partly because many of the kestrels were killed by eating prey that contained toxic chemicals, this species of bird became scarce in inner London in the late 1950s and early 1960s.

t: This patch of urban wasteground has been speedily colonised by Oxford ragwort, rosebay willowherb and buddleia. Butterflies and other insects feed on the flowers in summer and mice will almost certainly be sheltering in the rubble.

ow: Many cats in towns are feral ('gone wild'). They feed on scraps left out by residents and supplement their diet with rats and mice. Colonies of 30–40 have been found in big factories, hospitals and town squares. Like starlings, they are quick to locate warm spots, often rearing their litters in hot-air vents.

This two-spot ladybird (Adalia bipunctata) is an unusual product of polluted towns. Normally this species has black spots on a red background but some have been found with red spots on a black background. The black form seems to be more tolerant of polluted atmospheres than the red.

Nesting on concrete Many birds show remarkable versatility in the way they use concrete buildings. Pigeons are, of course, the best known city colonizers, finding rooftops and window ledges perfect substitutes for the cliffs and rocky caves they use in the wild. At the turn of the century, starlings discovered that Victorian gothic architecture, with its sheer walls and ornamental ledges, represented an ideal dormitory. Thereafter, urban roosting spread at a remarkable rate, the starlings foraging up to 20 miles outside big city centres and swarming in at night. Today, one of the largest roosts is in central Glasgow which, in winter, nightly plays host to upwards of 250,000 squabbling birds.

In coastal towns seabirds such as fulmars, herring gulls and kittiwakes emulate pigeons and will use rooftops and ledges for nesting. One riverside warehouse at North Shields, in Tyne and Wear, supports a breeding colony of over 100 pairs of kittiwakes on its window-sills. A large number of gulls have also come town dwellers: before 1940 it was rare see a gull nesting on a roof top, but by 19 some 7000 pairs were roof-nesters.

Warmth in winter Another attraction of city for all birds is the distinctive urb climate; London, for example, is on averag degree or two warmer and somewhat dr than its hinterland, an obvious bonus on lc winter nights. The brick and concrete bui ings retain a considerable amount of warm from heating systems. Warm ventilator sha and cooling towers make coveted roost si In fact the city can be a much better choice winter than the surrounding countryside. the winter of 1968, for example, after th weeks of snow London's blackbirds weigh 140g (5oz), but woodland blackbirds weigh only 80g (3oz). Clearly the city populatic were able to find sufficient food.

Cities also cause some curious side-effe in some of their wildlife inhabitants: dozi birds, mistaking the numerous street lig for daylight, not uncommonly burst into so in the dead of night. Trees are also confus by the artificially long day, and often leaf winter.

Predators on the prowl For birds, cit offer less risk of predation from animals su as weasels and stoats. However, the centre by no means devoid of predators. Kestre for example, have returned to many c centres to prey on sparrows. There has bee remarkable spread of foxes into urban are in recent years, making one of our traditic ally wildest animals a well-established feat of many large towns and cities. Several families have been recorded living well with reach of the centre of Birmingham. In Lc don, where the fox population is still growi cubs have been born only 3 miles from heart of the city, and in autumn and wint when foxes generally range further afie some make forays into the very centre.

Right: An enterprising urban coot has made use of bits of biscuit wrappings, cardboard and crisp bags to line its twig-based nest.

Below: Gulls nesting on roof tops instead of cliff ledges are now quite a familiar sight in towns, particularly coastal ones such as Whitby in Yorkshire.

INTRODUCED SPECIES AND GREAT ESCAPES

The natural ebb and flow in the populations of animal species results in some decreasing to the point of extinction and others increasing to become pests. These natural changes are slow and relatively infrequent, but where man has introduced new species, the process has been speeded up dramatically.

The British Isles have a limited number of animal species, compared with the rest of Europe. Some, such as the common dormouse, must have been widespread in Victorian times; when it was a nursery pet, now it is scarce. Others, such as the collared dove, once a rare visitor, are now established breeding species. Man has done much to influence the selection by changing or destroying habitats, or introducing new species, either intentionally or accidentally.

Introductions Some accidental introductions are of such antiquity that no details are known of the exact time when they were first made in the British Isles. The house mouse and the oriental cockroach, for example, have lived in close association with man for hundreds, if not thousands, of years and came here as involuntary passengers in ships. Other animal immigrants, originally brought here to be kept in captivity, escaped and took to life in the wild. The Soay sheep of St Kilda, and the wild goats which live in herds in several areas, belong to this category and are of great interest to students of the history of domestic animals, who see in them characteristics of ancient breeds of domestic animals. The American mink, also an escapee from domestication, is, on the other hand, a recent arrival whose success is well known.

In some cases no one is quite sure whether a particular species is introduced or truly wild,

Above: The crested porcupine (shown here) was the reported cause of forestry damage in Staffordshire in the 1970s. The related Himalayan porcupine, a native rodent of the central and eastern Himalayas, originally escaped from the Pine Valley Wildlife Park near Okehampton in Devon in 1969. Ever since then there has been great excitement when quills have been found in the undergrowth or in abandoned badger setts, and damage has been noted in conifer plantations. Porcupines appear to prefer to eat Norway spruce saplings in the British Isles, although in their native habitat they take mainly roots and farm crops.
In recent years there have been fewer reports of supposed porcupine damage to conifer plantations and no established populations of wild porcupine exist at present.

since its history is obscure, and the evidence is conflicting. For example, conventional wisdom says that the Exmoor pony, like all the other local British varieties of the horse, is a feral animal, a domesticated creature which has escaped from man's control and taken up a wild existence. So the Exmoor is an introduced animal. But is it? The Exmoor has many primitive features, for example an extra-thick wiry coat and strong bones, and it can survive the coldest and bleakest Exmoor winters without human help. Some zoologists are convinced that the Exmoor is a truly wild horse, with prehistoric ancestors.

Deliberate introductions These are even more numerous than accidental introduc-

Above: The ring-necked, or green, parakeet, a native of India, Africa, Malaysia and south-western China, has escaped from captivity here many times and is often seen in London and parts of the Home Counties.

Opposite: The pheasant was originally introduced as a game bird to Britain from Asia about 1000 years ago.

Below: The red-necked wallaby, a native of Tasmania, has a small wild population in England.

tions, and a comprehensive list would ta much space. Because the British Isles w cut off from Continental Europe before ma species which prefer milder climates F reached the British landmass, the fauna of British Isles is relatively impoverished.

Many steps were taken to enrich our fau particularly in the 19th century. The m reasons for introductions have been econo (the rabbit, for example), or for decorat (the mandarin and ruddy ducks and the dormouse, for example), or to provide sp (for instance, deer, pheasants, and rainb trout), and in come cases a combination these reasons.

Attempts at biological control are a m recent reason for introducing species: in ma cases a species becomes a pest because predator or parasite in its native habitat absent, therefore they in turn may be broug in. There is no good British example successful biological control, although so parallels may be seen in the way th myxomatosis, imported from South Ameri via France, has achieved a marked reducti in the rabbit population.

Some species (the mink, grey squirrel a rabbit) have been spectacular successes, t many introduced species fail completely establish themselves as self-perpetuati residents. Guinea pigs, for example, oft escape from captivity, yet wild colonies ne survive. Ferrets were released into the w in their thousands when the arrival of myx matosis made them temporarily redundant rabbit hunters and some colonies have surviv for long periods, even becoming permanen wild-living animals. Some species survive the wild on a limited scale, such as the nig herons which escaped from Edinburgh Z and the golden hamster, a frequent escap from pet shops.

Success or failure Part of the explanation for success or failure of a species may lie in the concept of the 'vacant niche'–an environment which does not have a species adapted to live in it already and can therefore support a new population of a particular species.

Some scientists say there is no such thing, since a niche is only evident when occupied by the appropriate animal. Yet the idea has appeal: attempts to re-introduce the wolf or the wild boar would probably be unsuccessful, because the habitat has been so changed by man that the resources they would need to survive in the British Isles are no longer there–their niche has disappeared.

On the other hand, until recently the British Isles had no mink. As we can see now, with the benefit of hindsight, the mink niche was vacant. Today the mink thrives in our countryside, neither competing too seriously with otters in our lakes, rivers and sea-shores, nor with stoats and weasels on land, and harvesting enough of our small wildlife to support itself without causing any widespread destruction (despite local damage to fish farms and waterfowl).

Sometimes, however, a colonist displaces another species. In much of the British Isles the grey squirrel appears to have displaced the native red, and in Europe, for example, the American mink has displaced the native European species. Preliminary research has shown that in these and similar cases there is no direct competition between the species, but rather that the species which contracts its range was already in retreat before the new-comer arrived. With the grey squirrel and the mink massive man-wrought alterations to the environment are the likely cause. When the newcomer arrived, better adapted to the changing conditions, the retreat was acceler-ated. The match between niche and new oc-cupant was then better, so the newcomer quickly replaced the old inhabitant and became an established species.

In the case of the small colonies of animals which spread only slowly, if at all, one can only assume that the resources in the habitat are inadequate for the animal's needs, so the invader is unable to build up a large popula-tion. The situation can persist for a long time, though a subtle change in environmental fact-ors can extinguish the colony, as has been the case with some colonies of the fat dormouse.

A similar argument probably explains why newly-established colonies are so precarious, taking time to reach a level where rapid ex-pansion is possible. The small colony, even in favourable conditions, is thinly dispersed and liable to serious depletion, even extinc-tion, as a result of quite small environmental changes. However, at a certain point–differ-ent in every case–conditions are right, and a new member of the British fauna, such as the Muntjac deer or wild mink, establishes itself in our countryside.

Above: The American mink had a humble beginning here on the edge of Dartmoor in the 1950s but it has now become a runaway success in most of mainland Britain.

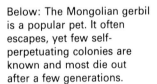

Right: The stick insect, a popular pet, lives wild on Tresco on the Scilly Isles. It seems to have got there accidentally, with some of the tropical and sub-tropical plants.

Below: The Mongolian gerbil is a popular pet. It often escapes, yet few self-perpetuating colonies are known and most die out after a few generations.

WALLABIES IN A COLD CLIMATE

Above: The red-necked wallaby gets its name from the rust-coloured patch on its shoulders. The red varies in intensity, and is less conspicuous in the wild.

Red-necked wallabies were introduced to British zoos from Australia over 100 years ago. Since then a few animals have either escaped or been released. A small population has survived in the wild for about 50 years—but today the future of these small kangaroos is far from secure.

The red-necked wallaby comes from Tasmania, an island off the south-eastern tip of Australia. Tasmania has a climate very similar to our own, which means that this particular species is accustomed to moderately cold temperatures. It has therefore done well in British zoos, and any visitor to Whipsnade will know that red-necked wallabies have the freedom of the grounds there and are very common.

Animals that have escaped or been released from captivity have established small colonies in the wild in at least two different parts of England. However, because wild wallabies are very vulnerable to disturbance by man, and their numbers are already precariously low, the location of these colonies has to be kept secret.

Excellent camouflage The front paws, hind feet and tail tip of the red-necked wallaby are black, the underside light grey, and the back a darker grey. This all provides remarkably good camouflage when the animal is still. There is no difference in colour between male and female, but the adult male is appreciably larger, and has a longer, blunter muzzle. The female has a more slender, tapered muzzle. The muzzle of the young male is similar to that of the female, and you can easily mistake a female for a young male until you notice the pouch.

Breeding The most interesting thing about

RED-NECKED WALLABY
(*Macropus rufogriseus*)
Length (head and body)
Male 65cm (25½in), female
61cm (24in).
Weight Male 13kg (28lb),
female 10kg (22lb).
Breeding season Generally
August, but considerable
variation.
Gestation period 30 days.
No of young 1.
Lifespan Max 19 years in
the wild.
Food Shrubs, grasses, herbs.
Predators None. However,
deaths caused by cars, and
as a result of disturbance by
man and dogs.
Distribution Must remain
secret, to protect few
remaining populations
in Britain.

wallabies is their manner of breeding. Like so many Australian mammals, they are marsupials. (They carry their young in a pouch situated on the lower abdomen.) Young marsupials are born in an under-developed state–prematurely by the stand-ards of other mammals–after a very short pregnancy. In the red-necked wallaby, preg-nancy lasts only 30 days, but to compensate for this the period of suckling is relatively long–around 280 days.

Courtship consists mainly of the male chasing the female, trying to stroke her tail, generally keeping as close as possible, and threatening any other male that comes near. If he annoys the female too much, she may turn round and box him with her front paws. Rival males may also indulge in boxing.

When the young wallaby is due to be born, the female sits down with tail extended for-ward between the legs, and licks the pouch and groin to clean them. The young wallaby is only about 10mm ($\frac{1}{2}$in) long, and its hind legs, so enormous in the adult, are minute in relation to the rest of its body; its eyes and ears are closed. However, its front legs are well formed, with strong claws, and with these it crawls up through its mother's fur, into the pouch, with no help at all from her. It then attaches itself firmly to a nipple and remains attached for about two months. After that, it begins to move around in the pouch, and at about seven months old it starts to poke out its head to see what is going on outside.

In Britain, mating occurs mostly in August, so that the young are probably born in September (birth itself has not been observed in the wild). In April, the young can be seen sticking their noses tentatively out of the mother's pouch, and by the end of June they leave the pouch altogether.

There is some variation in this timetable, since courtship occurs as late as December, and pouch young have been seen in Septem-ber. In the southern hemispheres, the time-table differs by six months, in order to match the seasons. Generally, the later part of pouch life and early freedom of the young wallaby coincide with the new growth of plant life in early summer whether this is June as in Britain or December as in Tasmania.

Free association Wallabies have no par-ticular home site and, although they tend to move about in small groups, no social struc-ture is apparent. Individuals move freely between groups. Juveniles stay away from these groups, perhaps because they are pushed out.

Wallabies have poor eyesight, but their sense of smell is good, and their hearing acute. The ears are extremely mobile, flicking back and forth like radar scanners to pick up the slightest sound. If greatly alarmed, wallabies hop off rapidly, downhill if possible, slapping the ground hard in the first few hops to warn other wallabies. Normally, however,

Above: The young wallaby does not poke its head out its mother's pouch until it i about seven months old. Two months later, it leaves the pouch altogether.

Left: A white line along the upper lip and whitish spots over the eyes are characteristic of the red-necked wallaby. The face o this young animal will light as it gets older. If it lives to old age, most of its muzzle will be white.

ey react to disturbance by crouching down, ther like hares, hoping to escape notice.

Feeding habits Wallabies generally spend e day in cover, hiding in scrub or on rough ound. At dusk, they become more active d feed intensively.

Wallabies are exclusively plant-eating (hervorous), feeding on a wide variety of rubs, grasses and other herbs. When ailable, heather is an important food urce. In spring wallabies eat the new shoots bilberry and in summer they eat a little acken as well as grass. They also take the oots of young pine trees, when they can ach them.

Wallabies have small mouths, and feed licately, using their front (incisor) teeth to te off the tastiest parts of the plants. When ting grass, they use their front limbs and il alternately with their back limbs, to tch themselves slowly forward in a 'five-gged' gait. They sit up to feed on heather or her shrubs, using their front paws to hold e selected shoots or pull them towards the outh. Wallabies are not known to drink ater, but they sometimes lick snow in inter.

Like ruminants, such as deer, sheep and ttle, wallabies have complicated stomachs ith fermentation chambers. These chambers e full of micro-organisms that break down herwise indigestible parts of food, parcularly cellulose.

When they are not feeding, wallabies spend lot of time grooming. They lick and nibble eir forequarters, and lick their front paws efore using them for face washing. The tail pulled slowly through the front paws and cked. Like other kangaroos, wallabies have n extra grooming device, a 'comb' on the nd foot, consisting of the two smallest toes. his is used vigorously to scratch the ears and e back of the head.

Heavy casualties It remains to be seen how ell the red-necked wallaby survives in ritain. One population of five animals, leased in 1940, increased to about 50 nimals by 1962, when the severe winter used many deaths. Since then, this popula- on has increased only very slowly.

Over the last 20 years numbers have fluctuated. There have been road casualties, and disturbance by people and dogs has lead to some deaths. The combination of severe winters and competition for food from sheep has also caused several deaths. The future is now uncertain for this, Britain's largest colony.

Given its apparent vulnerability to disturbance, severe winters and cars, it seems unlikely that the red-necked wallaby will ever become a pest here (as it has in New Zealand). We can only hope that tourists looking out for wallabies will keep their own disturbance to a minimum, and not chase the animals unnecessarily. Wallabies driven into less suitable habitats will no doubt fail to maintain their numbers and so die out. Also, if they stray on to surrounding farmland and eat vegetable crops, or get into timber plantations and nibble young shoots, they are likely to be killed by irate farmers and landowners. However, it is hoped that the red-necked wallaby, as our only wild marsupial, will continue to survive here.

Embryo-like young

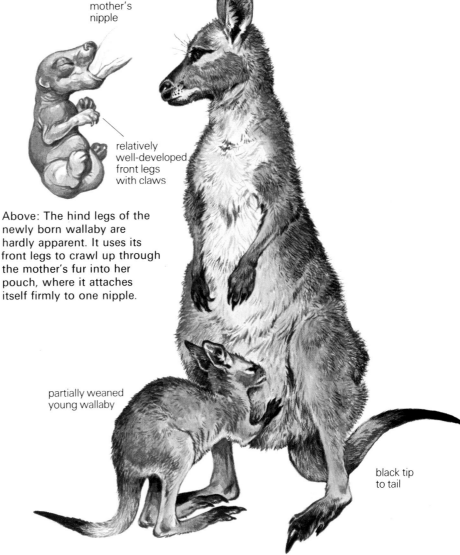

Below: When it is about eight months old, the young wallaby begins to make occasional sorties from the mother's pouch, in search of solid food. At around nine months, it leaves the pouch permanently, but it continues to suckle from the mother until it is at least a year old.

mother's nipple

relatively well-developed front legs with claws

Above: The hind legs of the newly born wallaby are hardly apparent. It uses its front legs to crawl up through the mother's fur into her pouch, where it attaches itself firmly to one nipple.

partially weaned young wallaby

black tip to tail

Left: The Latin name for the wallaby is *Macropus*, meaning 'big foot'. The long hind foot consists mainly of an enlarged fourth toe, but the fifth toe (our 'little' toe) is also quite large. The first toe (our 'big' toe) is missing, and the second and third toes are very small, closely joined together on the inside of the foot. The wallaby uses its smallest toes as a comb for grooming its ears and the back of its head.

167

MUNTJAC: SMALL DEER

Introduced from southern China during the last century, the muntjac deer – a very small species – has been spreading gradually throughout the countryside of England.

The Chinese muntjac deer, a native of southern China and Taiwan, was first brought to London Zoo in 1840. It was introduced to the grounds of Woburn Abbey by the Duke of Bedford in about 1900 and since then it has spread from the Abbey's evergreen shrubbery into nearby woodlands and out into the surrounding countryside. Since then it has established itself in the Home Counties and has spread as far as Nottinghamshire, the Welsh Marches, the West Country, Sussex and parts of East Anglia.

The muntjac is a small deer with a characteristic rounded back. The buck is considerably heavier in the neck and shoulders than the doe. The body colour is bright chestnut in summer but rather duller in winter, the big bucks being particularly dark in winter. The upper surface of the tail and back of the thighs is bright ginger in both summer and winter. The white undersurface of the tail is usually visible only in flight or fright, when it is raised, showing a bright white flash. When a muntjac is angry or aggressive the chestnut tail and the hair on the back of the legs can be fluffed up; in extreme aggression the whole of the body hair stands up, making the animal seem larger.

Simple antlers Only the bucks have antlers; at about 7cm (2¾in) long they are short in relation to the animal's body size when compared with those of other deer; they are also deciduous, falling off in May and June. The

Above: A Chinese muntjac buck. This species is sometimes known as the barking deer because of its hoarse bovine cough that it utters at four or five second intervals (although it is more usually silent).

Below: Muntjac deer are very small compared with other deer species found in Britain. Their closest relative is the Indian muntjac, found in India and other parts of Asia.

antlers are carried on bony, hairy projectio (pedicles) of the frontal bone. The bo pedicles start to grow when the muntjac four months old and take about three mont to mature; the straight, backward-pointi antlers are grown from May to Septembe and you may see animals with pedicles b no antlers (the pedicles looking, neverthele like antlers) all the year round. An anim born in January starts to grow pedicles April or May, but they are not fully form until August – too late for the antlers develop. The pedicles remain in velvet, with tiny button cap antlers, throughout t following winter.

Female muntjac bear dark haired marks place of antlers. They have a dark crow patch and less well-defined facial markin than the males. In both sexes the face lighter than the body colour, being yellow, occasionally a shade of orange.

The most interesting feature of muntja bucks is their protruding canine teeth. The are just visible, projecting from the upper ja as small tusks, and are thought to be used f defence and fighting purposes. Does al possess canine teeth, but these are muc smaller and less apparent.

Bramble habitat The favoured habitat the muntjac is bramble thicket, usual where it has grown in newly planted woodlar among young trees, or on wasteland or ev in gardens. Motorway banks, factory groun

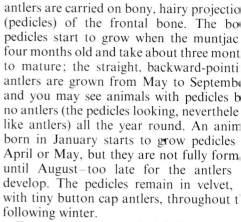

Ministry of Defence restricted areas are
o favoured.

Although muntjacs are shy animals, they
nefit from their association with man. Not
ly do they feed in gardens but in severe
ather they take shelter in garden sheds and
thouses, thus maintaining their popula-
ns. In Forestry Commission stands where
re has been no shelter in hard winters some
untjac have died.

Family animals Although muntjac are de-
ibed as solitary, they do in fact have a
nily structure. A buck and a doe will remain
hin the same area for a period of years.
lelity is difficult to prove, but the impres-
n is of pairs mated for life, although with
e death or injury of a partner a replacement
te (presumably solitary up until now) is
en within a matter of days.

Territories are marked by scent secreted
m glands on the head and below the eyes,
d on the pelvis and hind feet. Urine and
ces are also used as territorial markers—
e droppings, which are sometimes left
lividually but can collect gradually in
rines, are small, shiny, cylindrical black
llets pointed at one end and depressed at
e other. The deer often use their teeth to
ip the outer bark and tissues of plants and
oots and then they anoint the bared wood
th a secretion from the head glands.

If bucks are disturbed on their marked
rritory they fight with their canines and
tlers only as a last resort. Does behave
gressively towards other does, but relatives,
rticularly their own grown-up fawns, are
lerated. The muntjac registers aggression by
ising itself as high as it can on its four legs;
hair stands out and the animal presents
elf side-on to produce a silhouette of maxi-
um size. An animal wanting to show mini-
al aggression, or even submission, lies with
feet tucked in and its chin on the ground.

Continuous breeding The does normally
eed continuously. They are sexually mature
seven months old and drop a single fawn
ter a pregnancy of 210 days. Within two or
ree days of the doe giving birth the buck is
tively chasing her again, and copulation is
peated many times. If conception is not
hieved, oestrus appears to occur once a
ek on average.

Fawns are relatively large at birth and
eigh about 1kg (just over 2lb). They can
alk immediately and run within two or three
ys. For the first six to eight weeks their coats
e spotted but the pattern becomes gradually
oscured as a fluffy juvenile coat grows
rough the baby coat. They are milk-fed
uring the first two months, although they
art to graze at a few days old. The fawns
ve a characteristic cry—a penetrating
ueak uttered regularly that can be heard
om over 100 yards away. Lactating does
ll their young with a curious yelping sound.

As an introduced species, muntjac fit well
to our countryside. They are more widely

distributed in a given area than roe deer, and
do far less damage. They can become a
nuisance in gardens, however, unless fenced
out. Such trespassing may attract the attentions of 'sportsmen', and many deer carry
gunshot wounds or other injuries. An injured
or trapped deer has a penetrating cry.

It is seldom necessary to control muntjac
as their dispersal mechanism ensures against
a build-up of a population in a single area.
The first muntjac to arrive in a new area are
usually bucks, for it seems that bucks leave
home earlier and travel a greater distance
than does. Muntjac are often heard before
they are seen: their bark is distinctive; they
also squeak when sexually stimulated.

Above: A muntjac doe and
her fawn in Hertfordshire,
an area that is well
populated with this species.
They graze on most green
plants and even those that
are poisonous to other
animals, such as yew.
The picture on the left
shows a buck muntjac.

MUNTJAC DEER
(*Muntiacus reevesi*)
Size of adult Male about
48cm (19in); weighs 13.5kg
(30lb). Female 45cm (18in),
weighs 11.7kg (26lb).
Breeding season All year.
Gestation period 210 days.
No of young One.
Lifespan 15 years.
Food Bramble, ivy, yew,
dog's mercury, bluebells,
garden plants, grasses, food
from bird tables, fruits.
Predators Man, cats, dogs.
Distribution See map
below.

Muntjac distribution

MOST SUCCESSFUL BIRD SPECIES

Some bird species are on the edge of their range in Britain and Ireland, while others are so well suited to conditions here that their populations number in the millions. Here we look at some of the ways which can be used to measure 'success'.

e choice of a 'most successful bird species', en if restricted to birds of Britain and land, is one of great complexity as so many ds are judged to be successful, using a riety of different criteria. Do sheer numrs, for example, carry more weight than the ility to survive, albeit as a rarity, under verse conditions? Similarly, is the ability to ploit new habitats and food sources a eater measure of success, or the capacity to ke advantage of man's presence? We have opted the solution of awarding a number of izes', using different standards to award ch one. Then, from among these 'class ampions', we select a 'supreme champion' most successful species of all.

Birds as a group are among the most obile, versatile and adaptable of animals, d this makes the judge's task no easier. any, for example, exploit a variety of bitats, succeeding with difficulty in some d with ease in others. Migrant species, such waders, that breed far to the north inside e Arctic Circle, probably endure no more an average difficulty away from their eeding grounds, but need to be in perfect ysical condition if they are to make a ccess of the all-too-brief breeding season, th its treacherous weather. In between their o habitats they give another astounding monstration of their abilities: a migratory urney of several thousand miles, some of it ross the sea, and perhaps some over equally hospitable deserts. This is a magnificent hievement in terms of physique and navition, but one performed by millions of birds ice annually.

Most successful migrant Many of the igrants which use Britain and Ireland as ther their breeding or their wintering area rform roughly similar journeys. The title ntenders here are likely to come from nong those birds which pass through these lands on their way to even more distant calities. Though few breed here, the redcked phalarope is one contender under this eading. Wintering in tropical Africa, often at a, this tiny wader breeds well north into the rctic tundra. As part of its stratagem for ccess, the normal roles of male and female

Opposite page: The Brent goose deserves mention for persistence in the face of adversity. Sixty years ago, its main food plant, eelgrass, nearly died out, and the geese faced starvation. Survivors turned to winter wheat as an alternative food, and so the species held on until the eel-grass became plentiful once more.

Above right: The wren is our choice of champion for persistence in the face of adversity. In any really severe winter, millions of wrens die of starvation or heat loss; but within two or three years they are back to normal numbers—around ten million pairs.

Below: The peregrine has survived DDT poisoning, egg collecting and capture for sale to falconers.

are reversed: the female is larger and brighter, and takes the dominant role. Having chosen a mate, she lays, and then leaves the male to incubate the eggs and raise the brood singlehanded, while she procures a second mate and repeats the process, thereby increasing the chances of the survival of the species.

At least as remarkable, though for different reasons, is the wheatear. One race of this small member of the chat family breeds in Greenland, wintering well south in Africa. Some migrate via Iceland and Britain, but others, heading south, make their first landfall in Spain—a prodigious oceanic journey (including a crossing of the notorious Bay of Biscay) for such a small land bird.

These considered, perhaps the title should

after all go to a bird that does breed in considerable numbers in northern Britain and Ireland, the Arctic tern. No other migrant travels so far each year, and none sees so much daylight, for the Arctic tern leaves the 'perpetual day' of the Northern Hemisphere summer for the equivalent in the Southern Hemisphere, where it fishes off the ice in the Antarctic Ocean.

Persistence in adversity This is an altogether different category, but one no less varied. Contenders naturally include small resident birds such as the wren; often noisily abundant throughout the summer countryside, the wren's small size can be its undoing in periods of really severe weather. Days for feeding are short, and the nights which have to be endured are long, during the winter. An additional hardship occurs when frost or snow conceals food. Indeed, if ultra-low temperatures cause energy (in terms of stored fat) to be burnt up (in the process of keeping warm) faster than it can be gathered, then catastrophe may hit the wren.

Opposite right: Novelty is one of the criteria used in judging the class of entries for 'ability to cope with urbanisation'. The tawny owl is in a position to welcome urban spread, as this always brings sparrows, to which the owl has become partial. Brown rats, another urban species, do not escape its notice either. Invertebrate foods, particularly earthworms, form a significant part of the owl's diet, and therefore it can hunt successfully on school playing fields at night.

Below: The chaffinch—in winter, visiting birds from the Continent swell its population, making it our most numerous species.

In particularly harsh years, mortality can around 70% or 80%. But the wren show remarkable ability to bounce back from s adversity, and with considerable speed, often only two or three years elapse bef numbers are restored. This is the wren's cla to the title: in view of its large and succes population, we place it at the head of the cla

A survey of the peregrine falcon, carried because pigeon fanciers thought that pe grines were taking too many of their rac birds, showed a calamitous decline betwe the 1930s and the early 1950s. Some pe grines were shot during the wartime ye because they preyed on pigeons carry military messages, but the real culprit v discovered after some rather elegant resea had been carried out, investigating eggsh thicknesses.

The causes of breeding failure were trac to an excessive frailty of the eggshells, and cause of this was DDT. This was a warti product developed to control human tick a louse infestations. Post war, it became cheap, effective agricultural pesticide—but c of long environmental persistence. It accum lated along 'food chains' and poisoned predators at their summit, including peregrine. Ultimately the DDT was wi drawn, voluntarily, from agrochemical u and peregrine numbers began to recover.

Today, the main threats are egg collect and falconers seeking this noblest of falcons, with its thrilling 'stoop' at prey, keep in captivity. Despite the robbery dozens of eyries each year—quite illegally— peregrine is tolerating this additional ma made burden and holding its own.

The story of the red kite is broadly simil The tiny population—a few dozen birds—in mid-Wales oakwoods has held on agai threats from poison baits. These are often la for crows or foxes, but laid ignoring the f that the kite too is a carrion feeder. E collectors, too, are a serious hazard. In spite these, and with the help of bird protecti organisations such as the RSPB, the red k has in the last few years been more producti as a breeding bird than for decades.

Last in this category is the Brent goo When its main food plant, the marine e grass *Zostera*, was almost obliterated disease, Brent goose numbers crashed. Th the geese changed their diet: they began to e some seaweeds, and to fly inland to feed winter wheat shoots. This helped to stave disaster, as did a series of good summers on Arctic breeding grounds. Here, the norma savage weather ameliorated for several su cessive seasons, and fledging success was hig *Zostera*, too, has staged a comeback, a Brent goose numbers are now such that so farmers consider them a pest!

Coping unexpectedly with man Here t challengers have been selected on the basis novelty: the more routine cohabitants w man are considered in another catego

Breeding bird populations

Numbers in the chart are **in pairs**. Winter totals are different in many cases.
Key to species: **1** wren, **2** chaffinch, **3** blackbird, **4** house sparrow, **5** robin, **6** starling, **7** kestrel, **8** rock dove and feral pigeon (combined), **9** curlew, **10** tawny owl, **11** collared dove, **12** sparrowhawk, **13** little ringed plover, **14** peregrine, **15** golden eagle, **16** black-throated diver, **17** black redstart, **18** red kite.

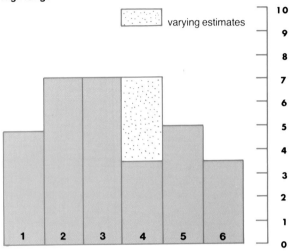

High range — millions

varying estimates

ban areas contain numerous rodents–rats
d house mice in particular–and both the
ny owl and the kestrel feed on these and on
 abundance of house sparrows. Gardens,
ks and playing fields are also home to an
ay of smaller animals, and perhaps in
ntrast to popular belief, both these preda-
s, with their astonishing powers of sight
d hearing, do feed for much of the time on
atures as small as beetles and worms.
But paramount in this category must be the
agpie. This alert, cautious member of the
ow family has turned its rural egg-stealing
y of life to good effect, following urban
kmen on their early morning rounds.
or-step deliveries of milk bottles are often
companied by boxes of chicken eggs, and
 magpies break open these cartons, con-
ning the contents of the eggs within.
Exploiting new environments Here pride of
ce must go to the little ringed plover,
loquially 'LRP' to birdwatchers. It was

Right: The information used to compile this chart has been collected over the last 25 years and is the latest across-the-board count of birds in Britain and Ireland.

Below: The collared dove has stabilised at a little over 50,000 pairs after 50 years of dynamic growth. It therefore wins the prize as the most promising newcomer, as well as the supreme championship.

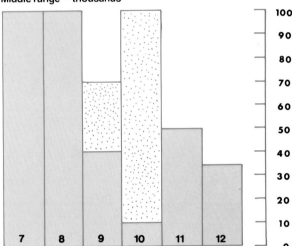

Middle range — thousands

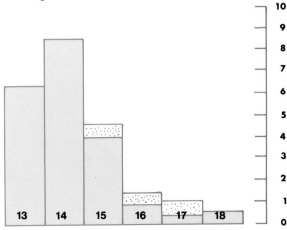

Low range — hundreds

almost unknown in Britain before the 1930s, but post-war building created new reservoirs and mineral extraction pits—for sand, ballast, clay and chalk—and these provided a novel environment that this migrant wader was quick to exploit in the south and east. The breeding population remains quite small, but the vast majority of LRP pairs nest on man-made sites; they seem to be quite untroubled by the constant comings and goings of heavy machinery nearby.

Most successful exploiter of man The challengers for this title are more predictable, with the house sparrow and starling leading the field. Both flourish in association with man, and the house sparrow rarely ventures far from man's activities or buildings. Some inner-city populations live a life with almost no 'outdoor' aspects and eat only man-provided food. An example of this is the sparrow population in a large main-line railway station. The starling, more mobile, more garrulous and more quarrelsome, is perhaps also wider-ranging in its exploitation,

Above: The magpie wins the prize for originality in coping with urbanisation.

Below: Starlings are great exploiters of man: here a group of them are feeding on slaughter-house offal at a rubbish tip.

Below left: The little ringed plover has established a British population of over 600 pairs. It has done so by spreading to a newly made habitat—mineral extraction pits.

especially in the range of farmland that it c successfully occupy. Grassland, orchards a cattle feeding areas all satisfy the starlin food requirements, and the species has esta lished itself successfully as a pest (so effect is its exploitation!) in many parts of the wo where it was thoughtlessly introduced by ea colonists.

Most successful newcomer Although in last few decades several birds have returr after a temporary absence to establish grea or lesser 'toe-holds' as breeding birds Britain, genuinely 'new' newcomers are l numerous. Cetti's warbler is one true ne comer, but there is only one serious contene for this particular title. The collared dove v unknown in Britain and Ireland before mid-1950s, but then the first few pairs collared doves settled in Norfolk and Ke Naturalists and ornithologists protected the few pairs with the utmost secrecy, but th efforts at conservation were overtaken events. Such was the strength of the tide tl swept the collared dove westwards acr Europe from its Asian homeland that witl two decades all of Britain and Ireland b been conquered and colonized, and in ma areas collared doves had reached such nu bers as to be considered a pest on poul farms and in grain storage silos. Now their c call and monotonous coo-*coo*-coo song is be heard year-round almost everywhere.

'Supreme Champion' A difficult choice w such a range of avian talents to choose fro Should emphasis be given to sheer numbe or to resilience, or to migratory prowess, adaptability? Only one of these birds wou qualify for a reasonably good score und each heading, and so the 'supreme' ti should logically fall to the phenomena successful collared dove.

A FARTHING FOR ITS SONG?

he perky, diminutive wren–Britain's smallest bird apart from the goldcrest and firecrest–is ideally suited to its foraging life in the undergrowth of woodland and hedgerow and, with ten million breeding pairs, is our most numerous species.

e wren, with its barred wn and grey plumage– ilar in both sexes–is l-camouflaged in the dergrowth it frequents. t you can identify the le by his exceptionally d 'churring' call.

In legend the familiar brown wren is condemned to live a skulking life of shame for cheating in the great election to find the king of the birds. The story goes that the birds decided to choose as their king the one which could fly the highest. Hoping to win the contest, the cheeky wren concealed himself in the plumage of the mighty eagle and hitched

a ride for most of the way, only emerging to outfly the eagle when it finally tired. The strength of this legend, which appears in many countries and cultures, testifies to Man's ancient association with and fondness for the perky little bird.

Tiny troglodyte The wren prefers to frequent holes and corners in cliff overhangs, derelict buildings, outhouses, tree roots and piles of boulders. Its scientific name means 'the cave-dweller'–a name not to be taken too literally, but nevertheless apt since the bird is one of the few able to exploit such recesses and cavities. It is an active little bird, full of verve and familiar in town and country.

The rounded, dumpy body, short whirring wings and cocked tail may look ungainly, but in fact the wren is superbly equipped for its ground-foraging way of life. It creeps about in the undergrowth in a characteristic crouched posture–very much like a small rodent–negotiating its way efficiently through narrow openings and working energetically through tangled vegetation, tree roots and

brambles. On a branch, its tail-cocked perching position is unmistakable.

Year-long songster The sexes are indistinguishable in plumage, but only the cock sings. For the size of the bird's body, the volume and carrying power of the song is remarkable. The male sings consistently throughout the year and song is important in his life. He uses one type of call – a vehement, rattling warble usually lasting a few seconds – for a variety of purposes: territorial warning and defence, courtship, attracting others to roost and communicating with partners. In the excitement of courtship and nesting, he will even sing with his beak crammed full of building materials!

Numerous nests The wren's breeding seaso starts from the second half of April onward It is catholic and often quaint in its choi of nesting sites, frequently ignoring natur recesses in hedge bottom, ivy bank or u turned tree root in favour of man-ma places such as outhouses or the corners gardens.

The cock builds several nests – outsiz domed structures of moss, dry grass, brack or leaves – to tempt his mate. The hen selec the one of her choice, lines it with feather then lays from five to twelve eggs and i cubates them by herself for 14 or 15 days. T glossy white eggs are often speckled wi minute black or red-brown spots at the lar end. When the young hatch, the male leav the female to do all the feeding. The hen us ally rears two broods a season, especially more vegetated areas where food is plentif The male bird – not the most diligent parents – may install several females in su cession in different nests.

Success story The wren is a successful a adaptable bird – something that is partic larly noteworthy since it is the only Eurasi representative of an extensive family otherwise exclusively New World birds. N only is the wren one of the most widespre of all our birds, it is also extremely numerou Densities of up to 100 pairs per squa kilometre have been recorded. At the sar time, the wren is vulnerable in hard winte when numbers may fall dramatically. Ho ever, the rate of recovery can be equa dramatic: after the cold winter of 1962-6 the wren recovered numbers faster than a other common bird.

The wren is almost entirely insectivorou Its diet is composed mainly of the larvae small moths, flies, beetles and other insec as well as spiders, mites and a limited varie of small soft-bodied invertebrates – probed, extracted or caught with the bir fine, slender, slightly curved bill. It is lit wonder that protracted hard weather – whi decimates insects – spells disaster for t wren. Unfortunately, it is our one gard visitor that is not drawn to bird tables, so it no use putting out extra food in the hope saving it from starvation. In times of plent however, there are probably up to ten milli breeding pairs of wrens in existence.

Quite a crowd One oddity of wren beha iour is communal roosting which sometim occurs in particularly severe weather. Wre are usually solitary at night, but large nu bers are sometimes found roosting in ve confined spaces, the birds huddled togeth in a feathery mass with tails pointing ou wards. As many as 30 or 40 individuals ha been found in one nest box, in tier on stifli tier. Obviously, the insulation obtained this crowding has a high survival value hard weather. It helps the birds retain t precious body heat they have gained fro hard-won insect food foraged during t

Wren (*Troglodytes troglodytes*); 10cm (3¾in) from beak to tail; distribution widespread; resident.

Above: A male wren singing to proclaim his territory. Apart from a series of loud warbling calls, the wren's repertoire includes cheery trills and a scolding 'tit-tit-tit' sound.

Right: The wren's domed nest, made of moss, dry grass and bracken and lined with feathers, makes a secure, snug home for the young. Some wrens prefer to nest in close proximity to Man and choose odd sites to build – such as in an old cap hung in a shed.

Above: A parent wren bringing a beakful of insects to its young in the nest. Its short wings make the wren's flight rapid and whirring. Note the characteristic white eye stripe.

ort winter daytime. After the young have dged in summer, but before they have come independent, parent birds can some-nes be seen shepherding their families to e safety of a communal roost.

Island races Wrens are not only found in oodland, farmland, river banks and sub-ban gardens—where we are most familiar th them; they also occur on sea cliffs and ountainsides. They even inhabit some of r furthest-flung islands, particularly Shet-nd, St Kilda and the Hebrides. On these ands the species has been isolated for 6000 ars or more and has produced distinctive, early separated local races. The island birds nd to be larger and greyer in colour and ve heavier chestnut-coloured barring on e back than their mainland relatives.

The wren hunt The wren frequents the vellings of Man more than any other bird, d it is not surprising that legends about it ound. One curious and ancient custom—e wren hunt—which originated over 1000 ars ago took place (in various forms) in

many parts of England, and was particularly popular in Ireland, parts of Wales and the Isle of Man. The hunt was specially associ-ated with St Stephen's Day (26th December). Wrens were hunted along hedgerows, and through woods with sticks, stones, bows and arrows or birch rods; any found were killed—often ritually. They were then borne through the town on an elaborate bier or specially constructed wren house by grotesquely dressed 'wren boys'—all to the accompani-ment of traditional wren-hunt songs. In many ceremonies, money was solicited by the wren boys for 'the burying of the wren'. The hunt persisted until very recent times, and in Ireland is still practised. Its origins go far back into history: it is said that a wren hop-ping on a drum awakened the Danes and foiled a stealthy Irish attack.

Fortunately for the wren, it has outlived the barbarous hunt; now, though we no longer have the farthing coin which carried the wren emblem and testified to its popular-ity, the bird is fully protected by the law.

Polygamy in birds

Most birds have only one mate; the advantage is that both parents help to rear young. Some birds, however, practise polygamy—having more than one mate. Male wrens often do this, especially where food is plentiful and the hen can feed the young on her own.

There are two types of polygamy. Simultaneous pairing can take place with two or more females (as with corn buntings). With successive polygamy, the male initiates consecutive broods with different females. Male wrens do both. The advantage is that the largest possible number of broods can be produced without the male increasing the size of his territory; also the female may have the opportunity to select more vigorous, active males—to the benefit of the species.

ell-adapted for creeping out in the undergrowth, e wren has an mistakable bobbing, jerky ethod of feeding on the ound.

TOWN AND COUNTRY PIGEONS AND DOVES

Pigeons and doves vary in size and colour but all have a plump body, small head and slender beak. They have succeeded in adapting to Man's urban sprawl, and have withstood the threat of the shotgun by rapid flight and consistent breeding.

Below: Turtle doves are thinly distributed on farmland south of a line between Durham and Lancashire (they are scarcer in west Wales and Cornwall). Their main food plant, which grows here, is fumitory.

There are about 300 species of pigeons and doves in the world, five of which occur in the British Isles. Whether you call them 'pigeon' or 'dove' is a matter of personal preference – though generally pigeons are large birds with short, square tails, and doves are more slightly built with long, rounded tails.

Cliff cousins Multicoloured town pigeo are a common sight in urban areas on buil ings, statues and railway stations as well as gardens. They are domesticated descendar of the rock doves, which now live only remote sea cliffs in north and west Scotla and the Atlantic coast of Ireland. These 'tr rock doves also occur around the Medite ranean, on coasts and near inland cliffs. Britain, however, it is their town cousins th thrive, with buildings for nest sites, amp supplies of bread and other scraps for foo and an extraordinary tolerance of Ma proximity.

In the early days of agriculture, most far had a dovecot, containing free-flying, do esticated rock doves, which were bred f their different colours and racing abilities. T domestic birds look quite different from t cliff-dwelling ones, but extensive interbree ing between the two has 'contaminated' but the most remote rock dove coloni However, breeding feral populations tend revert after a few years to the 'blue' color

n found in true rock doves.

Stock doves are easily confused with rock ves. Both have iridescent-green neck tches which they use in courtship display, t stock doves are less gregarious, more innspicuous birds and lack the bold markings their relatives. Once found only in south d east England, they have spread throught Britain with the increase in agriculture.

Woodpigeons have also increased dramcally in number and range, and are even lonising the Outer Hebrides and Shetland es. They are unusually tame birds in urban eas where their numbers are increasing. A oad, white crescent bisects each wing. It is ncealed when the wings are folded; in ght, however, it is obvious and recognised other pigeons as a hazard-warning signal. oodpigeons are larger than other British geons and have proportionately longer ls than stock doves. A good way to identify oodpigeons is by their bold white neck tch or ring–hence their other name 'ring' ve.

Collared doves take their name from the complete, white-bordered but otherwise ck neck collar. The smallest of our ident species, they spread from the Conent and have colonised most of the British es in the last 35 years with a dramatic pulation explosion. Associating closely with n and his cereal grain, collared doves are w common birds in villages and suburban as.

Turtle doves are even smaller than collared ves, with a shorter, more rounded tail. ey fly in a dashing manner, with quick cking wing-beats, and when overhead the ite belly appears outlined by darker wings d tail. Turtle doves spend the winter in frica, and return in late April to May.

Cooing songs Pigeons and doves have a aracteristic, monotonous call which they e to establish territories. The establishment territories helps to separate nests and duce the dangers from predators. Wood-

Rock dove/feral pigeon
Columba livia)
Stock dove
Columba oenas)
Turtle dove
Streptopelia turtur)
Collared dove
Streptopelia decaocto)
Woodpigeon
Columba palumbus)

Above: Unlike most birds, a woodpigeon does not need to lift its head to allow water to drain down the throat with each gulp.

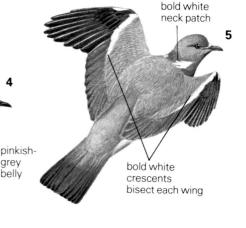

longer tail — 4
white belly — 3
pinkish-grey belly — 4
bold white neck patch — 5
bold white crescents bisect each wing
long tail

fine bars on neck patch
iridescent-green neck patch — 2
chestnut coloured small coverts — 3
small wing bars
lue-grey back
white rump
two large wing bars
ridescent-green neck patch — 1

pigeons, collared doves and stock doves have five, three and two-note rhythms respectively; they repeat each phrase several times in succession. The cooing of domestic and feral pigeons is well-known and seems not to have changed from that of rock doves. The turtle doves' soothing purr, which they sing hidden in deep cover, can easily go undetected. Alone among Britain's pigeons, the collared dove has a distinctive flight call: a harsh, nasal 'kwurr'.

Display flights Pigeons and doves also advertise their territory by flying in display positions. Rock and stock doves glide with wings held stiffly in a 'V'. Turtle and collared doves fly up and then parachute down with tail fanned and wings held below horizontal level. Woodpigeons have an undulating display-flight; they fly up, stall and 'clap' their wings two or three times, and then glide down before repeating the process. The claps, made on the downstroke of the wing-beat, are similar to the crack of a whip–contact between the wings is not important.

Nests Pigeons usually build their nests in trees, but also in holes, on ledges, and even on the surface of the ground. Sometimes you may see the conspicuous white eggs visible through the flimsy platforms of twigs. However as females incubate the eggs at night, and males take over during the day, the eggs are rarely left uncovered.

Pigeons lay only two eggs in each nest; but breeding continues until September or later and the parents raise at least two broods. Sometimes they make the second nest and the female lays her eggs even before the first brood has left. Pigeons and doves produce protein-rich pigeon milk – a cheesy curd that sloughs off from the lining of part of the crop;

Above: A special feature of pigeons and doves is their powder down feathers – small feathers of a crumbly material that breaks up into a dust to help in preening other feathers. If a bird flies into a window, this dust is shaken loose, leaving a remarkably detailed 'dust-shadow'.

Below: The stock dove has pale-grey feathers and hardly any noticeable white-coloured areas.

this is initially all the nestlings need. Late at feeding times, the parents regurgitate seed which they have gathered and stored in the crop. Each parent eventually feeds the young only twice a day, in the morning and evening.

Feral pigeons, particularly the dark-coloured types, may nest throughout the year and, on average, raise five broods. Turtle doves cut their breeding season short to migrate in August or September. Other species have their greatest breeding success in high summer, when there is plenty of food such as cereal grain.

Crop eaters Pigeons eat a wide variety of natural foods; woodpigeons, for example, eat weeds, acorns, tree flowers, ivy and beechnut. British pigeons, however, largely depend on agriculture – stock and turtle doves eat the weeds that grow beneath the crops but do not take the crops themselves. Resident pigeons and doves eat freshly sown grain and leftover on stubble.

Woodpigeons even take unripe corn, using their weight to drag the grain to ground level. They are equipped with a strong, hooked beak, ideal for tearing leaves, and to some have become Britain's worst pest. Four million breeding pairs and their offspring cause over £1 million damage every year. Wood pigeons perhaps create the greatest devastation when they cannot get at clover leaves which are covered by snow. Then they turn to the taller, but less nutritious brassicas. In short winter days they swallow more than their stomachs can cope with, and store the excess in their swollen-out crop to digest after dark.

Woodpigeons previously fed on leaves and seeds of woodland weeds and now exploit the bigger, better sources provided by farmers. Attempts to eradicate them have failed.

THE ENTERPRISING LITTLE RINGED PLOVER

As years go by, more and more little ringed plovers visit Britain in spring, ever since they first came in 1938. These birds are highly adaptable, and many pairs abandon their usual haunts on sand and shingle, intrepidly colonizing dry gravel pits, reservoir banks and other man-made habitats.

Above: Little ringed plovers inhabit dry, sandy areas, often inland. The three 'ringed' species of plover may all be found in similar habitats, and where the three nest in the same neighbourhood, birds of each species defend their territories against one another. Thus it may be for the sake of avoiding competition that little ringed plovers leave the coastal sites and nest inland.

Fifty years ago, little ringed plovers were rarely seen in this country; although they nested not far away on the Continent, their migration route took them southwards into Africa for the winter, and so they had little cause to come to Britain. Today, after a remarkable success story, we have several hundred breeding pairs.

Slowly spreading The recent and still continuing spread of these smart little wading birds is a result of their own adaptability and of man's help in opening up new habitats for them. For nearly a whole century they have expanded their breeding range in a northwesterly direction, so that they can be found in almost every European country, and right

across Asia to China and Japan. Typical habitats of the little ringed plover are sand and shingle banks beside lakes and rivers, but when the birds reached Britain they were quick to adapt to the very similar man-made alternatives: mostly gravel pits and reservoir banks.

Our first pair of little ringed plovers nested at the Tring reservoirs in Hertfordshire, in 1938. In 1944 a second pair was located, and the population has increased steadily ever since. There were over 100 pairs by 1960, over 400 by 1973 and over 600 by 1984; and they are now firmly established in most central and eastern counties of England; some have been found in North Wales and even in Scotland.

little ringed plover distribution

Ringed plover

more black on head

dark back

orange
base of beak

orange-yellow legs

Kentish plover

paler back and crown

more white on
head and throat

shorter bird with
longer legs and
larger head and beak

incomplete
black band

distinctive black legs

Little ringed plover

white lin
round cr

yellc
eye-

wing bar
extremely faint

The seven species of plover The little ringed plover is one of seven species of plover which you are likely to find in Britain or close by in France. All are compact-looking birds with medium-length legs, short necks and short, slightly bulbous beaks. Only one, the grey plover, has never nested in Britain, though it is a common winter visitor from Russia and Siberia to many coastal areas. The golden plover, which has a very similar plumage to the grey, breeds on the hills and moors of north and west Britain. The lapwing (or peewit) is the familiar 'green plover' of grassy farmland; and the dotterel is, in this country, a rare bird that breeds on only a few remote mountain tops.

The three remaining plovers all have 'ringed' plumage and are easily confused with one another. The Kentish plover has an incomplete black breast band and pale sandy upperparts. Although it no longer nests in Britain – the last regular pair bred in Sussex in 1956 – it remains common on other European coasts, and is still occasionally seen here.

Finally, the ringed and little ringed plovers, both with complete breast bands and pale brown upperparts, are so similar that even experienced ornithologists sometimes mistake them. At 15cm (6in) long, the little ringed is the smaller of the two; it is also more lightly built and has a finer bill, but at a distance and unless the two species are close together so that a comparison can be made, these differences are unreliable guides. In general, the little ringed plover is seen inland and the ringed plover on the coast, but again this is not a diagnostic feature.

The best way to identify the little ringed plover is to watch it flying and listen to its calls. Unlike the other 'ringed' plovers, it has no conspicuous wing bars – the wings appear completely brown – and its call is a short, characteristic descending whistle – 'pee-u'. In a really close view you can see that there is a yellow eye ring and a white stripe extending right over the crown – features not found on ringed or Kentish plovers. Also, the little ringed plover has a blackish beak (the ringed plover's beak has an orange base) and flesh-coloured legs rather than orange-yellow as in

the ringed, or black as in the Kentish plover. Immature individuals of all three species are much less distinctly marked, for example all have incomplete breast bands, so they are even more difficult to identify.

Settling to breed The first little ringed plovers arrive in mid to late March, but most arrive in April. Their first task is to find a territory: a place with some shallow water by which to feed, and a dry, stony or muddy area in which to nest.

Although males and females have identical plumage, you can spot the male when he lays claim to the territory with his noisy and conspicuous display flight, in which he flies about with curiously slow beats of his fully outspread wings, constantly calling out his trilling 'treea treea treea' song.

The male also takes the initiative in nest building; forming a hollow in the ground by squatting down, leaning forwards and rotating on the spot while at the same time scratching backwards with his feet. Attracted by the male's activities, and by his conspicuously fanned black, brown and white

Little ringed plover (*Charadrius dubius*); small wader; summer visitor (March-Aug). Length 15cm (6in).

Below: The scrape nest of a little ringed plover, in a typical site – a sandy, dry piece of flat ground. Newly dug gravel pits, ofter those still being worked, are ideal. Some choose natural sites beside lakes or rivers, but others make do even with industrial waste ground, where pools of rainwater provide sufficient insects and other invertebrates to keep the birds well fed.

oove: A nesting pair,
anging over at the nest
hile incubating. The birds
quat close together over the
est and make the change
ithout interrupting the
armth and cover for the
gs. In doing so, they
void exposing the eggs to
e view of hungry
edators.

elow: On hatching, the
ick already has acute
earing and sight, fully
rmed legs and a warm
oat of down. As soon as
e coat has dried, the
ick can walk and feed
self. Its parents lead
to the best feeding
ace, and, if danger
reatens, whistle the alarm.
l young chicks react
this sound, crouching
otionless and letting
eir camouflage work.

tail, the female then enters the newly formed
scrape – while her mate stands close by, flicking little stones back towards her. The com-
pleted nest is often lined with a few plant
stems, stones or fragments of shell. In May,
the female lays four well-camouflaged stone-
like eggs; each is buff-coloured with brown
spots.

Hazards abound Little ringed plovers
always choose open nest sites on the ground,
and are therefore vulnerable to several
dangers, and their camouflage, instinct and
cunning are tested to the full. They are remarkably tolerant of disturbance by anglers,
workmen and heavy machinery in their
neighbourhood, leaving their nest only if
threatened by a direct approach; but their
greatest danger is from the ever watchful
crows and magpies, which need only a few
seconds to fly in and steal the eggs. At one
regular breeding site, this particular problem
has been overcome by placing a wire mesh
cage over the nest, with holes large enough to
allow free passage for the plovers but too
small for the crows.

Deceiving the eye Camouflage plays a
large part in the life of the little ringed plover.
A sitting bird is much more difficult to spot
than you might expect. From a side or face-
on view, the boldly patterned head and breast
break up the bird's outline so effectively that
it becomes almost impossible to tell that the
bird is there, and from above the mud-
coloured back and crown blend marvellously
into the surroundings.

Helpless, hungry chicks in an open nest
would make easy targets for predators, but
when little ringed plover chicks hatch they are
already well equipped for survival. Development within the egg continues to an advanced
stage, so that within hours of hatching the
chicks are able to fend for themselves to an
astonishing degree. Within four weeks they
can fly.

The little ringed plover's last line of defence
is one of cunning – the distraction display.
When, for example, a dog threatens to approach too closely to the eggs or brood, the
adult plover quietly makes its way round
behind the dog. Then with loud calls and conspicuous flapping about on the ground, it
pretends to be injured – trailing a 'broken'
wing in a manner that entices the dog. In such
a situation, most dogs forget the eggs and
young, and chase the apparently easy meal,
which of course moves away from its family
and then escapes with ease.

Methods of hunting All plovers hunt primarily by sight, although they use their sense
of touch, too, for you may sometimes see
them thrust their beaks well into soft ground.
In general, however, they are better adapted
for surface food. Little ringed plovers search
for insects in the same way that thrushes
search for worms: running a few paces and
then pausing to scan the ground, and only
reaching down when food is in sight.

Above: The tiny, brightly coloured tree frog (*Hyla arborea*) is an agile climber, spending most of its life in reeds, shrubbery and trees, often high above the ground. Small ridges on the sole of the frog's foot help it get a grip on irregular surfaces, while adhesive, disc-like pads on its toes (below) create a suction effect by muscular contraction. The vacuum is broken when the muscles relax, rounding out the central pad and allowing it to be lifted free.

disc-like
sucking pads

FROGS FROM FAR AWAY

Each breeding season, small colonies of exotic frogs remind us of their successful introduction with their unusually loud and urgent calls.

There have been many attempts over the years to introduce 'exotic' frogs to Britain. Most, like the tree frogs brought from Australia, and the painted frogs and stripeless tree frogs from southern Europe and North Africa, have met with limited success.

Three species have established themselves in Britain. The marsh frog, now a permanent member of our fauna, is the most successful. The edible frog has also survived, though on a smaller scale. The third species, the tiny European or common tree frog, is resident at a single site in England, where a small population has survived for about 70 years.

Close relatives Marsh and edible frogs are very closely related; at one time, indeed, the marsh frog was considered to be a subspecies of the edible frog. In fact, the two species are capable of interbreeding quite successfully and, because of the nature of their genetic makeup, the offspring are usually true edible frogs, rather than hybrids sharing the features of both parents.

The edible frog is slightly larger than the common frog. It has a distinctive greenish livery, spotted with black, and sports a yellowish stripe down its back. The species is celebrated for its hind legs, which are considered a delicacy in French cuisine.

The marsh frog, like the edible frog, is a handsome amphibian. In the words of the man who first introduced them in numbers, its colour ranges from 'a shrill emerald green to a blackish olive bronze'. Today, most specimens are of the latter sort; they have a rather warty back, and they generally lack the edible frog's dorsal stripe. The adult marsh frog is also distinguishable by its

rmidable bulk. It can reach a length of
cm (6in) from nose to rump, compared to
e 7.5cm (3in) of the edible frog.
The tree frog is unrelated to the other in-
oduced species and is the smallest of all,
ching a maximum size of 5cm (2in). It
ries in colouring from bright green to
llow or brown, with a dark stripe along
ch of its sides.

Arrival of the edible frog The British edible
og has a complex pedigree, being derived
om French, Belgian, West German and
alian stock. The earliest recorded introduc-
ons were made between 1837 and 1842 by
eorge Berney who, with the aid of large
mpers lined with water lily leaves, imported
oout 1500 specimens. These were released in
e Cambridgeshire Fens and further stocks
re subsequently set free in many parts of
itain, as far north as south-east Scotland.
Although some populations thrived for
any years, others dwindled to extinction or
uld only be maintained by 'topping up'
th further importations. By 1976, the
ecies was scattered over at least eight sites
three southern English counties – Norfolk,
rrey and Sussex. The biggest colony – over
thousand strong – is in Surrey and is still
owing.

Success of the marsh frog Compared with
e edible frog, which cannot be said to have
really firm foothold in the British country-
de, the marsh frog is well entrenched and
sily the most successful amphibian ever
troduced here. Romney Marsh in Kent was
s first major stronghold, and still is. Here
2 Hungarian specimens, rescued from the
ssection laboratories at University College,
ondon, were liberated in the winter of
934-5.
The release site, a network of dykes, canals,
eres and streams criss-crossing lush sheep

pastures, turned out to be an ideal habitat.
Marsh frogs were soon found all over the
Marsh, their spread due to successful reproduction and rapid dispersal along the
waterways.

Wide-ranging appetites One factor which
has helped the marsh frog in its efforts to
establish itself is its remarkably omnivorous
nature. Apart from spiders and insects –
including bees, beetles, grasshoppers and
earwigs – its diet also includes snails and
fishes.
Marsh frogs, and to a lesser extent edible
frogs, also include the young stages of other
frogs in their diet, and sometimes may even
eat the young of their own species. This

Above: The future of this young marsh frog (*Rana ridibunda*) depends on the extent to which farming and other land practices make inroads into its marshy habitats. Although established in the localities shown in the map (below), the populations in Romney Marsh, the site of its first introduction, may already be threatened by the changeover from traditional sheep farming to arable farming, which alters the ditch system so favourable to the frogs.

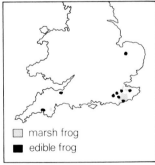

marsh frog
edible frog

Left: The paired vocal sacs of this male edible frog help to amplify its croaking, which attracts the females in the breeding season. In the last century, edible frogs were known for their vocal powers, and nicknamed 'Cambridgeshire nightingales' or 'Whaddon organs', after their places of release.

underlines the aggressive superiority of the marsh frog in the amphibian community. It may also help to explain why the extension of its range in Romney Marsh and elsewhere seems to have been matched by a reduction in the fortunes of common frogs in these areas.

Tree frogs, being much smaller, prey mostly on insects and spiders. They compete for food only with small birds, such as tits and warblers, which share their leafy habitat. However, as tree frogs are active mostly at night, they can forage largely unmolested. Furthermore, they have a chameleon-like ability to change their skin colour to suit their surroundings, making detection doubly difficult.

Build-up to mating In winter, the hazards of frozen ponds and streams and diminishing food supplies force these species into hibernation, usually under water. Whereas the common frog emerges from its winter retreat in March, marsh frogs wait until early April, and tree frogs even later.

May is a month of intense activity as courtship gets under way. Although tree frogs rarely come to ground in summer, they resort to pools and ponds for courtship and breeding purposes. The urgent croaking of the amorous males, heard mostly at night, is marvellously powerful for so small a creature, and conveniently allows an annual check on the well-being of the colony.

Male marsh and edible frogs are equally voluble and the combined chorus of a sizeable colony, maintained day and night, can be almost overpowering. The vocal sacs, one at each corner of the mouth, balloon out to lend

their singing its full-throated, resonant quality. This is particularly important during the breeding season, for courtship purposes.

In this courtship, the males of the introduced species attract the females by their powerful croaking, then encourage them to approach so that their potential as mates can be assessed. This contrasts markedly with the ritual of the common frog, in which both sexes do no more than converge simultaneously in a seething mass to mate and spawn in their traditional ponds. The females of the introduced species, having no need of self-advertisement, are much less vocal and barely audible to the human ear at a distance of more than a few yards.

Above: Marsh frogs vary widely in colour, from bright green to the more usual olive green or bronze. In common with edible frogs, they lose their distinctive colour if kept in captivity. Marsh frogs reach a length of 15cm (6in) compared to the 10cm (4in) maximum length of the common frog. Their large size enables them, on occasion, to include small birds and nestlings in their diet.

Mighty leapers

Leaping frogs, like this edible frog (left), can cover great distances in one leap. One marsh frog is on record as having cleared 145cm (57in) in one leap, although a jump of 63 to 76cm (25 to 30in) would be more usual. The illustration below shows how the muscles in the frog's legs relax and contract in leaping.

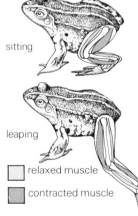

sitting

leaping

relaxed muscle

contracted muscle

FOREIGN FISHES

Some of the most familiar fish in our waters, such as the carp, are not native, but were introduced centuries ago. Not so the tropical species that make a surprising appearance – they are abandoned pet fish.

Man is often responsible for carrying animals and plants with him as he moves around the world. In many cases this is accidental – plants are carried in ships' ballast, and stray seeds in grain or in animal fodder. In other cases it is deliberate – the introduction of the grey squirrel to Britain is a well-known example. Many of the best-known instances involve animals introduced to islands which, because of their generally sparse fauna, provide ideal opportunities for the exotic animal to thrive.

This is illustrated by the freshwater fishes introduced to the British Isles. Compared with the mainland of Europe we have relatively few native freshwater fishes – at most 33 species, as against about 145 in Europe. As a result, some introduced species have thrived particularly well.

Common carp Some of the non-native species were introduced so long ago that they are now rarely thought of as 'foreign fish'. The carp is a typical example. No one knows for certain when it was introduced to the British Isles (it is native to the Danube and eastwards, including Greece), but it has been here so long most people regard it as one of our native fish. It was first mentioned in print as a British fish around 1496, but it was not common then. Archaeologists have found other evidence in the form of carp bones in Tudor remains in the south of

Above: Stocking a river with trout fry from a hatchery, which takes place in spring. Later in the year slightly larger fish, known as fingerlings, are used. Large numbers of these fish die in their new homes before reaching maturity.

Below: Rainbow trout in a hatchery, where they are bred to be used as stock for anglers in hundreds of lakes and rivers. There are only six established breeding colonies of rainbow trout in the 'wild'.

England, but nothing so far in earlier sites.

Today, the carp is widely distributed in Britain, but it frequently owes its presence to anglers who have stocked lakes with it. The related crucian carp is certainly a native fish, although it is often claimed as an introduction, largely as a result of some authors calling it the 'Prussian' carp. Its bones have been identified in Roman archaeological sites in London.

Rainbow trout Two members of the salmon family–the rainbow trout and the brook charr–are more recently introduced fishes. The rainbow trout was first introduced to England in 1884. Its original range is the coastal drainage area of the Pacific coast of North America from Alaska virtually to Mexico, and several rainbow trout hatcheries were established along this coastline. The rainbow trout has been distributed to many parts of the world from these hatcheries, although ironically several of the original populations in its native range have become extinct.

Brook charr originally came from eastern North America, roughly from Quebec to South Carolina, and this species has also been widely re-distributed. It was first introduced to Britain in 1869 and many subsequent introductions were made, a number of these resulting in established breeding populations. In the last ten years in Britain, some fish hatcheries have raised large num-

bers of brook charr, mainly for angling lakes, and the species is becoming much more familiar in British lakes and rivers.

Weighty wels Most of the introduced fishes in Britain have proved to be rather slow to establish themselves and have not spread, or have only done so with the help of man. One example is the European catfish known as the wels–a rather unattractive looking fish with several long barbels around its mouth. It is native to the Danube and eastwards, where it grows to a huge size, reportedly 5m (16ft), with a weight of 306kg (675lb). Its introduction to various places in the British Isles during the last century was usually accompanied by controversy over the

Above: The rainbow trout (*Salmo gairdneri*) can be distinguished from the native brown trout by the coloured band on its side and its spotted body.

Below: The pumpkinseed (*Lepomis gibbosus*), pictured here with rudd, is North American cold water fish. There are two populations in Britain, in Somerset and Sussex, which were probably established when pet aquarium fish were released into the ponds.

Introduced fish facts

Above: The zander (*Stizostedion lucioperca*), known as a pike-perch although only related to the perch, reaches an average length of 45cm (18in) with a weight of 1kg (2lb).

Above: The wels (*Silirus glanis*) is a member of the catfish family. It has a slimy, scaleless skin and measures on average 100cm (39in), with a weight of 10kg (22lb).

Above: The brook charr (*Salvelinus fontinalis*), also known as the brook trout, shown here in breeding colours. It reaches 65cm (25½in) in length, 3kg (6½lb) in weight.

dom of releasing such a large fish in British
ters. Eventually, the only populations to
ome established were those in the lakes at
oburn Abbey (some of these were later
ased into neighbouring Bedfordshire and
ckinghamshire lakes), and the reservoirs
Tring in Hertfordshire. The largest speci-
n caught by an angler in Britain was
en from Tring in 1970; it weighed 19·7kg
lb 8oz).

Tropical guppies Much less impressive in
ms of size, but considerably more attract-
ly coloured, were two populations of
ppies which survived for several years, one
he River Lee at Hackney, London and the
er in the St Helen's canal in Lancashire.
th were living in warm water discharges –
former from a power station and the
er from a glassworks. With the closure of
power station and the presence of pre-
tors, the River Lee's guppies disappeared,
t the St Helen's canal fish continued to
ive. This canal is also the habitat of
eral other tropical fish species, which are
en caught by anglers. They all came from

Above: Guppies (*Poecilia
reticulata*), more familiar
as aquarium fish, have
established populations in
freshwater. The release of
former pet fish is now
illegal, but has led to the
presence of goldfish in
numerous lakes and rivers.

ht: The bitterling
odeus amarus), a rare
oduced fish, has a
cinating method of
roduction, involving a
d party, the swan mussel,
a host for the eggs. When
y hatch after 2-3 weeks,
young swim away.

ow: The Chinese grass
p (*Ctenopharyngodon
lla*) has been
perimentally introduced
a possible solution to
problem of clearing
ed-choked ponds.

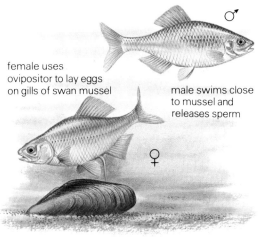

female uses
ovipositor to lay eggs
on gills of swan mussel

male swims close
to mussel and
releases sperm

a local pet shop which, when it closed,
released its stock into the canal.

The spread of the zander Such fishes have
fitted easily into their new environment and
caused few problems. The same cannot be
said of the zander, a European relative of the
perch, but a much larger fish, which was
released in the early 1960s into the Great
Ouse Relief Channel. Curiously, zander
have lived in the lakes at Woburn Abbey
since the 1870s without causing great problems, but once they were released into the
river system of the Great Ouse, they began
to increase their numbers and range greatly.
Throughout the 1960s and 1970s the zander
spread through the Great Ouse system, and
by the late 1970s they began to turn up in
other river systems elsewhere in the country.

Their success in establishing themselves is
due to a number of factors, one of which is
that they are particularly well adapted to life
in the slow-flowing, sparsely vegetated, rather
murky waters that comprise so many of our
lowland rivers. They are also efficient predators, finding the large numbers of rather
small cyprinid fishes (members of the carp
family – bleak, roach and dace especially),
living in such waters easy prey. As a result,
they are extremely abundant in many of the
waterways to which they have found their
way. The spread of the zander has been
partly natural, because most of the rivers of
East Anglia are interconnected, but it has
also been aided by anglers who have taken
fish from one water and released them illegally
in another.

Predatory problems The spread of the
zander has meant that the numerous cyprinid
fishes which made up so much of the catch
of anglers have become scarce. The other
predators native to these waters, perch and
pike, are now fewer and smaller. The addition
of a third, and possibly better adapted,
predator in the form of the zander has
affected both competing predators and prey
and has caused considerable changes in the
fish life of these rivers. Unfortunately, the
zander cannot now be controlled and there
is little doubt that it will spread in the next
decade or two to the whole of lowland Britain.

189

INDEX

The entries listed in **bold** type refer to main subjects. The page numbers in *italics* indicate illustrations. Medium type entries refer to the text.

ACKNOWLEDGEMENTS

Photographic Credits Heather Angel/Biofotos 18 (bottom), 32, 34 (bottom), 37, 47 (middle), 54, 58, 62 (bottom), 70 (bottom), 76 (top right), 84 (bottom), 97, 105 (bottom left), 110 (top), 111, 114 (top), 116, 121, 132 (top), 139 (top), 156 (middle), 166 (bottom), 172, 174 (bottom right), 180 (top), 187, 188 (bottom), 189; Aquila (J Anthony) 119 (left), (S Downer) 101 (top left), 102 (bottom right), (Rodney Foster) 25 (bottom), (J V Harrison) 131 (top), (N Harwood) 23, (M & V Lane) 70 (top), 148, (M Leach) 168 (bottom), (R Siegal) 83, (A Wharton) 74 (bottom), (D Whitaker) 171 (bottom), (M Wilkes) 67, 71; A-Z Botanical Collection 49; Ian Beames (16 top, bottom), 19 (middle), 60 (top), 63, 91 (bottom), 92 (bottom), 170, 171 (top), 186 (top); Biofotos/ Geoffrey Kinns (150 top); Bruce Coleman (Jen and Des Bartlett) 162 (bottom), (Jane Burton) 16 (middle), 44, (56 left), 61 (bottom), 93, 162 (top), 169 (bottom), (Eric Crichton) 98 (top), (S Dalton) 177, (A Deane) 159 (bottom), (J Grande) 59 (top), 184, (Dennis Green) 156 (top), (C Molyneux) 96-7, 99 (top), (Hans Reinhard) 34 (top), 35, 154, 163, (Leonard Lee Rue) 164 (bottom), (Frieder Sauer) 185 (bottom), (James Simon) 164, (Kim Taylor) 14, 75, (Rod Williams) 166 (top); Michael Chinery 76 (top left), 138 (top), 139 (bottom), 153 (top); Adrian Davies 40 (bottom), 104 (bottom), 122 (bottom), 165, 173 (top); Martin Dohrn 104 (top); Geoff Dore 117 (top); Steve Downer 85 (top), 86 (top); Bob Gibbons Photography 18 (top), 68, 79 (top), 130 (right), 132 (middle), 174 (bottom left); Dennis Green 21 (bottom), 25 (top), 31, 106, 181, 183 (bottom); Jeremy Gunn-Taylor 138 (bottom); Brian Hawkes 158; Graham Hirons 41 (top), 155 (top, bottom); George Hyde 72, 136 (bottom); Gillian Kerby 159 (top); Mike Leach 55, 85 (middle), 94 (bottom), 100, 149 (bottom), 174 (top); Richard Littleton 61 (top); John Mason 43, 51, 124 (top), 127 (top); Richard Mills 33 (top), 76 (bottom), 105 (top, bottom right), 113 (top), 117 (bottom), 146, 160 (top), 176 (top); Pat Morris 38, 39, 86 (bottom), 91 (top), 101 (bottom), 103 (bottom left), 107 (bottom), 122 (top), 124 (bottom), 127 (bottom left), 153 (bottom), 160 (bottom); NHPA (A Barnes) 108 (bottom right), (M Clark) 168 (top), 169 (top); (Stephen Dalton) 8, 123, 126, 130 (left), 142-3, 145 (top), 149 (bottom), 186 (bottom), (J B Free) 128 (top), (J Goodman) 41 (bottom), 42 (bottom), 59 (bottom), 118 (right), 188 (top), (S Harris) 25 (middle), (Brian Hawkes) 33 (bottom), 62 (top), 95 (top), (E A Janes) 29, 147 (bottom), 180 (bottom), (D Jeffrey) 176 (bottom), (R Knight) 112 (bottom), (W Murray) 87 (top), (K Preston-Mafham) 48, 73, (Ivan Polunin) 125 (top), (R Shaw) 119 (right), (J Tallen) 156 (bottom), (Michael Tweedie) 134, (Bill Wood) 125 (bottom); Nature Photographers 89, (S Bisserot) 60 (bottom), 118 (left), 120 (top), 132 (bottom), 161, 164 (middle), (Frank Blackburn) 66, 77, 152, 175, 178, 183 (top), (D Bonsall) 117 (middle), (B Burbidge) 157 (top), (N Callow) 45 (top), (Kevin Carlson) 27, 108 (top), 140, (Richard Crane) 20, (Ettlinger) 33 (middle), (K Handford) 101 (top right), (M Harris) 151 (top), (C Hill) 90, 114 (bottom), (J Hunt) 109, (Mike Leach) 150 (bottom), (C K Mylne) 56 (right), 92, 155 (middle), (Owen Norman) 10, 19 (top), 157 (bottom right), (W Paton) 22, 24, 69 (middle), 84 (top), (Picozzi) 57 (bottom), 95 (bottom), (J Reynolds) (bottom), (Don Smith) 69 (bottom), 103 (top), (P Sterry) 21 (top), 47 (top), 74 (top), 141 (middle), (middle), 185 (top), (Maurice Walker) 182, (Derek Washington) 13 (bottom); Naturfoto 50, 64 (left); Natural Selection 11 (top); E Neal 57 (top); John Neale 173 (bottom); W S Paton 144 (bottom); Bernard Picton 42 (middle); Keith Porter 128 (bottom), 129, 131 (bottom); J F Preedy 12, 88 (middle, bottom); Premaphotos Wildlife/K Preston Mafham 46, 78 (top, bottom), 79 (middle), 131 (middle), 136 (top), 141 (bottom), 157 (bottom left); Presstige/Tony Tilford 13, 94 (top); Richard Revels 117 (middle), 133 (bottom); John Robinson 11 (bottom), 28, 30, 64 (right), 80, 85 (bottom), 102 (top), 103 (bottom right), 108 (bottom left), 141 (top), 144 (top), 153 (middle), 179; Valerie Russel 98 (bottom), 99 (bottom); Seaphot 120 (bottom); Tony Stone Associates 82; Swift 36, 110 (bottom), 145 (bottom left); R Tidman 112 (top left); Michael Tweedie 45 (bottom), 47 (bottom), 79 (bottom), (bottom right), 128 (middle), 135, 137; Bill Vaughan 151 (bottom); Woodfall Wildlife Pictures 40 (top), 42 (top); ZEFA 6-7, 53.
Front cover: Bruce Coleman Ltd/Hans Reinhard

Index compiled by Kate Chapman BA ALA, Society of Indexers.